HEAT

BLACKIE & SON LIMITED
66 Chandos Place, LONDON
17 Stanhope Street, GLASGOW

BLACKIE & SON (INDIA) LIMITED
103/5 Fort Street, BOMBAY

BLACKIE & SON (CANADA) LIMITED
TORONTO

HEAT

A TEXTBOOK FOR HIGHER CERTIFICATE AND INTERMEDIATE STUDENTS

BY

M. NELKON, M.Sc.(Lond.), A.K.C.
William Ellis School, London:
Visiting Lecturer, Northampton Polytechnic, London

BLACKIE & SON LIMITED
LONDON AND GLASGOW

First published 1949

Printed in Great Britain by Blackie & Son, Ltd., Glasgow

PREFACE

This textbook aims at a clear presentation of the fundamental principles of Heat to a Higher Certificate and Intermediate standard, and assumes a school certificate knowledge of the subject. Numerically worked examples from past examination papers of the various Boards have been included in the text to illustrate the topics, and the calculus has been used only where necessary.

It is not possible here to comment on more than a few of the points which have been borne in mind in the presentation of the subject. The basic principles of thermometry and pyrometry have been fully discussed; the importance of the mass of the gas in Gas Equations has been emphasized; the methods of measuring the mechanical equivalent of heat have been given prominence; and the First Law of Thermodynamics has been applied to isothermal and adiabatic changes. The units of the various quantities encountered have been stressed throughout the text, and some straightforward questions have been set at the beginning of each exercise to test a knowledge of the fundamental points of the corresponding chapter.

I am grateful to P. Parker, M.Sc., A.M.I.E.E., Senior Lecturer in Physics, Northampton Polytechnic, London, for his assistance at all stages of preparation of this book. I am also indebted to J. Duffey, B.Sc., Ph.D., William Ellis School, London, for reading parts of the text. Any errors outstanding are the responsibility of the author, who would be glad to receive notice of them. I acknowledge with thanks the permission of the following examining boards to reprint questions set in their past examinations: London University; Northern Universities Joint Board; Cambridge Local Examinations Syndicate; Oxford and Cambridge Joint Board; Central Welsh Board.

M. N.

CONTENTS

CHAPTER I

Principles of Thermometry

1. Temperature.

When we wash in water from a " cold " tap, and then in water from a " hot " tap, we experience different sensations; we say that the " temperature " of the water is different in the two cases. The *temperature* of an object may be defined as its degree of hotness (or coldness), and a *thermometer* is an instrument which measures temperature.

If a finger is placed in hot water and then in a warm liquid A, the latter feels cold. If the finger is now placed in cold water and then in A, the latter feels warm. It can hence be seen that the sense of touch is a very unreliable method of estimating temperature, and to overcome any human element, scientists make use of liquids and other substances such as gases to measure temperature. This will be discussed fully later (p. 3).

2. Centigrade, Fahrenheit, Réaumur systems of numbering temperature scales.

The earliest thermometer was constructed by GALILEO in 1593, and improvements were suggested and carried out by numerous other scientists. NEWTON was one of the first to point out that the construction of a thermometer necessitates the marking on it of two fixed temperatures, which are known as the **fixed points** of the thermometer. Since the *temperature of melting ice* is practically constant under normal conditions, this temperature is chosen as the " lower fixed point " of all thermometers. The *temperature of steam at a pressure of* 76 *cm. of mercury* (*normal* *pressure*) is chosen as the "upper fixed point" of thermometers; a correction is required when the pressure is not 76 cm. of mercury, as the temperature of steam varies with pressure (p. 124).

There are several methods of numbering the temperature scales. In the *centigrade* system of temperature, first suggested by CELSIUS in 1742, the lower fixed point is given the number 0; the upper fixed point is given the number 100; and the interval between them is divided into 100 equal parts or *degrees*. The centigrade system is adopted for general scientific use.

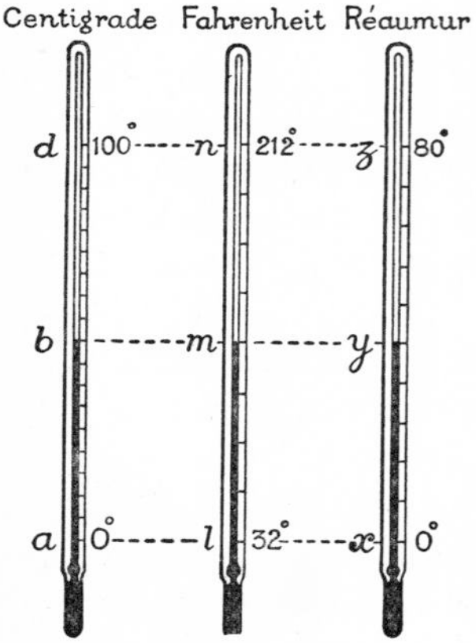

Centigrade Fahrenheit Réaumur

d 100° ---- n 212° ---- z 80°

b ------ m ------ y

a 0° ----- l 32° ---- x 0°

Fig. 1.1

In the *fahrenheit* system, suggested by FAHRENHEIT about 1720, the lower fixed point is given the number 32, the upper fixed point is given the number 212, and the interval between them is divided into 180 degrees. The fahrenheit system is used by engineers in this country.

The *réaumur* system, still used on the Continent, has the lower fixed point marked as 0, the upper fixed point as 80, and the interval between them is divided into 80 degrees (see fig. 1.1). It can be seen that a change from 32° to 212° on the fahrenheit scale is equivalent to a change from 0° to 100° on the centigrade scale, i.e. 180° F. change = 100° C. change.

Suppose C is the temperature on the centigrade system which is the same as the temperatures F and R on the fahrenheit and réaumur systems respectively. Then, if C corresponds to the mercury level at b (fig. 1.1), F to the level m, and R to the level y, we have

$$\frac{\mathrm{ab}}{\mathrm{ad}} = \frac{\mathrm{lm}}{\mathrm{ln}} = \frac{\mathrm{xy}}{\mathrm{xz}},$$

from which it follows that

$$\frac{C}{100} = \frac{F - 32}{180} = \frac{R}{80}.$$

This formula can be used to convert a temperature from one system to another.

3. The mercury thermometer scale.

The most common type of thermometer, used in everyday life, is a *mercury-in-glass* thermometer, which consists essentially of a capillary tube of uniform bore having a bulb at the lower

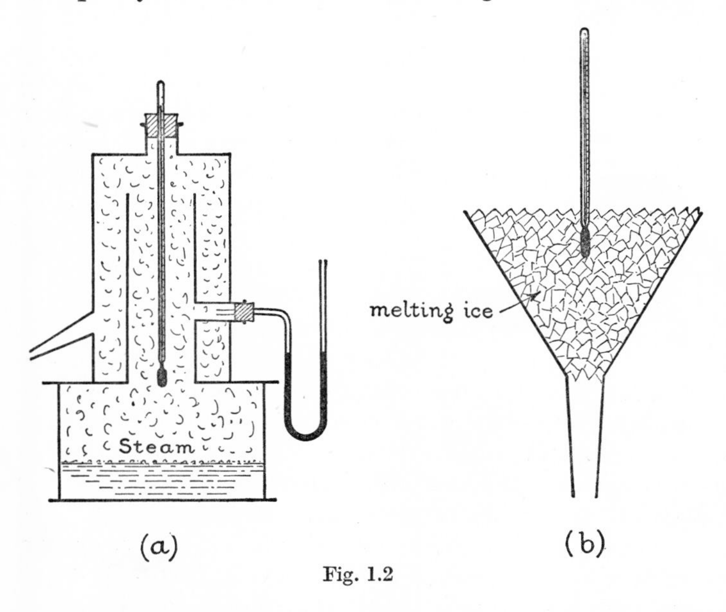

Fig. 1.2

end filled with mercury. The upper fixed point is determined with the aid of a *hypsometer*, which contains steam circulating round the thermometer (fig. 1.2a). The inner walls of the hypsometer are also at steam temperature, and thus prevent radiation from the thermometer, which would lower the latter's temperature. The lower fixed point is determined before the upper fixed point by placing the thermometer in pure melting ice, and the constancy of the mercury level is tested by raising the thermometer a little, when the level should remain constant (fig. 1.2*b*). When the thermometer is subjected to changes of temperature, changes occur in the *volume* of the mercury, which therefore rises or falls in the capillary part of the tube.

Suppose v_0 is the volume of the mercury filling the bulb and the lower part of the capillary tube at the temperature of melting ice, and v_{100} is the volume of the mercury at the steam temperature when the pressure is 76 cm. of mercury: the difference $(v_{100} - v_0)$ in the volumes, which is called the *fundamental interval*, is divided into 100 equal parts or *degrees*; and if v_t is the volume of the mercury when the thermometer is used to measure the temperature t of a substance, then t is *defined* in degrees centigrade by the relation

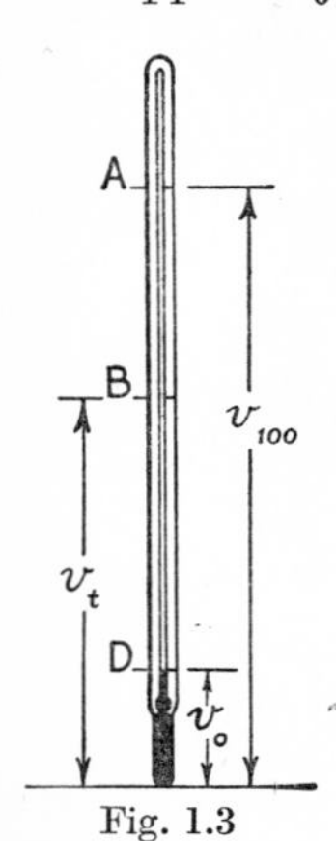

Fig. 1.3

$$\frac{t}{100} = \frac{v_t - v_0}{v_{100} - v_0}. \quad . \quad . \quad . \quad (1)$$

To illustrate the meaning of this definition, suppose the mercury level reaches D at the lower fixed point, A at the upper fixed point, and B when the temperature is t (fig. 1.3). The volume $(v_t - v_0)$, the numerator of the right-hand fraction in (1) above, is the volume of the mercury between B and D, and the volume $(v_{100} - v_0)$ is the volume of the mercury between A and D.

If the bore of the capillary tube is uniform, these two volumes are respectively proportional to the *lengths* BD and AD. It then follows from the relation (1) that the number corresponding to a temperature of 50° C. is marked midway between D and A; that 25° C. is one-quarter of DA from D, and so on. For this reason a uniform capillary tube is used in a mercury thermometer, and the temperature is read from divisions equally spaced on the length of the capillary tube.

The mercury-in-glass thermometer is a convenient one for everyday use. But it has a limited range from about —40° C., when mercury freezes, to about 350° C., when mercury boils; and it is not employed when a very accurate measurement of temperature is required (see p. 6).

4. Alcohol-in-glass thermometers are used in Arctic regions or when very low temperatures are measured, as alcohol freezes at about —112° C. Alcohol has the disadvantage of boiling at 78° C., however, and takes some time to reach the temperature it is required to measure; it also wets the sides of the glass, unlike mercury.

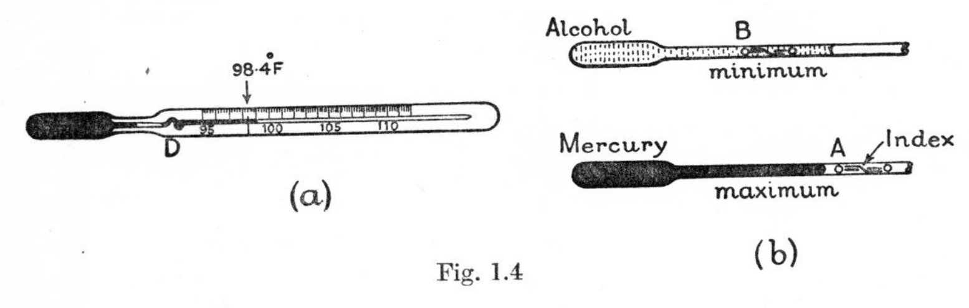

Fig. 1.4

5. The clinical thermometer is a mercury thermometer which has (i) a constriction at the lower end, (ii) a small temperature range (fig. 1.4*a*). The constriction at D prevents the mercury thread in the capillary tube rejoining the mercury in the bulb when the thermometer is taken out of the patient's mouth. The temperature of a person in normal good health is usually taken as 98·4° F.

6. Maximum and minimum thermometers are used at meteorological stations for determining the maximum and minimum temperatures over a period of time. One type of maximum thermometer contains mercury, with a small steel index above it, so that the steel index is pushed along the tube as the temperature rises but remains in the same position when the temperature falls (fig. 1.4*b*). The end A of the index thus corresponds to the maximum temperature. One type of minimum thermometer is illustrated in fig. 1.4*b*, and contains a small index inside alcohol. When the temperature rises the alcohol flows past the index. When the temperature falls, the " skin " of the liquid pulls back the index, so that the minimum temperature corresponds to the right end of the index B.

7. Disadvantages of the mercury-in-glass thermometer.

The mercury-in-glass thermometer has several disadvantages for accurate temperature measurement. For example, the glass contracts very slowly after it is heated to obtain the upper fixed point of the thermometer, so that the zero mark moves up slowly, causing error in the readings; there is always a part of the thermometer not in contact with the object whose temperature is measured; and the bulb expands slightly when the thermometer is used in an upright position, owing to the pressure of the mercury on it. Most important of all, when a mercury thermometer is used to measure temperature, the glass tube, as well as the mercury, changes in volume, and the observed expansion of the mercury is thus less than the true expansion by the volume change of the glass. Now the glass expansion is about 10 per cent of that of the mercury for the same temperature change, which means that the glass expansion *must* be taken into account in accurate measurement of temperature. Unfortunately no accurate correction can be made for the glass expansion, as the changes in volume of glass with temperature are very irregular.

8. The constant-volume gas thermometer scale.

One method of reducing the error due to the expansion of the glass, to the point of making the error negligibly small, is to use a substance which has a very large expansion relative to glass. As we shall discuss more fully later (p. 57), the variation with temperature of the *pressure of a gas at constant volume* is relatively about 200 times as great as the volume change of glass with temperature, and the pressure varies regularly when the temperature changes. On this account, scientists are generally agreed that a gas thermometer is the most accurate type of thermometer, and an elaborate type of gas thermometer is used at the National Physical Laboratory (N.P.L.) for accurate temperature measurement.

A simple form of *constant-volume gas thermometer* is illustrated in fig. 1.5. A bulb B contains the gas, and is connected by a capillary tube to a mercury manometer. The volume of the gas is kept constant by moving the open tube R up or down until the mercury level reaches a fixed mark A on the glass, and the difference in levels of the mercury, h cm., is measured. The pressure, p, of the gas is then given by $p = (H + h)$ cm. of mercury, where H is the atmospheric pressure read on the barometer.

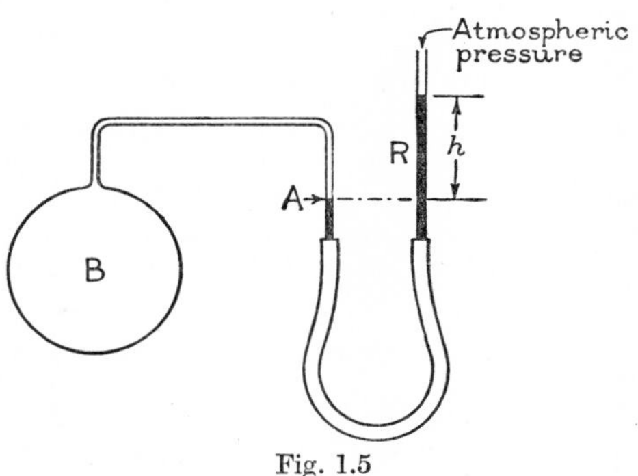

Fig. 1.5

The pressure, p_0, of the gas is determined when the bulb is immersed in melting ice, and this reading is the "lower fixed point" of the thermometer (p. 1). The bulb is surrounded by steam and the new pressure, p_{100}, is determined at constant volume, and is the "upper fixed point" of the thermometer. *The fundamental interval,* $p_{100} - p_0$, *between the two pressure values is divided into* 100 *equal parts,* just as in the mercury thermometer the interval between the volumes of mercury at 0° C. and 100° C. was divided into 100 equal parts (p. 2). The bulb is immersed in a liquid, for example, whose temperature t is required, and the new pressure, p_t, at constant volume is observed. The temperature t is then calculated from the relation

$$\frac{t}{100} = \frac{p_t - p_0}{p_{100} - p_0}, \quad . \quad . \quad . \quad . \quad . \quad . \quad (2)$$

which is the *definition* of temperature on the constant-volume gas thermometer scale.

Example 1.—Suppose that the pressure of hydrogen in a constant-volume gas thermometer is 74·0 cm. mercury at the temperature of melting ice; 108·4 cm. at the temperature of steam at normal pressure, and 87·2 cm. at the temperature t of a liquid. Then, from (2), the temperature t is given by

$$\frac{t}{100} = \frac{87{\cdot}2 - 74{\cdot}0}{108{\cdot}4 - 74{\cdot}0},$$

from which $t = 38{\cdot}4°$ C.

The resemblance between the relations

$$t/100 = (v_t - v_0)/(v_{100} - v_0) \text{ and } t/100 = (p_t - p_0)/(p_{100} - p_0),$$

which define respectively the temperatures on the mercury and constant-volume gas thermometers, should be carefully noted by the reader.

9. Constant-volume gas thermometer (accurate form).

The essential features of an accurate constant-volume gas thermometer are shown in fig. 1.6; it was designed by Harker and Chappuis. The bulb B contains nitrogen or hydrogen, and is connected by a capillary tube to a manometer M. The volume

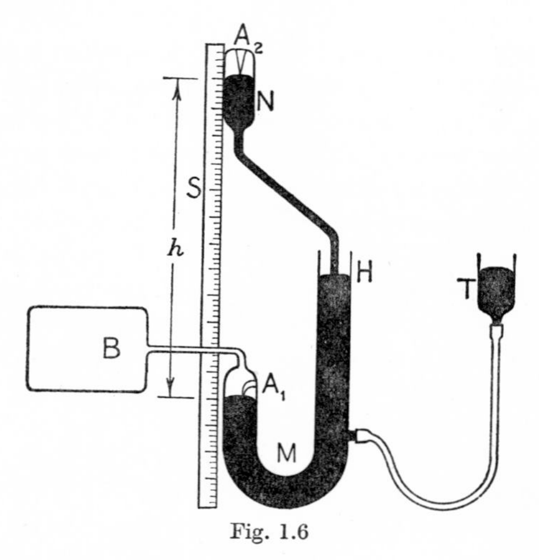

Fig. 1.6

of the gas is kept constant in all measurements of pressure by bringing the mercury level to the tip of the pointer A_1, which can be done by raising or lowering the tube T. A barometer NH is incorporated in the instrument so that the pressure of the gas can be directly determined at the place where the temperature is actually measured, and hence a vacuum exists above the mercury level in N.

When a measurement is taken, the level of the mercury in N is brought to the tip of a pointer A_2 by raising or lowering N, and the reading on the scale S which is at the same height as the tip of A_2 then corresponds to the level of mercury at the top of the barometer. The reading h on S corresponding to the tip of A_1 now gives a measure of the gas pressure in the bulb B. Only a very small percentage of the gas is in the space outside the bulb B, so that only a very small correction is required for this gas, which cannot be brought to the same temperature as that in B. The thermometer range is about 1500° C. to —200° C.

10. The platinum resistance thermometer scale.

The electrical resistance of pure platinum increases with increasing temperature, and this property of platinum was first extensively investigated in 1877 by CALLENDAR with a view to constructing a new type of thermometer. The resistance of a metal can be measured to a high degree of accuracy by means of a special Wheatstone bridge arrangement, and the *platinum resistance thermometer* is now an accurate instrument for measuring temperature.

Fig. 1.7*a* illustrates the essential features of a platinum resistance thermometer. A fine platinum wire is wound on a mica frame M, and is connected to one side A of a Wheatstone bridge arrangement by means of the leads L. To neutralize the resistance introduced by L, " compensating " or " dummy " leads C are used which have the same resistance as L. The leads C are placed beside L, and are connected to the side B of the Wheatstone bridge *opposite* to A. The whole arrangement is placed inside a tube from which nearly all the air has been removed, and the leads are kept apart by discs of mica D. To measure the resistance R_P of the platinum wire the leads are connected to a slide-wire Wheatstone bridge, shown in fig. 1.7*b*. Then, at a balance,

$$\frac{R_1}{R_2} = \frac{R_P + R_L + (a - x)\rho}{R_L + S + (a + x)\rho},$$

where R_L is the total resistance of the leads, $2a$ is the length of the wire, x is the length of wire from the balance-point to the

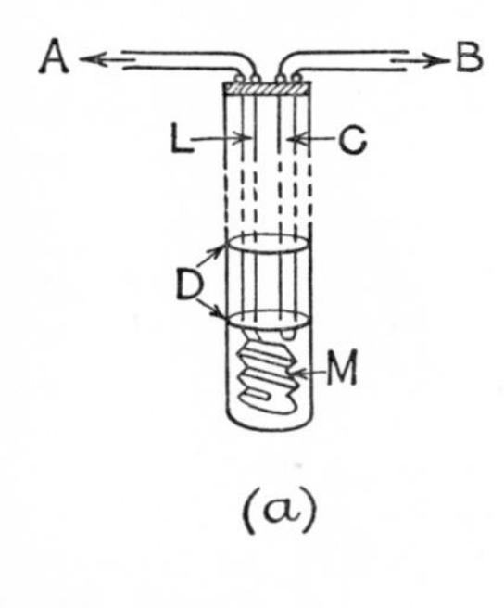

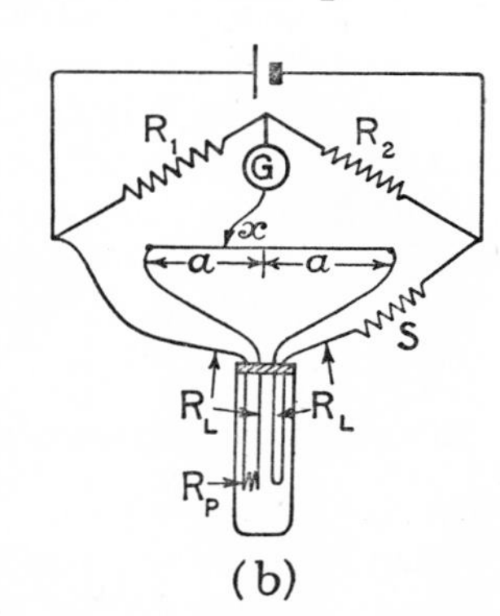

Fig. 1.7

middle, ρ is the resistance per unit length of the wire, and S is a variable known resistance. In practice R_1 is made equal to R_2, and hence

$$R_P + R_L + (a - x)\rho = R_L + S + (a + x)\rho$$

$$\therefore\ R_P = S + 2x\rho.$$

Thus the resistance of the leads is eliminated by the use of the "dummy" leads, and it can be seen that the resistance measured is always that of the platinum wire alone.

The resistance R_0 of the platinum wire at the temperature of melting ice corresponds to the "lower fixed point" of the thermometer, and the resistance R_{100} at the temperature of steam at normal pressure corresponds to the " upper fixed point ". *The interval between these two resistance values is divided into* 100 *equal parts or degrees.* The resistance R_t of the wire at an unknown temperature t_p is measured, and the latter is calculated from the relation

$$\frac{t_p}{100} = \frac{R_t - R_0}{R_{100} - R_0}. \qquad \qquad (3)$$

The relation in (3) is the *definition* of temperature on the platinum resistance thermometer scale, and the reader will again note the resemblance between this expression and those which define the temperature as determined by the mercury and gas thermometer scales (pp. 4, 7).

Example 2.—Suppose $R_0 = 6{\cdot}284$ ohms, $R_{100} = 7{\cdot}321$ ohms, and that the resistance R_t is 6·726 ohms when the thermometer is placed in warm water. The temperature t_p of the water is then given by

$$\frac{t_p}{100} = \frac{6{\cdot}726 - 6{\cdot}284}{7{\cdot}321 - 6{\cdot}284},$$

from which $t_p = 42{\cdot}6°$ C.

The platinum resistance thermometer has the wide range of about —200° C. to 1200° C., and is very accurate. One disadvantage is the time required to make the bridge balance when measuring a temperature.

11. Thermoelectric thermometer.

If two unlike metals A, B, such as copper and iron, are joined together, and one of the junctions H is heated, an e.m.f. is developed in one direction, say AHB, and a current flows (fig. 1.8*a*). The thermoelectric e.m.f., as it is called, depends on the difference in temperatures between C, the " cold " junction, and H, the " hot " junction, and is obtained by a conversion of heat energy to electrical energy.

The *thermoelectric thermometer* utilizes the thermoelectric e.m.f. Fig. 1.8*b* represents a nickel wire A and a Nichrome wire B inside an iron tube T, with a high-resistance millivoltmeter G connected to A and B by very long leads. When the end of T is placed in contact with a hot object, an e.m.f. is developed in the circuit, and the temperature is read directly from the scale on G, which is calibrated in degrees centigrade or fahrenheit with the aid of a platinum resistance or gas thermometer.

Nickel and Nichrome can be used for temperatures up to about 1200° C. For higher temperatures the tube must be made of silica, and metals with higher melting-points, such as tungsten

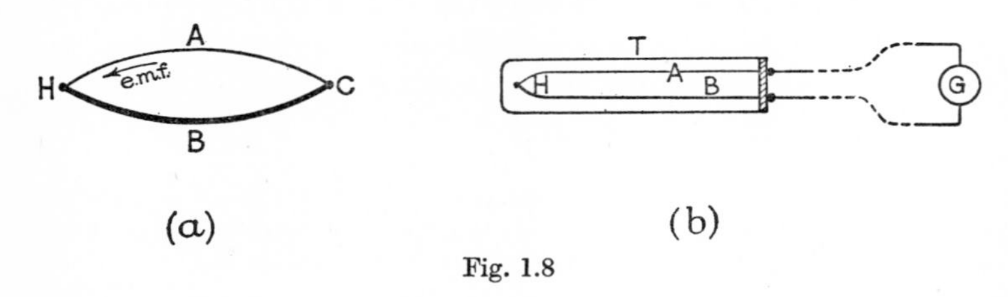

Fig. 1.8

and molybdenum, or platinum and an alloy of platinum, are used. The thermoelectric thermometer has a wide range of about —200° C. to 1400° C., and is very useful for measuring varying temperatures. It is also used for measuring the temperatures of blast and glass furnaces, and thus enjoys a wide use in industry.

12. A comparison between the mercury, gas, and platinum resistance thermometer scales.

If the temperature of a liquid is measured by a mercury thermometer, then by a constant-volume gas thermometer, and then by a platinum resistance thermometer, the results obtained are not the same; for example, the temperatures on the respective thermometer scales might be 28·2° C., 28·0° C., 28·1° C. A little thought will show that this is not a surprising result. In one case the property used to measure temperature is the change in volume of mercury with temperature changes; in another case the pressure variation with temperature of a gas at constant volume is used; and in the third case the variation of electrical resistance with temperature. *Thus the numerical value given to a temperature depends on the type of thermometer used.* The differences in the values are comparatively small in practice, and may be obtained from tables which have been compiled, using the temperature on the *gas thermometer* scale as a reference standard.

The student should clearly understand that the centigrade, fahrenheit, and réaumur systems are methods of numbering scales. We thus have temperatures in °C., or °F., on the mercury, gas, and platinum resistance thermometer scales.

13. International scale of temperature.

In 1887 an international meeting of scientists set up a scale of temperature which was to be used internationally. It was decided to transfer all temperatures to the constant-volume hydrogen thermometer scale, the melting-point of ice being taken as 0° C. and the temperature of steam at normal atmospheric pressure being taken as 100° C. Hydrogen, however, is not an ideal or perfect gas (p. 72), and it appeared to be better to transfer temperatures to an ideal scale first suggested by Lord Kelvin in 1848. Temperatures on this scale are called *degrees Kelvin* (°K), see p. 58. As it is difficult to realize the Kelvin scale practically, an international meeting in 1933 decided to adopt a scale known as the *International Temperature Scale*, on which the melting-points and boiling-points of pure substances are allotted definite numerical values, and the temperatures between these points are obtained from specified formulæ. The international temperature scale is the nearest practical approach to the Kelvin scale.

Example 3.—Describe a constant-volume air thermometer, and explain how an interval of one centigrade degree is defined on the scale of this instrument. The following readings were obtained with a constant-volume air thermometer:

	Level of mercury in closed limb, mm.	Level of mercury in open limb, mm.
Bulb in melting ice	136	112
Bulb in steam at 76 cm. pressure ..	136	390
Bulb at room temperature	136	160

Calculate the room temperature. (*O. & C.*)

First part.—(See p. 8.) The interval of one centigrade degree is defined as $(p_{100} - p_0)/100$, where p_{100}, p_0 are the respective pressures at the temperatures of steam under normal pressure, and melting ice.

Second part.—The temperature t of the room is given by

$$\frac{t}{100} = \frac{p_t - p_0}{p_{100} - p_0},$$

using the notation and diagram on p. 7. Now $p_0 = H - (13{\cdot}6 - 11{\cdot}2)$ cm., where H is the barometric pressure in centimetres of mercury, $p_t = H + (16{\cdot}0 - 13{\cdot}6)$ cm., and $p_{100} = H + (39{\cdot}0 - 13{\cdot}6)$ cm.

$$\therefore\ p_t - p_0 = 4{\cdot}8 \text{ cm.}, \ p_{100} - p_0 = 27{\cdot}8 \text{ cm.}$$

$$\therefore\ \frac{t}{100} = \frac{4{\cdot}8}{27{\cdot}8}.$$

$$\therefore\ t = 17{\cdot}3^\circ \text{ C.}$$

Examples on Chapter I

1. In a mercury thermometer the volumes of the mercury at 0° C. and 100° C. are 0·400 c.c. and 0·432 c.c. respectively. Calculate the temperature when the volume of the mercury is (i) 0·408 c.c., (ii) 0·428 c.c., (iii) 0·390 c.c.

2. What advantages has alcohol over mercury as a thermometric liquid? List the advantages of mercury as a thermometric liquid.

3. What is the definition of temperature on the platinum resistance thermometer scale? The resistances of the thermometer are 6·750 and 7·350 ohms respectively at the temperatures of melting ice and steam at normal atmospheric pressure. At room temperature the resistance is 6·846 ohms. Find the temperature of the room. Would this be exactly the same temperature as that obtained by a mercury thermometer? Give a reason.

4. Name the errors inherent in the mercury thermometer. What do you regard as the chief source of error?

5. What is the definition of temperature on the constant-volume gas thermometer scale? The pressure of the gas at 0° C. in such a thermometer is 65·00 cm. mercury, at 100° C. it is 91·60 cm. When it is used to measure the temperature of two liquids, the pressure becomes (i) 82·00 cm., (ii) 108·70 cm. respectively. What are the two temperatures?

6. Describe how a thermocouple is used to determine the temperature of a molten metal.

7. Name the thermometer you consider most accurate for measuring the following temperatures: (i) 80° C., (ii) −50° C., (iii) 1000° C., (iv) 280° C. What thermometers do you consider to be most convenient for measuring these temperatures, if a very accurate value is not required?

8. Explain the principles used in establishing a scale of temperature. Give an account of *two* experiments you could perform, using quite distinct physical properties, in order to determine the temperature of a liquid bath (about 110° C.), without using a mercury or other liquid thermometer, but using normal laboratory equipment. (*L.H.S.C.*)

9. State precisely what is meant by the statements that the temperature of a certain body is (*a*) "t° C. on the constant-volume air scale," and (*b*) "t_p° C. on the platinum scale." Draw a labelled diagram of a constant-volume air thermometer. Describe how you would use it to find the boiling-point of a solution of common salt. How would the boiling-point compare with that of pure water, and how would it vary with the concentration of the solution? (*L.H.S.C.*) [See also p. 126.]

10. Describe a clinical thermometer and point out how its construction makes it (*a*) sensitive, (*b*) quick acting, (*c*) self-registering. Give reasons for and against the use of mercury as a thermometric fluid. (*C.H.S.C.*)

11. How is a centigrade temperature defined on (*a*) a constant-volume gas thermometer, (*b*) a platinum resistance thermometer? Give an account of platinum resistance thermometry. (*O. & C.*)

12. Describe a simple form of constant-volume air thermometer, and give an account of the method you would employ to determine the boiling-point of a liquid by the use of such a thermometer. Point out the precautions you would take to ensure an accurate result. (*C.W.B.*)

13. Describe how you would use *either* (i) a constant-volume *or* (ii) a constant-pressure air thermometer to calibrate a mercurial thermometer. If the difference of mercury level in a constant-volume air thermometer is -2 cm. when the temperature of the bulb is 10° C. and $+22$ cm. when the bulb is at 100° C., what is the height of the barometer? (*L. Inter.*) [See also p. 61.]

14. A certain temperature t, such as the melting-point of a solid, is expressed on the centigrade scale. Explain what is the value of t on (*a*) an ideal gas centigrade scale, (*b*) on a platinum resistance centigrade scale. Describe a platinum resistance thermometer and explain how it may be used to measure a temperature. (*L. Inter.*)

15. Discuss the measurement of temperature, and explain how temperature is defined on the scale of a given type of thermometer. When used to measure temperatures of about 300° C. the readings on the scale of an accurate mercury thermometer are about 2° higher than those of an accurate air thermometer. Why is this, and what reasons, if any, are there for adopting one scale rather than the other? (*O. & C.*)

16. How is centigrade temperature defined (*a*) on the scale of a constant-pressure gas thermometer, (*b*) on the scale of a platinum resistance thermometer? A constant mass of gas maintained at constant pressure has a volume of 200·0 c.c. at the temperature of melting ice, 273·2 c.c. at the temperature of water boiling under standard pressure, and 525·1 c.c. at the normal boiling-point of sulphur. A platinum wire has resistances of 2·000, 2·778, and 5·280 ohms at the same temperatures. Calculate the values of the boiling-point of sulphur given by the two sets of observations and comment on the results. (*L. Inter.*)

17. Describe some form of electrical resistance thermometer. For what range of temperatures is it particularly useful? How would you use an electrical resistance thermometer to measure the melting-point of lead? (*C.H.S.C.*)

CHAPTER II

The Expansion of Solids

Observation shows that the length of a solid varies with temperature (p. 20), and that a very large force is exerted by the solid when the expansion, or contraction, is opposed (p. 26). These phenomena cause many inconveniences in everyday life, and the variation in length is allowed for in the design of pendulums of clocks, and in the construction of railway lines and bridges. The Forth bridge, for instance, has roller bearings at both ends to allow for changes in its length with temperature; if the bridge were fixed at both ends it would be subjected to an exceptionally severe strain in expansion or contraction, owing to the large force exerted. On the other hand, the expansion of solids with increasing temperature is utilized commercially in the design of thermostats and balance wheels of watches (pp. 22, 23).

1. Coefficient of linear expansion.

Different solids expand by different amounts when heated through the same temperature range. The most useful way of providing information concerning the linear expansion of a solid is to give the expansion of *unit* length of the solid when it is heated through a temperature change of *one* degree, as the expansion of any other length of the solid for any other temperature change can then be easily calculated by simple proportion. The *coefficient of linear expansion* (α) of a solid is defined as *the increase in length of unit length when the temperature increases by* 1° C. The magnitude of α depends on the initial temperature of the solid, though the variation of α with temperature is extremely small.

When the solid is heated over a wide range of temperature, e.g. from 14° C. to 54° C., we refer to the *mean coefficient* of linear expansion (α_m) in this temperature range, and this is defined as " the average increase in length of unit length for 1° C. change in temperature, in the temperature range 14° to 54° C." Thus if the length of a solid increases from 120 cm. at 14° C. to 120·2 cm. at 54° C., the mean coefficient in this temperature range

$$= \frac{120 \cdot 2 - 120}{120 \times (54 - 14)} = 0 \cdot 000\,04 \text{ per °C.}$$

Experiment shows that the mean coefficient of expansion of a solid varies only very slightly with different temperature ranges.

2. Some magnitudes of linear coefficient of expansion.

From the above calculation for the mean coefficient, α_m, it can be seen that

$$\alpha_m = \frac{\text{change in length}}{\text{original length} \times \text{change in temperature}}.$$

The same formula also holds for the linear coefficient α. Since a " length " is present in the numerator and the denominator, the ratio of these two quantities is a number; it can thus be seen that the *units* of linear coefficient are simply "*per °C.*", or "*per °F.*", without any mention of a length.

The mean coefficient of linear expansion of brass is about 0·000 018 per °C.; thus 1 cm. (or 1 ft.) of brass expands by 0·000 018 cm. (or 0·000 018 ft.) when its temperature rises 1° C. The mean coefficient of linear expansion of iron is about 0·000 011 per °C., while that of glass is about 0·000 008 per °C. Since a change of 1° C. is equivalent to a change of (9/5)° F., the linear coefficient of brass can also be expressed as 0·000 018 per (9/5)° F., or 0·000 018 × 5/9 per °F. Thus the linear coefficient of brass is 0·000 010 per °F.

Quartz and *fused silica* have extremely low linear coefficients, so that vessels of these materials have a negligibly small expansion when the temperature rises. *Pyrex*, the material used for cooking dishes, has a very small coefficient, which prevents the glass from cracking when the temperature rises or falls. *Invar* is an alloy of steel and nickel which has a very low linear coefficient, and is used in a thermostat for domestic gas cookers and as the pendulum material of a standard clock.

3. Formulæ.

Suppose a piece of brass 120 cm. long at 0° C. is heated to a temperature of 40° C. Assuming that the mean linear coefficient of expansion of brass is 0·000 018 per °C., it follows that the expansion is 0·000 018 × 120 × 40 cm., by simple proportion. In the same way, if a solid has a length l_0 at 0° C., a mean linear coefficient α, and the temperature rises to t° C., then

$$\textit{increase in length} = \alpha l_0 t. \quad . \quad . \quad (4)$$

Consequently the new length l_t of the solid at t° C. = original length + increase = $l_0 + \alpha l_0 t$.

$$\therefore \quad l_t = l_0(1 + \alpha t). \quad . \quad . \quad . \quad . \quad (5)$$

Further, since $(l_t - l_0)$ is the increase in length when a length l_0 at 0° C. increases to a length l_t at t° C., the linear coefficient is given by

$$\alpha = \frac{l_t - l_0}{l_0 \times t}. \quad . \quad . \quad . \quad . \quad . \quad (6)$$

Similar formulæ are obtained if we start with a length of the same solid at a temperature other than 0° C.; and since the mean coefficient of the solid has very nearly the same magnitude as before, we shall assume that the mean coefficient is still given by α. Thus if l_1 is a length of the solid at t_1° C., and l_2 is the new length at a higher temperature t_2° C.,

$$\alpha = \frac{l_2 - l_1}{l_1 \times (t_2 - t_1)},$$

from which

$$l_2 = l_1[1 + \alpha(t_2 - t_1)].$$

4. A laboratory method for determining the mean coefficient of expansion.

The mean linear coefficient of expansion of a solid can be found by the apparatus illustrated in fig. 2.1. One end A of a solid rod is fixed, while the other end B is free to expand, and the rod is surrounded by an insulating jacket P. The movable screw S of a spherometer is turned until it makes contact with the end B (a bell-circuit, not shown, can be used to find when contact is made), and the reading on the spherometer is taken.

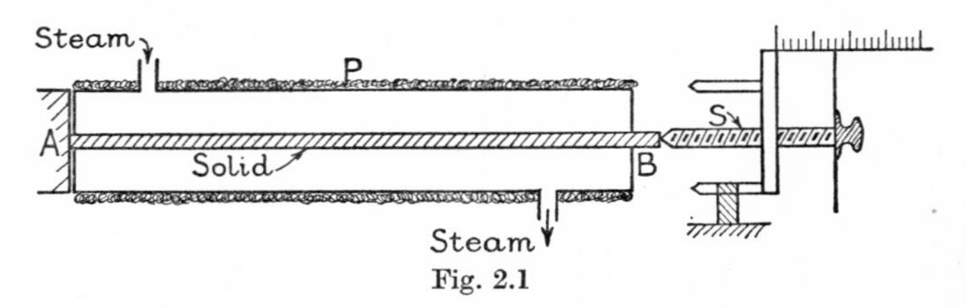

Fig. 2.1

Suppose it is 1·436 cm., and the original length of the rod is 98·6 cm. The screw S is then turned back to allow the rod to expand, steam is passed into the jacket, and after a time the screw is turned to make contact with B again. The new reading is noted; suppose it is 1·224 cm. The expansion of the rod is thus 1·436 — 1·224, or 0·212 cm. If the initial temperature of the rod is 15° C. and the steam temperature is 99·8° C., the mean coefficient over the temperature range is given by

$$\text{mean coefficient} = \frac{\text{increase in length}}{\text{original length} \times \text{temperature rise}}$$

$$= \frac{0{\cdot}212}{98{\cdot}6 \times (99{\cdot}8 - 15)} = 0{\cdot}000\,025 \text{ per } {}^\circ\text{C.}$$

5. The comparator method for measuring the linear coefficient of expansion.

An accurate method of measuring the linear coefficient of expansion of a solid is illustrated by fig. 2.2. It is known as a "comparator method" for a reason explained later, and is used at the International Bureau of Weights and Measures.

A standard metre bar P, one with marks on it exactly one metre apart, and the bar Q whose linear coefficient is required, are on separate trolleys inside a trough T containing water at 0° C. The bar Q (not shown) has scratches on it about one metre apart. The trolleys move on wheels which enable the marks on P and Q to be brought in turn under the microscopes M_1 and M_2, which are supported by massive concrete pillars X.

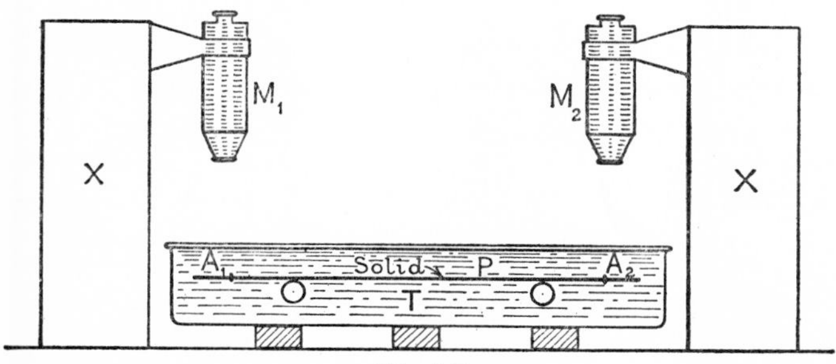

Fig. 2.2

The standard metre bar P is viewed first, and both microscopes are then adjusted by micrometer screws (not shown) until the two marks A_1, A_2 on P are exactly under the cross-wires in each eyepiece. The distance between the cross-wires is then exactly one metre. P is now wheeled out of view, Q is brought into its place, and the two microscopes are adjusted until the two marks on Q are under the respective cross-wires. Knowing the total shift s of the two microscopes, the length l between the two marks on Q is obtained by adding (or subtracting) s from one metre. The temperature of the trough is now increased and maintained constant, and the microscopes are again adjusted so that the marks on Q are in line with the cross-wires. The net shift of the microscopes is equal to the expansion of a length l of the bar Q and, knowing the rise in temperature, the linear coefficient α can be calculated.

Owing to the massive concrete pillars on which they are mounted, the microscopes are not affected by any change in temperature. This method of determining the linear coefficient is known as the comparator method because the original length of the rod is obtained by comparing it with a standard metre bar.

Effects of Expansion

6. The bimetallic strip.

If equal lengths of brass and iron are riveted or welded together as shown in fig. 2.3*a*, they are said to form a " bimetallic strip ". When the strip becomes warm it begins to curve with the brass on the outside, as the linear coefficient of brass is greater than the linear coefficient of iron (fig. 2.3*b*). For a similar reason,

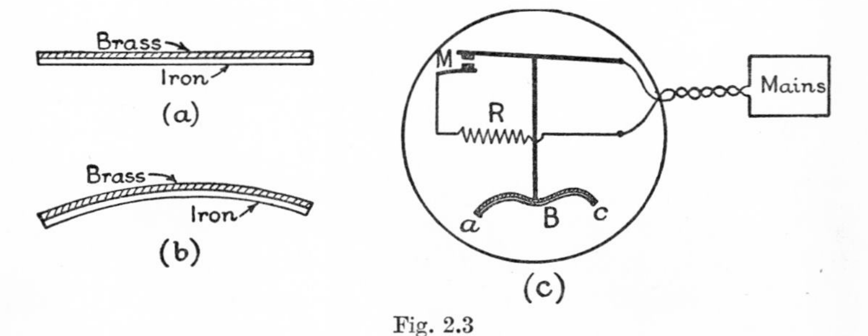

Fig. 2.3

a bimetal coil, fixed at one end, begins to rotate when its temperature rises. The phenomenon is utilized in a variety of domestic and industrial appliances, e.g. in thermostats inside gas heaters and electric irons. Fig. 2.3*c* shows diagrammatically how a curved bimetal strip B, fixed at a and c, breaks the circuit in an electric iron when the temperature of the heater coil R becomes excessive. In this case B expands upwards, breaking the circuit at M. If the temperature falls, B contracts and the circuit is re-made at M.

7. The compensated balance-wheel.

The period of oscillation of a balance-wheel of a watch depends on the elasticity of the hair-spring and the dimensions of the wheel. When the temperature rises, the elasticity of the hair-spring decreases and the wheel expands, causing the watch to slow down. To compensate for temperature changes the balance-wheel rim is made from a bimetallic strip, with the more expansible metal on the outside (fig. 2.4), so that when

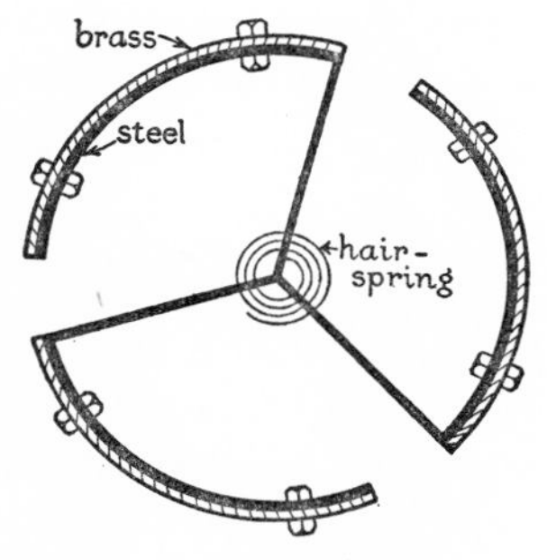

Fig. 2.4

the temperature rises the radius increases; but the rim curves inward and thus decreases the dimensions of the wheel. In this way a " compensation " can be arranged for the altered elasticity of the spring and the change in the radius of the wheel.

8. Harrison's compensated pendulum.

By using two different metals, Harrison designed a pendulum whose length remained fairly constant as the temperature varied, and thus won a Government prize in 1761 for the most accurate timekeeper. Harrison's compensating pendulum is illustrated in fig. 2.5; S represents a steel rod and B a brass rod. The length of the pendulum remains constant if the length from the point of suspension D to the middle of the bob A is constant, and this condition will be obtained if the expansion of the total length of the steel rods S in the downward direction is always equal to the expansion of the total length of the brass rods B in the upward direction, no matter what change occurs in the temperature.

Suppose l_s, l_b are the *total* lengths of the steel and brass rods respectively, and α_s, α_b the corresponding linear coefficients. If the rise in temperature is t, the increase in length of the steel rods in a downward direction is $\alpha_s l_s t$, and the increase in length of the brass rods in an upward direction is $\alpha_b l_b t$. Thus if the length between D and the pendulum bob is to be kept constant, $\alpha_s l_s t = \alpha_b l_b t$. Hence

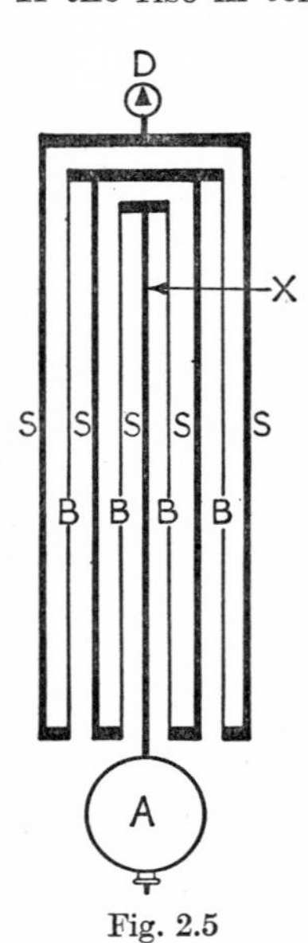

Fig. 2.5

$$\frac{l_s}{l_b} = \frac{\alpha_b}{\alpha_s}.$$

Assuming the linear coefficients of brass and steel are 0·000 018 and 0·000 011 per °C. respectively, $\alpha_b/\alpha_s = 3/2$ approximately. Thus $l_s : l_b = 3 : 2$ approximately. This condition is fulfilled in fig. 2.5, as there are 3 steel and 2 brass rods on either side of a vertical line drawn through the centre of the middle rod X.

9. Alteration in the period of a simple pendulum.

We shall now consider the effect of temperature change on the magnitude of the period of a simple pendulum.

The period T of a simple pendulum of length l is given by $T = 2\pi \sqrt{(l/g)}$, where g is the acceleration due to gravity; if l is in centimetres, g is 981 cm. per sec.^{2} (approx.). Since 2π is a number, and g is a constant at a given place on the earth, it follows that T is proportional to the square root of the length l.

$$\therefore T \propto \sqrt{l}. \qquad \text{(i)}$$

Suppose that a clock has a metal pendulum and is correct in autumn. In summer, when the length of the metal increases, the period of the clock becomes greater, from (i), and the clock will therefore lose. In winter the clock will gain, as the length of the pendulum decreases.

Example 1.—Suppose we require to find how much a clock will lose in a month of 30 days if the average temperature is 18° C., assuming the clock is accurate at 8° C. and has then a period of exactly 2 sec. If the length of the pendulum is l_1 at 8° C., and this increased to l_2 at 18° C., we have, from (i),

$$\frac{T_2}{T_1} = \sqrt{\frac{l_2}{l_1}},$$

where T_1, T_2 are the respective periods at 8° C. and 18° C.

But
$$l_2 = l_1[1 + \overline{18 - 8} \,.\, \alpha],$$

where α is the mean coefficient of linear expansion of the pendulum wire.

$$\therefore \quad \frac{T_2}{T_1} = \sqrt{\frac{l_1(1 + 10\alpha)}{l_1}} = \sqrt{(1 + 10\alpha)}.$$

But $T_1 = 2$ sec., and $\alpha = 0{\cdot}000\,011$ per °C. if the wire is made of iron,

$$\therefore \quad \frac{T_2}{2} = \sqrt{(1 + 10 \times 0{\cdot}000\,011)} = \sqrt{1{\cdot}000\,11}$$

$\therefore$ $T_2 = 2 \times \sqrt{1{\cdot}000\,11} = 2{\cdot}000\,11$ sec.
$\therefore$ in 2·000 11 sec. the clock registers 2 sec.
$\therefore$ in 2·000 11 sec. the clock loses 0·000 11 sec.
$\therefore$ in 1 sec. the clock loses $\frac{1}{2} \times 0{\cdot}000\,11$ sec. to a good approx.
$\therefore$ time lost in a month of 30 days $= \frac{1}{2} \times 0{\cdot}000\,11 \times 30 \times 24 \times 3600$
$= 143$ secs. $= 2$ min. 23 sec.

10. The incorrect metal rule.

If a metal rule or scale is graduated correctly when the temperature is 15° C., for example, the scale gives incorrect values when it is used at a different temperature, because of the change in length of the metal. The steel measuring tapes used by surveyors thus require some correction to be made to the results obtained when they are used.

Suppose that a metal rule is graduated correctly in centimetres at 15° C.; 1 cm. on the scale is then accurately 1 cm. long at this temperature. At a temperature of 18° C., however, the 1 cm.

on the metal scale has expanded to $(1 + 3\alpha)$ cm., where α is the mean coefficient of linear expansion of the metal, as the rise in temperature is 3° C. Thus if a length measured by the metal rule at 18° C. is 20 cm., the true length is greater than this value, and is equal to $20(1 + 3\alpha)$ cm., using the relation $l_2 = l_1[(1 + \alpha(t_2 - t_1)]$ (p. 19). Thus, in general, if the rule is calibrated correctly at t_1° C., a length measured as l_1 by the rule at t_2° C. has a true length l_2 given by $l_2 = l_1[1 + \alpha(t_2 - t_1)]$.

11. The force in a bar when it expands or contracts.

If a metal bar is fixed at one end and heated, observation shows that the great force exerted when it expands is sufficient to break a cast-iron pin placed against it at the other end. On account of the tremendous forces concerned, gaps must be made in railway lines to allow for the expansion.

The magnitude of the force F in a bar when it expands or contracts depends on the value of Young's modulus E for the metal concerned. Suppose that the latter is made of iron of linear coefficient 0·000 011 per °C., and is heated so that its temperature increases by 150° C.

$$\text{Now } E = \frac{\text{stress in bar}}{\text{strain in bar}}, \text{ by definition,}$$

$$= \frac{F/A}{e/l},$$

where A is the area of cross-section of the bar, and e is the extension of the original length l when the iron is heated.

Thus $$F = EAe/l, \text{ from above.}$$

But the increase in length $e = \alpha lt$ (see p. 19),

$$\therefore F = EA\alpha lt/l = EA\alpha t.$$

Suppose that the area of cross-section of the bar is 0·5 sq. in. Then, since $E = 14{,}000$ tons per sq. in. (approx.) for iron,

$$F = 14{,}000 \times 0{\cdot}5 \times 0{\cdot}000\,011 \times 150 = 11{\cdot}55 \text{ tons wt.}$$

This is the magnitude of the force exerted by the bar when it expands. The force exerted when the bar contracts is calculated in a similar manner, and is also given by the formula $F = EA\alpha t$, as the reader should verify.

12. The coefficient of area (superficial) expansion.

Besides expanding in length, solids expand in area when their temperature increases. Thus a metal cistern increases in surface area when the water it contains becomes hotter.

Suppose that a metal square of side l_0 cm. at 0° C. is heated to a temperature of t° C. The new length of the side of the square then becomes $l_0(1 + \alpha t)$, where α is the linear coefficient, and hence the increase in the area of the square $= l_0^2(1 + \alpha t)^2 - l_0^2$.

$$\therefore \text{ increase in area } = l_0^2(2\alpha t + \alpha^2 t^2).$$

The coefficient of area (superficial) expansion β is defined as "the increase in area of unit area at 0° C. for 1° C. rise in temperature".

$$\therefore \text{ coefficient of superficial expansion } \beta = \frac{l_0^2(2\alpha t + \alpha^2 t^2)}{l_0^2 \times t}$$

$$= 2\alpha + \alpha^2 t.$$

But $\alpha^2 t$ is very small compared to 2α, because α is small and of the order 0·000 01.

$$\therefore \beta = 2\alpha.$$

Thus the linear coefficient is *doubled* to obtain the superficial or area coefficient.

13. The coefficient of volume (cubical) expansion.

When a solid, or a glass vessel, becomes hot, the volume changes as well as the length. Suppose that a *hollow cube* has each side of length l_0 at 0° C. and is heated to a temperature of

$t°$ C. If α is the linear coefficient, each side expands to $l_0(1 + \alpha t)$. The new volume of the cube is thus

$$l_0^3(1 + \alpha t)^3 = l_0^3(1 + 3\alpha t + 3\alpha^2 t^2 + \alpha^3 t^3),$$

and subtracting the original volume l_0^3,

$$\text{increase in volume} = l_0^3(3\alpha t + 3\alpha^2 t^2 + \alpha^3 t^3).$$

The coefficient of cubical (volume) expansion γ of a solid is defined as the "increase in volume of unit volume at 0° C., when the temperature increases by 1° C."

$$\therefore\ \gamma = l_0^3(3\alpha t + 3\alpha^2 t^2 + \alpha^3 t^3)/(l_0^3 \times t) = 3\alpha + 3\alpha^2 t + \alpha^3 t^2.$$

But $3\alpha^2 t + \alpha^3 t^2$ is very small compared to 3α, since α is very small,

$$\therefore\ \gamma = 3\alpha.$$

Thus the cubical coefficient of glass is $(3 \times 0{\cdot}000\,008)$ per °C. if the linear coefficient of glass is 0·000 008 per °C.

Consider the expansion of a *solid* cube of side l_0 at 0° C. when it is heated to a temperature of $t°$ C. The new volume is then $l_0^3(1 + \alpha t)^3$, since each side increases in length to $l_0(1 + \alpha t)$, and it can therefore be seen from above that *the expansion of a hollow vessel is exactly the same as if it were a solid vessel occupying the same volume.* We shall have occasion to use this result when we deal with the expansion of liquids (p. 38).

Example 2.—Explain what is meant by saying that the coefficient of linear expansion of brass is 0·000 019 per deg. C. How would you determine this coefficient over the range 0°— 100° C.? The barometric height, as read at 12° C. by a brass scale correct at 0° C., is 76·52 cm. What is the actual height of the mercury column at 12° C.? (*N.J.M.B.*)

First part.—See text.

Second part.—The length of 76·52 cm. on the brass scale is correct only at 0° C. The brass scale expands when the temperature rises to 12° C., and the new length l_2 of 76·52 cm. of brass at 0° C. is given by

$$\begin{aligned} l_2 &= l_1[1 + \alpha(t_2 - t_1)] \\ &= 76{\cdot}52[1 + 0{\cdot}000\,019(12 - 0)] \\ &= 76{\cdot}52 \times 1{\cdot}000\,228 = 76{\cdot}54. \end{aligned}$$

Thus the actual height of the mercury column at 12° C. is 76·54 cm.

Example 3.—Define Young's modulus for the material of a wire. The diagram shows an iron wire AB stretched inside a rigid brass framework and rigidly attached to it at both ends, A and B. The length of AB at 0° C. is 300 cm. and the diameter of the wire is 0·6 mm. What extra tension will be set up in the stretched wire when the temperature of the system is raised to 40° C.? (Take the coefficient of linear expansion of iron as 0·000 012 per °C., the coefficient of linear expansion of brass as 0·000 018 per °C.; Young's Modulus for iron as $2 \cdot 1 \times 10^{12}$ dynes per sq. cm.) (*L.H.S.C.*)

$$\text{Young's modulus } E = \frac{\text{stress}}{\text{strain}} = \frac{F/A}{e/l} \text{ (see p. 26).}$$

$$\therefore \quad F = EAe/l.$$

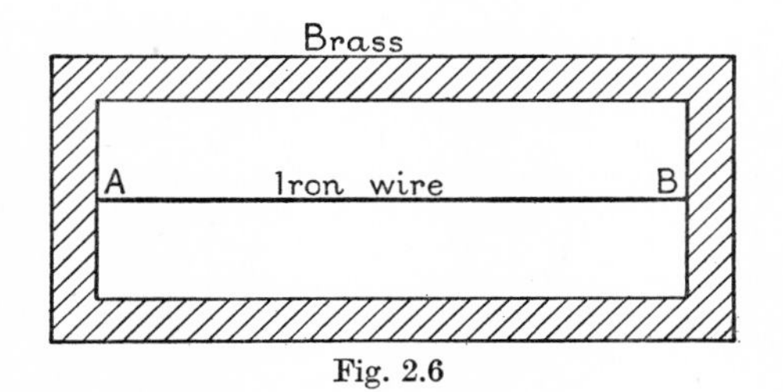

Fig. 2.6

When the system is heated, the brass expands to a length $300(1 + 40\alpha) = 300(1 + 40 \times 0 \cdot 000\,018) = 300 \cdot 216$ cm. The iron wire would normally have expanded to $300(1 + 40 \times 0 \cdot 000\,012)$, or 300·144 cm.; hence the extension e due to its attachment to the brass $= 300 \cdot 216 - 300 \cdot 144 = 0 \cdot 072$ cm.

The "original" length l of the iron $= 300 \cdot 144$ cm.

$$\begin{aligned} \therefore \text{ extra tension in wire } F &= EAe/l \\ &= 2 \cdot 1 \times 10^{12} \times (\pi \times 0 \cdot 03^2) \times 0 \cdot 072/300 \cdot 144 \\ &= 14 \cdot 24 \times 10^5 \text{ dynes,} \end{aligned}$$

as the area A of the cross-section of the wire $= \pi r^2 = \pi \times 0 \cdot 03^2$ sq. cm.

EXAMPLES ON CHAPTER II

1. The linear coefficient of expansion of brass is 0·000 018 per °C. Calculate its linear coefficient per °F. and per °R. State the superficial (area) coefficient and the cubical coefficient of brass on the centigrade scale.

2. The length of a steel rule at 4° C. is 30·00 yards. Calculate (i) its length at 30° C., (ii) its increase in length in inches at 15° C. (Mean linear coefficient of steel = 0·000 012 per °C.).

3. An aluminium roof at 8° C. has dimensions 40·00 ft. by 60·00 ft. What is the new area (i) at 20° C., (ii) at 0° C.? (Mean linear coefficient of aluminium = 0·000 022 per °C.)

4. What is the relation between the period T of a simple pendulum and its length l at a given place on the earth? The length of an iron simple pendulum is 100·00 cm. at 5° C. and the period is 2 sec. What is the period at 26° C. if the mean linear coefficient of iron $= 11 \times 10^{-6}$ per °C.?

5. A bimetal strip is made of brass and iron, and is originally straight. Draw a sketch of the strip when the temperature (*a*) decreases, (*b*) increases.

6. Write down an expression for the force in a steel rod fixed at both ends when it is heated. Calculate the force in kilograms weight if a steel girder of cross-sectional area 100 sq. cm., initially at 4° C., is prevented from expanding when the temperature rises to 18° C. (Mean linear coefficient of steel $= 12 \times 10^{-6}$ per °C., Young's modulus for steel $= 2 \times 10^{12}$ dynes per sq. cm.)

7. Draw a sketch of a compensated balance-wheel of a watch, and explain how its period is kept constant.

8. Describe a method of measuring the coefficient of linear expansion of a substance. Show that the coefficient of cubical expansion of a homogeneous substance is three times its coefficient of linear expansion. (*O. & C.*)

9. What is meant by the statement that the coefficient of linear expansion of iron is 0·000 012 per degree C.? How would you show experimentally that for brass this quantity is about 0·000 018 per degree C.? If a strip of iron and a strip of brass are welded together to form a straight bimetal strip at room temperature, what would happen if the strip were (*a*) raised to a high temperature, (*b*) lowered to a temperature below 0° C.? Describe one application of the bimetal strip in a device in common use. (*L.H.S.C.*)

10. Describe an accurate method for determining the coefficient of thermal expansion of a solid in the form of a rod. The pendulum of a clock is made of brass whose coefficient of linear expansion is $1{\cdot}9 \times 10^{-5}$ per degree C. If the clock keeps correct time at 15° C., how many seconds per day will it lose at 20° C.? (*O. & C.*)

11. A steel wire 8 metres long and 4 mm. in diameter is fixed to two rigid supports. Calculate the increase in tension when the temperature falls 10° C. [Linear coefficient of expansion of steel $= 12 \times 10^{-6}$ per degree centigrade, Young's modulus for steel $= 2 \times 10^{12}$ dynes per sq. cm.] (*O. & C.*)

12. Explain what is meant by the statements that (*a*) Young's modulus for steel is 2×10^{12} c.g.s. units, (*b*) the coefficient of linear expansion of steel is $1{\cdot}2 \times 10^{-5}$ per °C. Describe an accurate method of measuring *one* of these quantities. A steel rod of diameter 1·0 cm. is clamped firmly at each end when its temperature is 25° C., so that it cannot contract on cooling. What will be the tension in the rod at 0° C.? (*C.H.S.C.*)

CHAPTER III

The Expansion of Liquids

When a mercury (or an alcohol) thermometer is used to measure the temperature of hot water, the volume of the mercury (or the alcohol) increases so that the thread travels along the capillary tube. Thus liquids expand when their temperature increases. Generally, liquids expand much more than solids when they are heated through the same temperature range (see below). The change in volume of a liquid with temperature is utilized in the convection system of heating, which supplies hot water from taps, and fishes and other animal life are able to live in lakes when the temperature is below freezing-point on account of the way in which the volume of water changes with temperature (p. 47).

1. The coefficient of expansion of a liquid.

A liquid occupies a *volume* and we can thus deal only with the volume changes of a liquid with temperature.

The *coefficient of expansion of a liquid* is defined as *the increase in volume of unit volume when its temperature increases by* 1° C., which is a similar definition to that given for a solid (p. 17). The difference is that we are here dealing with changes in volume, i.e. a cubical coefficient, and not changes in length. The magnitude of the coefficient of expansion of a liquid is about ten times as great as the magnitude of the linear coefficient of expansion of solids; e.g. the coefficient of expansion of water is about 0·000 2 per °C., whereas the linear coefficient of brass is about 0·000 018 per °C. The coefficient of expansion of a given liquid depends on its initial temperature.

The *mean coefficient* of expansion of a liquid γ is defined as the "average increase in volume of unit volume for 1° C. rise in temperature in the temperature range concerned". Thus if the volume of water at 14° C. is 270 c.c. and the volume at 60° C. is 273 c.c., the mean coefficient between 14° C. and 60° C. is given by

$$\frac{273 - 270}{270 \times (60 - 14)} = 0{\cdot}000\,24 \text{ per °C.}$$

2. Formulæ.

Suppose v_0 is the volume of a liquid at 0° C. and v_t is the volume at t° C. The mean coefficient of expansion of the liquid is then given by

$$\gamma = \frac{v_t - v_0}{v_0 \times t}, \quad . \quad . \quad . \quad . \quad . \quad . \quad . \quad (7)$$

by definition of γ. Further, the increase in volume of the liquid from 0° C., which is $(v_t - v_0)$, is given by

$$\text{increase in volume} = \gamma v_0 t, \quad . \quad . \quad . \quad . \quad (8)$$

and the volume v_t is thus $(v_0 + \gamma v_0 t)$.

$$\therefore \; \boldsymbol{v_t = v_0(1 + \gamma t)}. \quad . \quad . \quad . \quad . \quad . \quad . \quad (9)$$

Similar formulæ are obtained when the liquid is originally at a temperature other than 0° C. For example, if v_1 is the volume of a liquid at t_1° C., v_2 is the volume at t_2° C., and γ is the mean coefficient of expansion in this temperature range, then $v_2 = v_1[1 + \gamma(t_2 - t_1)]$.

3. The absolute (true) and apparent coefficients of expansion of a liquid.

A liquid must always be contained in a vessel of some kind. If the liquid is heated the vessel expands as well as the liquid, and the observed or *apparent* increase in volume of the liquid is equal to the difference between the actual or *absolute* expansion of the liquid and that of the vessel. If the vessel expands more than the liquid, the latter will appear to decrease in volume, and this may be observed to occur when a liquid is first warmed in a glass vessel, as the heat has then not yet reached the liquid. We must therefore distinguish between the absolute or true coefficient of expansion of a liquid and its apparent coefficient.

The *absolute* (*true*) *coefficient of expansion* of a liquid γ is defined as the actual or true increase in volume of unit volume when the temperature increases by 1° C. (p. 32). The *apparent coefficient of expansion* of a liquid (γ_{app}) is defined as the observed increase in volume of unit volume when the temperature increases by 1° C. Thus the apparent coefficient does not take into account the expansion of the containing vessel, and it should be obvious that the apparent coefficient (γ_{app}) is *less* than the absolute (true) coefficient γ. It can be shown that, approximately,

$$\gamma = \gamma_{app} + c, \quad . \quad . \quad . \quad . \quad . \quad (10)$$

where c is the cubical coefficient of the material of the container (see below). Thus the value of c must be known if γ_{app} is measured in an experiment and the absolute coefficient γ is required. Suppose, for example, that the linear coefficient of glass is 0·000 008 per °C; then the cubical coefficient of glass $c = 3 \times 0{\cdot}000\,008 = 0{\cdot}000\,024$ per °C. (p. 28). If the apparent coefficient of a liquid in glass is found by experiment to be 0·000 45, the absolute coefficient $\gamma = 0{\cdot}000\,45 + 0{\cdot}000\,024 =$ ·0000 47 per °C., to two significant figures.

4. To show $\gamma = \gamma_{app} + c$, approximately.

Consider a vessel filled with a liquid of volume v_1 at t_1° C. to a level A (fig. 3.1*a*), and suppose an etching or scratch is made at this level on the container. If the liquid is heated to t_2° C., the vessel expands to a volume v_1' at a level B, which is the new height of the etching if we assume the base of the vessel is fixed so that it cannot expand. At the same time the volume of the liquid increases to a value v_2 (fig. 3.1*b*), and if the level of the liquid is now at D, the apparent expansion of the liquid is the volume between B and D, which is $(v_2 - v_1')$. The original volume of the liquid is the volume v_1, and hence the apparent coefficient of expansion of the liquid is given by

$$\gamma_{app} = \frac{\text{apparent increase in volume}}{\text{original volume} \times \text{temperature change}}$$

$$= \frac{v_2 - v_1'}{v_1(t_2 - t_1)},$$

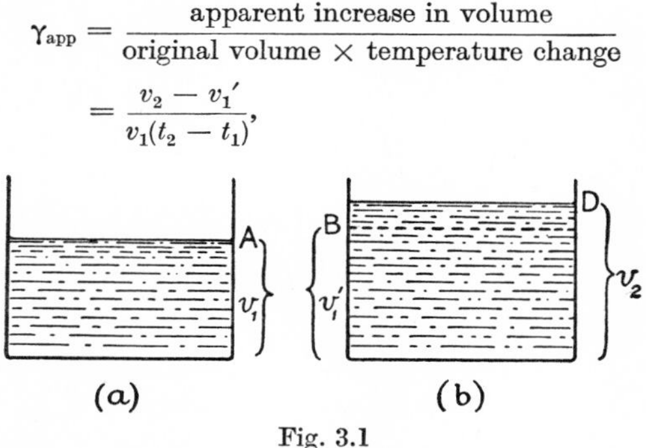

Fig. 3.1

where t_2, t_1 are the final and initial temperatures of the liquid. Now $v_2 = v_1[1 + \gamma(t_2 - t_1)]$ and $v_1' = v_1[1 + c(t_2 - t_1)]$, to a good degree of approximation.

$$\therefore \quad \gamma_{app} = \frac{v_1[1 + \gamma(t_2 - t_1)] - v_1[1 + c(t_2 - t_1)]}{v_1(t_2 - t_1)}$$

$$= \frac{(\gamma - c)(t_2 - t_1)v_1}{v_1(t_2 - t_1)} = \gamma - c.$$

$$\therefore \quad \gamma = \gamma_{app} + c.$$

5. The relation between the absolute coefficient γ of a liquid and its density d.

When a given mass of liquid is heated its volume increases, and hence the density (mass/volume) of the liquid decreases. There is a simple relation between the density values of a liquid at various temperatures and its absolute coefficient of expansion γ, and as this relation is at the basis of many of the methods of determining γ, the following deserves the close attention of the reader.

Let $\quad m =$ the mass of a liquid,

v_0, $v_t =$ the volumes at 0° C. and t° C. respectively,

and $\quad d_0$, $d_t =$ the densities at 0° C. and t° C. respectively.

Since mass = volume × density, it follows that

$$m = v_0 d_0, \text{ and } m = v_t d_t.$$

$$\therefore\ v_0 d_0 = v_t d_t.$$

$$\therefore\ \frac{d_0}{d_t} = \frac{v_t}{v_0}.$$

But $v_t = v_0(1 + \gamma t)$, p. 33, and hence $\frac{v_t}{v_0} = 1 + \gamma t$.

$$\therefore\ \boldsymbol{\frac{d_0}{d_t} = 1 + \gamma t}. \quad . \quad . \quad . \quad . \quad . \quad (11)$$

When a liquid is heated from a temperature of t_1° C. to t_2° C., it can be proved by an exactly similar method that

$$\frac{d_1}{d_2} = 1 + \gamma_m(t_2 - t_1),$$

where d_1, d_2 are the densities at t_1° C., t_2° C. respectively, and γ_m is the mean coefficient of expansion of the liquid between these temperatures.

It should be noted that, in general, the density of a liquid is greater at a lower temperature than a higher one, since the volume of a given mass of liquid becomes smaller when the temperature decreases. Thus the density d_0 at 0° C. is usually greater than the density d_t at t° C., where t is greater than zero.

Example 1.—What do you understand by the statement "The mean coefficient of expansion of mercury is 182×10^{-6} per °C."? The density of mercury at 20° C. is 13·55 gm. per c.c. At what higher temperature will this figure be in error by 1 per cent? (*N.J.M.B.*)

First part.—The statement means that: The average expansion of 1 c.c. of the mercury for 1° C. rise in temperature is 182×10^{-6} c.c. over the temperature range considered.

Second part.—Suppose t is the temperature in °C. At this temperature the density is less than 13·55 by 1/100 of 13·55.

$\therefore$ density d_2 at t° C. = 13·55 − 0·1355 = 13·4145 gm. per c.c.

But density d_1 at 20° C. = 13·55 gm. per c.c.,

and $d_1/d_2 = 1 + \gamma(t_2 - t_1)$, with the usual notation.

$$\therefore \frac{13{\cdot}55}{13{\cdot}4145} = 1 + 0{\cdot}000\,182(t - 20),$$

since $\gamma = 182 \times 10^{-6}$.

$$\therefore t - 20 = \frac{13{\cdot}55 - 13{\cdot}414\,5}{13{\cdot}414\,5 \times 0{\cdot}000\,182} = 55{\cdot}6.$$

$$\therefore t = 75{\cdot}6° \text{ C.}$$

Determinations of the Apparent and Absolute Coefficients of Expansion

6. The specific gravity bottle, or weight thermometer, method.

One of the simplest methods of determining the *apparent coefficient* of expansion of a liquid is to fill a specific gravity bottle P quite full of liquid. Instead of a specific gravity bottle, a glass vessel Q of the shape shown in fig. 3.2 is sometimes used; Q is known as a "weight thermometer".

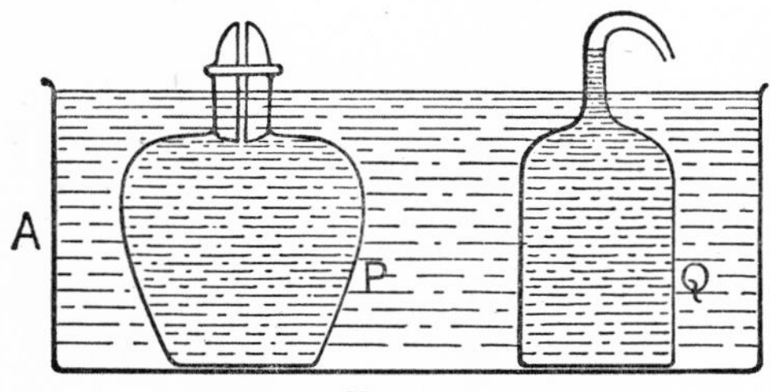

Fig. 3.2

The mass of liquid filling the vessel is first measured. The vessel is then placed in a water bath A and is heated to a known temperature. Since the liquid expands, some of it is expelled from the vessel through the opening at the top, and when the vessel is reweighed, the mass of liquid left in the vessel is determined.

Suppose m_1, m_2 are the masses of the liquid filling the bottle at temperatures $t_1°$ C., $t_2°$ C., where t_2 is greater than t_1; v_1, v_2 are the respective volumes of the liquid; and d_1, d_2 are the respective densities of the liquid. Then, since mass = volume × density,

$$m_1 = v_1 d_1,\ m_2 = v_2 d_2.$$

$$\therefore\ \frac{m_1}{m_2} = \frac{v_1 d_1}{v_2 d_2} = \frac{v_1}{v_2} \times \frac{d_1}{d_2}. \quad . \quad . \quad . \quad . \quad \text{(i)}$$

Now the ratio d_1/d_2 concerns the mean coefficient of expansion γ of the liquid between the temperatures $t_1°$ C., $t_2°$ C., and $d_1/d_2 = 1 + \gamma(t_2 - t_1)$, p. 36. On the other hand, it should be carefully observed that the ratio v_1/v_2 concerns the *mean cubical coefficient of expansion c of the material of the vessel,* since a liquid always conforms to the shape of the vessel containing it. Thus $v_2 = v_1[1 + c(t_2 - t_1)]$, and hence $\dfrac{v_1}{v_2} = \dfrac{1}{1 + c(t_2 - t_1)}$.

Substituting for v_1/v_2 and d_1/d_2 in (i), we have

$$\frac{m_1}{m_2} = \frac{1}{1 + c(t_2 - t_1)} \times 1 + \gamma(t_2 - t_1) = \frac{1 + \gamma(t_2 - t_1)}{1 + c(t_2 - t_1)}.$$

Cross-multiplying and simplifying for γ, we obtain

$$\gamma = \frac{m_1 - m_2}{m_2(t_2 - t_1)} + \frac{m_1}{m_2} . c. \quad . \quad . \quad . \quad . \quad (12)$$

A convenient approximation can be made in this expression for γ by considering the results of a typical experiment. The original mass of liquid m_1 was 62·41 gm., and the mass of liquid m_2 left after heating was 59·70 gm. Thus

$$\frac{m_1}{m_2} . c = \frac{62{\cdot}41}{59{\cdot}70} c, \text{ and hence } \frac{m_1}{m_2} c = c$$

to a good degree of approximation. Consequently, it can be stated, from the expression for γ in (12), that

$$\gamma = \frac{m_1 - m_2}{m_2(t_2 - t_1)} + c,$$

to a good degree of approximation. Hence

$$\gamma - c = \frac{m_1 - m_2}{m_2(t_2 - t_1)}.$$

But $$\gamma - c = \gamma_{\text{app}},$$

where γ_{app} is the apparent coefficient of expansion of the liquid.

$$\therefore \gamma_{\text{app}} = \frac{m_1 - m_2}{m_2(t_2 - t_1)}.$$

Since $(m_1 - m_2)$ is the " mass of liquid expelled " on heating, and m_2 is the " mass of liquid *left* ", it follows that

$$\gamma_{\text{app}} = \frac{\textit{mass expelled}}{\textit{mass}\ \text{LEFT} \times \textit{temperature rise}}. \quad . \quad (13)$$

The specific gravity bottle, or weight thermometer, thus enables the apparent coefficient of expansion of a liquid to be easily found. If the absolute coefficient of the liquid is required, the cubical coefficient c of the vessel's material must be added to the apparent coefficient; but this method does not give a very accurate value for the absolute coefficient, as c is not known to a high degree of accuracy. If the specific gravity bottle, or the weight thermometer, were made of quartz or Pyrex, the magnitude of c would then be so small as to be negligible in comparison with the magnitude of γ_{app}. In this case the absolute coefficient of the liquid can be accurately measured by the specific gravity bottle or weight thermometer method.

Example 2.—When a glass weight thermometer filled with mercury at 0° C. is heated to 100° C., 7·785 gm. of mercury overflow and 450·0 gm. remain in the thermometer. Using glycerine in place of mercury, the corresponding figures are 2·173 gm. and 41·00 gm. The coefficient of expansion of mercury is 0·000 183 per °C. Determine (*a*) the coefficient of linear expansion of the glass, (*b*) the coefficient of volume expansion of the glycerine. (*N.J.M.B.*)

(*a*) Apparent coefficient of mercury

$$\gamma_{app} = \frac{\text{mass expelled}}{\text{mass left} \times \text{temp. rise}}$$

$$= \frac{7{\cdot}785}{450{\cdot}0 \times 100} = 0{\cdot}000\ 173 \text{ per } ^\circ\text{C.}$$

But the absolute coefficient of mercury $\gamma = \gamma_{app} + c$, where c is the cubical coefficient of glass.

$$\therefore\ c = \gamma - \gamma_{app} = 0{\cdot}000\ 183 - 0{\cdot}000\ 173$$
$$= 0{\cdot}000\ 010 \text{ per } ^\circ\text{C.}$$

$\therefore$ linear coefficient of glass $= \frac{1}{3} \times c = \frac{1}{3} \times 0{\cdot}000\ 010 = 0{\cdot}000\ 003\ 3$ per °C.

(*b*) Apparent coefficient γ_{app} of glycerine

$$= \frac{\text{mass expelled}}{\text{mass left} \times \text{temp. rise}}$$

$$= \frac{2{\cdot}173}{41{\cdot}00 \times 100} = 0{\cdot}000\ 530 \text{ per } ^\circ\text{C.}$$

$\therefore$ absolute coefficient of glycerine $= \gamma_{app} + c$

$$= 0{\cdot}000\ 530 + 0{\cdot}000\ 010 = 0{\cdot}000\ 540 \text{ per } ^\circ\text{C.}$$

7. The hydrostatic (Archimedes' principle) method for the apparent coefficient of expansion.

Besides the weight thermometer method, there is a hydrostatic method for determining the apparent coefficient which utilizes Archimedes' principle.

In this method, an object which can sink below the surface of the liquid (a 200 gm. brass weight, for example, or a loaded glass bulb) is first weighed in air, and then weighed when it is totally immersed in the liquid at room temperature, t_1° C. say. The liquid is then heated to a new constant temperature t_2° C., and the new apparent weight of the sinker is again measured.

Suppose w_0, w_1, w_2 are the respective weights of the sinker in air, in the liquid at t_1° C., and in the liquid at t_2° C. Now Archimedes' principle states that *the apparent loss in weight of a body immersed in a liquid is equal to the weight of liquid displaced by the body.* In the present case, $(w_0 - w_1)$ is the apparent loss in weight of the sinker at $t_1°$ C., and $(w_0 - w_2)$ is the apparent loss in weight at $t_2°$ C. Thus if v_1, v_2 are the volumes of the liquid displaced at $t_1°$ C., $t_2°$ C. respectively, and d_1, d_2 are the corresponding densities of the liquid, then

$$\frac{w_0 - w_1}{w_0 - w_2} = \frac{v_1 d_1}{v_2 d_2} = \frac{v_1}{v_2} \times \frac{d_1}{d_2}. \quad . \quad . \quad . \quad . \quad \text{(i)}$$

Now v_1, v_2 concern the mean cubical coefficient c of expansion of the *sinker*, so that $v_2 = v_1[1 + c(t_2 - t_1)]$. Thus

$$\frac{v_1}{v_2} = \frac{1}{1 + c(t_2 - t_1)}.$$

Also, d_1, d_2 concern the mean coefficient of expansion γ of the *liquid*, so that

$\frac{d_1}{d_2} = 1 + \gamma(t_2 - t_1)$, see p. 36. Substituting for v_1/v_2 and d_1/d_2 in (i),

$$\therefore \frac{w_0 - w_1}{w_0 - w_2} = \frac{1 + \gamma(t_2 - t_1)}{1 + c(t_2 - t_1)}. \quad . \quad . \quad . \quad \text{(ii)}$$

It can now be seen that, if w_0, w_1, w_2, c, t_1, t_2 are all known, the mean coefficient of expansion γ of the liquid can be calculated.

An advantage of the "Archimedes' principle" method is that it can be used to measure the variation of the coefficient of expansion of a liquid with temperature. Thus if the liquid is heated from 15° C. to 35° C., the expression in (ii) enables its mean coefficient between these two temperatures to be calculated; if the liquid is heated from 35° C. to 60° C., the expression in (ii) enables the mean coefficient from 35° C. to 60° C. to be calculated; and so on. To obtain accurate results a sensitive balance must be used.

8. Balancing columns (Dulong and Petit) method for determining the absolute coefficient of expansion of a liquid.

In the weight thermometer and Archimedes' principle experiments, it will be noted that the absolute coefficient of expansion of the liquid can only be determined if the cubical coefficient of the vessel in the one case, and that of the sinker in the other case, are known. In 1808, however, DULONG and PETIT devised a method for determining the absolute coefficient of expansion of a liquid *without* any reference to the cubical coefficient of the container.

Fig. 3.3 illustrates the principle of the method. The liquid is placed in a U-tube, one limb of which is maintained at a constant temperature $t_1°$ C., and the other at a higher temperature

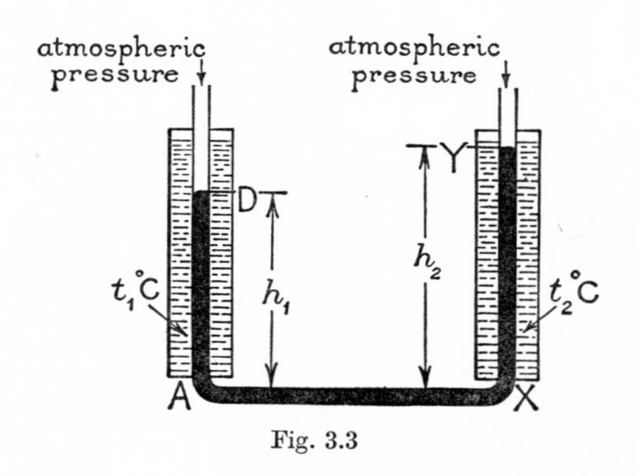

Fig. 3.3

$t_2°$ C. When conditions are steady the liquid level Y in the latter limb will be higher than the level D of the liquid in the other limb.

Suppose that the base AX of the U-tube is horizontal, and that the height AD is h_1, and the height XY is h_2. Then, since A and X are points in the same horizontal level of the liquid,

$$\text{the pressure at A} = \text{the pressure at X}. \quad . \quad . \quad \text{(i)}$$

Now the pressure p at a point h cm. below the surface of a liquid of density d gm. per c.c. is given by $p = hdg$ dynes per sq. cm., where g has the numerical value of 980 *cm./sec.*^{2} Thus, since both limbs of the U-tube are open, the pressure at A is $B + h_1d_1g$, where B is the atmospheric pressure and d_1 is the density of the liquid at $t_1°$ C.; and the pressure at X is $B + h_2d_2g$, where

d_2 is the density of the liquid at t_2° C. Consequently, from (i),

$$B + h_1 d_1 g = B + h_2 d_2 g. \quad . \quad . \quad . \quad . \quad \text{(ii)}$$

$$\therefore \; h_1 d_1 = h_2 d_2.$$

$$\therefore \; \frac{d_1}{d_2} = \frac{h_2}{h_1}.$$

But
$$\frac{d_1}{d_2} = 1 + \gamma(t_2 - t_1), \text{ p. 36,}$$

where γ is the mean coefficient of expansion of the liquid.

$$\therefore \; 1 + \gamma(t_2 - t_1) = \frac{h_2}{h_1}.$$

$$\therefore \; \gamma(t_2 - t_1) = \frac{h_2}{h_1} - 1 = \frac{h_2 - h_1}{h_1}.$$

$$\therefore \; \gamma = \frac{h_2 - h_1}{h_1(t_2 - t_1)}. \quad . \quad . \quad . \quad . \quad (14)$$

Thus if $(h_2 - h_1)$, h_1, t_2, t_1 are measured, the *absolute* coefficient γ of the liquid can be calculated.

It will be noted that the coefficient of expansion of the vessel does not enter into the calculation for γ, or in the final expression for γ given in (14). Of course, the limb XY of the vessel expands if it is heated; but the pressure at X depends only on the *height* of the liquid above this point, and the level Y of the liquid accordingly adjusts itself to make the pressure at X equal to the pressure at A. Dulong and Petit's "balancing column" method, as it is sometimes called, thus enables a direct determination of the absolute coefficient of expansion of a liquid to be made.

9. Determination of the absolute coefficient of mercury by Callendar and Moss.

From the theory of Dulong and Petit just given in equation (14), the absolute coefficient $\gamma = (h_2 - h_1)/[h_1(t_2 - t_1)]$. Now $(h_2 - h_1)$ is the difference in levels of the liquid at D, Y (fig. 3.3), and is very small, perhaps 0·4 cm. Thus if γ is to be determined with accuracy, the difference in levels must be measured very accurately, and hence a travelling microscope must be used. Since h_1 is a comparatively big length, e.g. 65 cm., a small error in this measurement will make very little difference to the value of γ, and hence h_1 may be measured with a metre ruler.

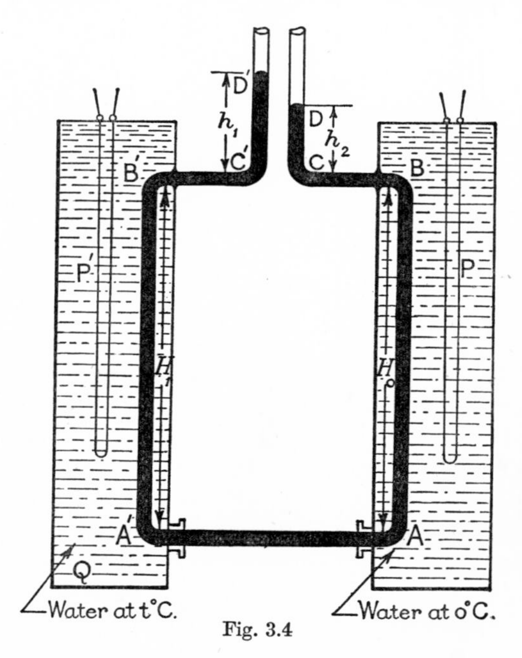

Fig. 3.4

In 1911 CALLENDAR and MOSS made a very accurate determination of the absolute coefficient of expansion of mercury by the method of balancing columns (fig. 3.4). Mercury was contained in a glass tube whose open ends were brought together at D′, D, and the column of mercury in A′B′ was maintained at a constant high temperature by a liquid bath Q. The mercury in AB was kept at the constant temperature 0° C. by continuously circulating ice-cold water round it. The rest of the mercury was also maintained at 0° C. by wrapping pieces of blotting-paper dipped in melting ice round A′A, B′C′, C′D′, CD.

Suppose A′B′ $= H_1$, AB $= H_0$; C′D′ $= h_1$, CD $= h_2$; the temperatures of A′B′, AB $= t°$ C., 0° C.; d_0, $d_t =$ the respective densities of mercury at 0° C. and $t°$ C.; and $B =$ the atmospheric pressure. Then *if* A′A *is kept horizontal*,

$$\text{pressure at A}' = \text{pressure at A}.$$

$$\therefore\ B + H_1 d_t g + h_1 d_0 g = B + H_0 d_0 g + h_2 d_0 g.$$

$$\therefore\ H_1 d_t = (H_0 + h_2 - h_1) d_0.$$

$$\therefore\ \frac{d_0}{d_t} = \frac{H_1}{H_0 + h_2 - h_1}.$$

But

$$\frac{d_0}{d_t} = 1 + \gamma t,$$

$$\therefore\ 1 + \gamma t = \frac{H_1}{H_0 + h_2 - h_1}.$$

$$\therefore\ \gamma = \frac{H_1 - H_0 + h_1 - h_2}{(H_0 + h_2 - t_1)t}. \qquad . \quad . \quad (15)$$

The heights H_1, H_0, and the length $(h_1 - h_2)$ were measured accurately by a cathetometer, which is a travelling microscope moving in a vertical direction. The temperatures were measured by resistance thermometers, P′, P. In order to increase the difference in levels of the mercury, thus increasing the sensitivity, Callendar and Moss used six " hot " and six " cold " tubes (instead of one " hot " and one " cold " tube as shown in fig. 3.4); they connected them so that six of the tubes were maintained at the same high temperature and six were at a temperature of 0° C. REGNAULT had carried out a similar experiment to measure the absolute coefficient of expansion of mercury in 1847, but had used only one " hot " and one " cold " tube.

10. " Reducing " the barometric height to 0° C.

The barometric height is recorded at meteorological stations at intervals during the day. Since mercury expands when its temperature increases, the temperature must also be recorded at the time the barometric height is measured, and for purposes of comparison, it is usual to calculate the height of mercury *at* 0° C. which would have the same pressure as that observed. The "correction" of the barometric height to 0° C. involves the linear expansion of the brass or steel scale provided with the barometer, as well as the coefficient of expansion of the mercury, and the following example illustrates how the correction is made.

Example 3.—If l is the coefficient of linear expansion of a solid, explain carefully why $3l$ may be used as the coefficient of cubical expansion. The height of a mercury barometer read with a steel scale is 754 millimetres at 20° C. What will it read at 0° C.? (Coefficient of linear expansion of steel 0·000 012 per °C.; coefficient of cubical expansion of mercury 0·000 182 per °C.) (*O. & C.*)

First part.—See p. 27.

Second part.—Suppose that the steel scale reads correctly at 0° C. Then at 20° C. the reading of 754 mm. on the steel scale is smaller than the true length, h_t, which is given by

$$h_t = 754(1 + 0{\cdot}000\,012 \times 20). \quad . \quad . \quad . \quad . \quad . \quad \text{(i)}$$

Let h_0 = the required height of the barometer at 0° C.
Then, since the pressures at 0° C. and 20° C. are the same,

$$h_0 d_0 g = h_t d_t g,$$

where d_0, d_t are the densities of mercury at 0° C., 20° C. respectively.

$$\therefore\ h_0 = h_t \frac{d_t}{d_0} = \frac{h_t}{1 + 20\gamma},$$

since $\dfrac{d_t}{d_0} = \dfrac{1}{1 + \gamma t}$ (p. 36), where γ is the cubical coefficient of mercury, 0·000 182 per °C. But $h_t = 754(1 + 0{\cdot}000\,012 \times 20)$, from (i).

$$\therefore\ h_0 = \frac{754(1 + 0{\cdot}000\,012 \times 20)}{1 + 0{\cdot}000\,182 \times 20}$$

$$= \frac{754(1 + 0{\cdot}000\,24)}{1 + 0{\cdot}003\,64} = 751{\cdot}44 \text{ mm.}$$

Thus the height at 0° C. = 751·44 mm.

11. The anomalous expansion of water.

Most liquids expand when they are heated, so that the density (mass/volume) decreases with increasing temperature. Water, however, is one of the few exceptions to this rule, as it is known by experiment that the density of water at normal pressures *increases* from 0° C. to 4° C., i.e. the density variation is anomalous in this temperature range. Beyond 4° C., the density of water decreases with increasing temperature, like most liquids, so that water has a maximum density at 4° C. Fig. 3.5 illustrates roughly the variation of the density of water with temperature.

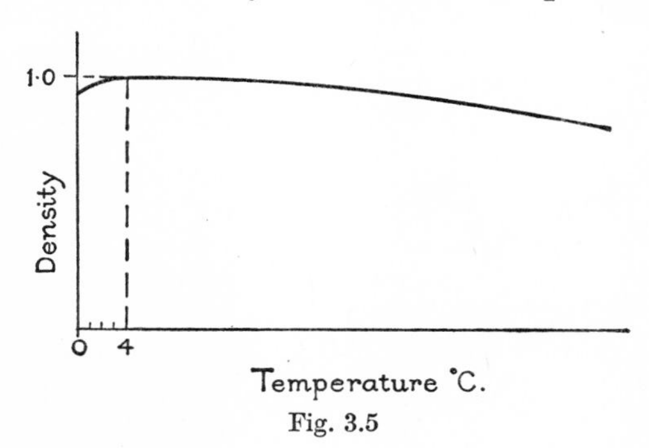

Fig. 3.5

The temperature of maximum density of water was first obtained by HOPE in 1804; he used a tall cylinder containing water, with a freezing mixture F round the middle (fig. 3.6*a*). Observations were taken on two thermometers T_1, T_2, which were placed respectively in the upper and lower parts of the water, and it was found that the lower thermometer first fell from 15° C., say, to a temperature of 4° C., and then remained constant at this temperature (fig. 3.6*b*). After this the upper thermometer T_1 began to fall in temperature from 15° C., until ice was formed at the top, when the temperature reached 0° C. (fig. 3.6*b*).

Hope's results are easily explained. When the temperature of the water in the middle of the cylinder M is first lowered (fig. 3.6*a*), the density of the water here is increased, and hence the water falls to the bottom. This convection process continues until the water below M is all at 4° C. When the water at M is cooled *below* 4° C., the density of the water increases and hence it rises to the top; thus the temperature of the water at the top diminishes until ice is eventually formed. These results show that in winter-time lakes and rivers contain water at 4° C. at

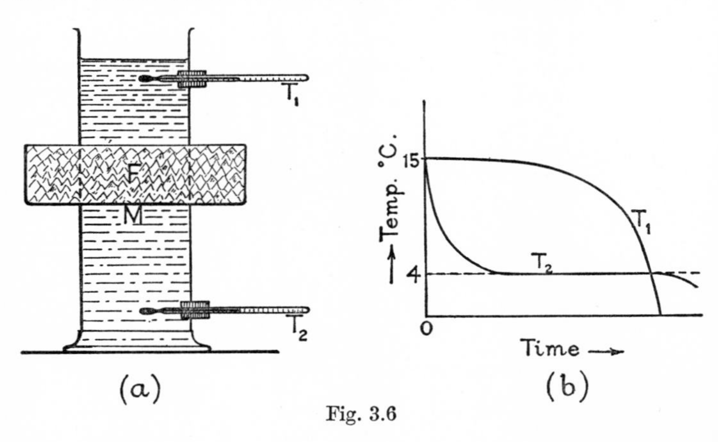

Fig. 3.6

the bottom, although the temperature of the air outside may be below freezing-point, enabling fishes and other creatures to live in water under arctic conditions.

12. Joule and Playfair devised a more sensitive method than Hope's for finding the temperature of maximum density of water. They used two tall cylinders, A and B, connected across the top and bottom by tubes, the lower tube having a tap T (fig. 3.7). A and B are filled with water, and with T closed, the temperature of A was made slightly greater than 4° C., while the temperature of B was made slightly lower than 4° C. The tap T was then opened, and the movement of a float F in the upper connecting tube was observed. If F was stationary, there was no convection current in the water system; the density of the water in A is then equal to that in B, as the pressure on one side of T is equal to the pressure on the other side when there is no convection current. Now the density-temperature curve (fig. 3.5) is *symmetrical* for small temperatures on either side of its maximum value; and hence, if the temperature of A is t_1° C., and that of B is t_2° C. when the float is stationary, the temperature of maximum density is $\frac{1}{2}(t_1 + t_2)$, the average of t_1 and t_2. In this way Joule and

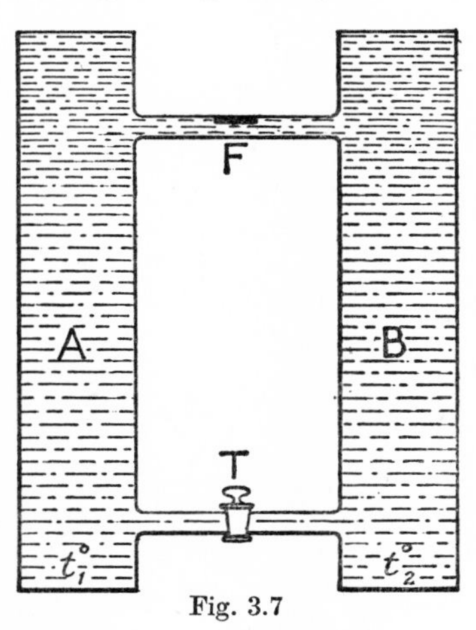

Fig. 3.7

Playfair estimated that water had a maximum density at 3·95° C. Later experiments showed that the temperature of maximum density of water varies with the external pressure.

Example 4.—Distinguish between the coefficients of real and apparent expansion of a liquid. Deduce an expression relating the density of a liquid, at different temperatures, with a coefficient of expansion.

A glass bottle, volume 50 c.c. at 0° C., is filled with paraffin at 15° C. What is the mass of the paraffin? The density of paraffin at 0° C. is 0·82 gm. per c.c.; the coefficient of real expansion of paraffin for the range 0° to 15° C. is 0·000 9; and the coefficient of linear expansion of glass is 0·000 009, both per deg. C. (*N.J.M.B.*)

First part.—See text.

Second part.—Coefficient of cubical expansion of glass = 3 × 0·000 009 = 0·000 027.

$\therefore$ volume of bottle at 15° C. = 50(1 + 0·000 027 × 15).

$$\text{Density of paraffin at } 15^\circ \text{ C.} = \frac{d_0}{1+\gamma t} = \frac{0{\cdot}82}{1+0{\cdot}000\,9\times 15} \quad \text{(see p. 36).}$$

$$\therefore \text{ mass of paraffin at } 15^\circ \text{ C.} = \text{volume} \times \text{density}$$

$$= 50(1+0{\cdot}000\,027\times 15)\times \frac{0{\cdot}82}{1+0{\cdot}000\,9\times 15}$$

$$= 50{\cdot}02\times \frac{0{\cdot}82}{1{\cdot}013\,5}$$

$$= 40{\cdot}47 \text{ gm.}$$

Example 5.—Describe a method of measuring the coefficient of expansion of a liquid which is independent of the expansion of the vessel containing the liquid. A weight thermometer of fused silica holds 5·00 gm. of a liquid at 25° C.; when heated to 100° C., 0·400 gm. overflows. Assuming that the liquid expands uniformly throughout the range and that the effect of the expansion of the silica is negligible, how much more liquid will overflow when the temperature is raised to 200° C.? Justify any formula you quote. (*L.H.S.C.*)

First part.—See " Dulong and Petit's method," p. 41.

Second part.—The apparent coefficient of expansion of the liquid

$$= \frac{\text{mass expelled}}{\text{mass left} \times \text{temp. rise}}$$

$$= \frac{0{\cdot}4}{4{\cdot}6\times 75} = 0{\cdot}001\,16 \text{ per } ^\circ\text{C.}$$

Suppose m gm. of the liquid overflow when the temperature rises from 100° C. to 200° C. Then $(4{\cdot}6 - m)$ gm. = mass left in vessel.

But
$$\text{apparent coefficient} = \frac{\text{mass expelled}}{\text{mass left} \times \text{temp. rise}},$$

$$\therefore\ 0{\cdot}001\,16 = \frac{m}{(4{\cdot}6-m)100},$$

$$\therefore\ 0{\cdot}001\,16\times 100(4{\cdot}6-m) = m.$$

$$\therefore\ 1{\cdot}116m = 0{\cdot}534.$$

$$\therefore\ m = 0{\cdot}478 \text{ gm.}$$

The proof of the " apparent coefficient " formula is given on p. 38.

Example 6.—Describe, giving the theory, a method of determining the real expansion of a liquid, if a solid which has a known coefficient of expansion and will sink in the liquid, is provided.

A loaded glass bulb weighs 156·25 gm. in air, 57·50 gm. when immersed in a liquid at 15° C., and 58·57 gm. when immersed at 52° C. Calculate the mean coefficient of real expansion of the liquid between 15° C. and 52° C. (Coefficient of linear expansion of glass = 0·000 009 per deg. C.) (*C.W.B.*)

First part.—See text.

Second part.—Upthrust on bulb at 15° C. = 156·25 − 57·50
= 98·75 gm. wt.,

and upthrust at 52° C. = 156·25 − 58·57
= 97·68 gm.wt.

But upthrust = wt. of liquid displaced, from Archimedes' principle.

$$\therefore\ 98{\cdot}75 = v_1 d_1, \text{ and } 97{\cdot}68 = v_2 d_2,$$

where v_1, v_2 are the volumes of the *glass* at 15° C. and 52° C. respectively, and d_1, d_2 are the corresponding densities of the *liquid*.

$$\therefore\ \frac{v_1 d_1}{v_2 d_2} = \frac{98{\cdot}75}{97{\cdot}68}. \qquad \text{(i)}$$

But
$$v_2 = v_1[1 + 0{\cdot}000\,027(52 - 15)],$$

since the cubical coefficient of glass is 3 × 0·000 009; and if γ is the real coefficient of expansion of the liquid,

$$d_1/d_2 = 1 + \gamma(52 - 15).$$

Substituting for v_1/v_2 and d_1/d_2 in (i),

$$\frac{1 + 37\gamma}{1 + 37 \times 0{\cdot}000\,027} = \frac{98{\cdot}75}{97{\cdot}68}. \qquad \text{(ii)}$$

Solving this equation for γ, we obtain

$$\gamma = 0{\cdot}000\,32 \text{ per deg.}$$

Note.—The left side of equation (ii) can be simplified to $1 + 37(\gamma - 0{\cdot}000\,027)$ from the binomial theorem, to a very good approximation, leading to rapid calculation of γ.

Examples on Chapter III

1. The volume of mercury at 0° C. in a mercury thermometer is 6·800 c.c. Calculate the volume of the capillary tube from 0° C. to 100° C. if the mean absolute cubical coefficient of mercury is 0·000 18 per °C., assuming the glass has a negligible expansion.

2. Draw a diagram of the apparatus you would use to determine the apparent coefficient of expansion of a liquid, and its absolute (real) coefficient.

3. A glass vessel is filled with 200 c.c. of water at 10° C. and heated to 60° C. The mean absolute coefficient of expansion of water is 0·000 3 per °C., and the mean *linear* coefficient of glass is 0·000 009 per °C. Find the new volume of the water, (i) neglecting the glass expansion, (ii) taking the glass expansion into account.

4. What is the relation between the density of a liquid at t° C. and its density at 0° C. in terms of the cubical coefficient of expansion? If the density of mercury at 30° C. is 13·52 gm. per c.c., calculate its density at 0° C. and at 100° C. (Mean cubical coefficient of mercury = 0·000 18 per °C.)

5. In words, what is the formula for the apparent coefficient of expansion of a liquid in the weight thermometer (specific gravity bottle) method? In what circumstances would the formula also give the absolute (true) coefficient? Calculate the mean apparent coefficient if the mass of liquid filling the vessel is 64·62 gm. at 15° C. and 61·84 gm. at 100° C. What is the mean absolute coefficient if the linear expansion of the vessel's material is 0·000 009 per °C.?

6. (i) Why does the "balancing column" (Dulong and Petit) method provide the absolute coefficient of expansion of a liquid, and not the apparent coefficient? (ii) Name an advantage and a disadvantage of the "Archimedes' principle" method of determining the apparent coefficient of expansion of a liquid.

7. In what range of temperature is the expansion of water anomalous? Draw a sketch showing the variation of the density of water with temperature from 0–100° C., and state briefly how (i) Hope, (ii) Joule and Playfair determined the temperature of the maximum density of water.

8. Describe and explain a method of measuring the absolute coefficient of expansion of a liquid. A mercury barometer with brass scale reads 76·530 cm. at 20° C. What would the reading be at

0° C., the atmospheric pressure remaining the same? [Cubical expansion of mercury = 0·000 181 per deg. C., linear expansion of brass = 0·000 019 per deg. C.] (*L.H.S.C.*)

9. Distinguish between the coefficients of real and apparent expansion of a liquid, and describe an experiment to determine the coefficient of apparent expansion of paraffin in glass. A glass vessel holds 40 gm. of paraffin at 0° C. What mass of paraffin will it hold at 70° C.? The coefficient of volume expansion of paraffin is 9×10^{-4} per deg. C., and that of glass 24×10^{-6} per deg. C. (*N.J.M.B.*)

10. Define the terms "apparent" and "absolute" coefficients of expansion of a liquid, and show how the former is found by means of a weight thermometer. A litre flask, which is correctly calibrated at 4° C., is filled to the mark with water at 80° C. What is the weight of water in the flask? [Coefficient of linear expansion of the glass of the flask = $8{\cdot}5 \times 10^{-6}$; mean coefficient of cubical expansion of water = $5{\cdot}0 \times 10^{-4}$.] (*O. & C.*)

11. Show how in general the density of a liquid at a temperature t° C. is related to that at 0° C. for small values of t. Describe and illustrate, by reference to experiments, the anomalous behaviour of water in this respect. A glass sinker has a mass M in air. When weighed in a liquid at temperature t_1 the apparent mass is M_1, and when weighed in the same liquid at temperature t_2 the apparent mass is M_2. If the coefficient of cubical expansion of the glass is β, find α, the real coefficient of expansion of the liquid. (*L.H.S.C.*)

12. Describe in detail one method of determining the mean coefficient of absolute expansion of mercury between 0° C. and 100° C. Give the theory of the method. (*C.H.S.C.*)

13. Describe and explain a method of determining directly the coefficient of real expansion of mercury. A mercury thermometer is to be made with glass tubing of internal bore 0·5 mm. diameter, and the distance between the fixed points is to be 20 cm. Estimate the internal volume of the bulb and stem below the lower fixed point. The coefficient of expansion of mercury is 0·000 180 and the coefficient of linear expansion of glass is 0·000 009, both in centigrade units. (*N.J.M.B.*)

14. How can you show that the density of water does not fall steadily as the temperature is raised from 0° C. to 100° C.? What does your experiment indicate about the expansion of water? What importance has this result in nature? (*C.H.S.C.*)

15. Why is mercury used as a thermometric fluid? Compare the advantages and disadvantages of the use of a mercury-in-glass

thermometer and a platinum resistance thermometer to determine the temperature of a liquid at about 300° C.

A dilatometer having a glass bulb and a tube of uniform bore contains 150 gm. of mercury which extends into the tube at 0° C. How far will the meniscus rise up the tube when the temperature is raised to 100° C. if the area of cross-section of the bore is 0·8 sq. mm. at 0° C.? Assume that the density of mercury at 0° C. is 13·6 gm. per c.c., that the coefficient of expansion of mercury is $1{\cdot}82 \times 10^{-4}$ per deg. C., and that the coefficient of linear expansion of glass is $1{\cdot}1 \times 10^{-5}$ per deg. C. (*N.J.M.B.*)

16. Describe how you would use a specific gravity bottle to find the coefficient of expansion of paraffin oil relative to glass between 0° and 50° C. A specific gravity bottle contains 44·25 gm. of a liquid at 0° C. and 42·02 gm. at 50° C. Assuming that the coefficient of linear expansion of the glass is 0·000 01 per deg. C., (*a*) compare the densities of the liquid at 0° C. and 50° C., (*b*) deduce the coefficient of real expansion of the liquid. Prove any formula employed. (*N.J.M.B.*)

17. Define the coefficients of linear and cubical expansion, and derive the relation between them for a particular substance. Describe, and give the theory of, a method for finding *directly* the absolute coefficient of cubical expansion of a liquid.

The bulb of a mercury-in-glass thermometer has a volume of 0·5 c.c. and the distance between successive degree marks is 2 mm. If the coefficient of linear expansion of glass is 10^{-5} per °C. and the coefficient of cubical expansion of mercury is $1{\cdot}8 \times 10^{-4}$ per °C., find the cross-sectional area of the bore of the stem. (*C.H.S.C.*)

18. Describe how to measure the coefficient of apparent expansion of a liquid using a weight thermometer. Show how the result can be calculated from the observations.

A specific gravity bottle of volume 50·0 c.c. at 0° C. is filled with glycerine at 20° C. What mass of glycerine is contained in the bottle if the density of glycerine at 0° C. is 1·26 gm. per c.c., and its coefficient of real expansion is $5{\cdot}2 \times 10^{-4}$ per deg. C.? Assume that the coefficient of linear expansion of the glass is 8×10^{-6} per deg. C. (*N.J.M.B.*)

CHAPTER IV

The Expansion of Gases

Mechanical engineers who design engines of all types must know how the gases inside them expand and contract when they are subjected to changes of temperature and pressure. On this account the subject of "The Expansion of Gases" has considerable practical importance.

Unlike solids and liquids the volumes of gases are considerably affected by small changes of pressure, and hence we cannot specify the condition or state of a given mass of gas without a knowledge of its pressure as well as its volume and temperature. It can thus be seen that the pressure, volume, and temperature of a gas must be taken into account when its expansion is studied, and it is logical to examine the changes of volume with temperature *while the pressure is kept constant,* then to examine the changes of pressure *while the volume is kept constant,* and, finally, to combine the two sets of results. Accordingly we begin with a study of the expansion of a gas at constant pressure.

1. Expansion of a gas at constant pressure. Charles' law.

CHARLES, about 1780, was among the first scientists to carry out an investigation into the expansion of a given mass of gas at constant pressure. The simple form of apparatus shown in fig. 4.1*a* can be used for this purpose, and contains air trapped by mercury in a glass bulb B of uniform cross-section. When the level of the mercury in the open tube C is adjusted, by moving C, so that it is the same as the level of the mercury in B, the pressure of the air is atmospheric pressure (fig. 4.1*a*). Steam is passed into a jacket round B, and when the temperature on the thermometer A is steady, C is moved so that the levels of the mercury are the same in B and C, and the length of the air column in B is read from a metre ruler S. The steam is then cut off, and the temperature of the air in B begins to decrease. A number of readings of the length of the air-column in B, and the corresponding temperature, are now taken, the levels of the mercury being adjusted each time to be the same, so that the pressure of the gas is kept constant at the atmospheric pressure.

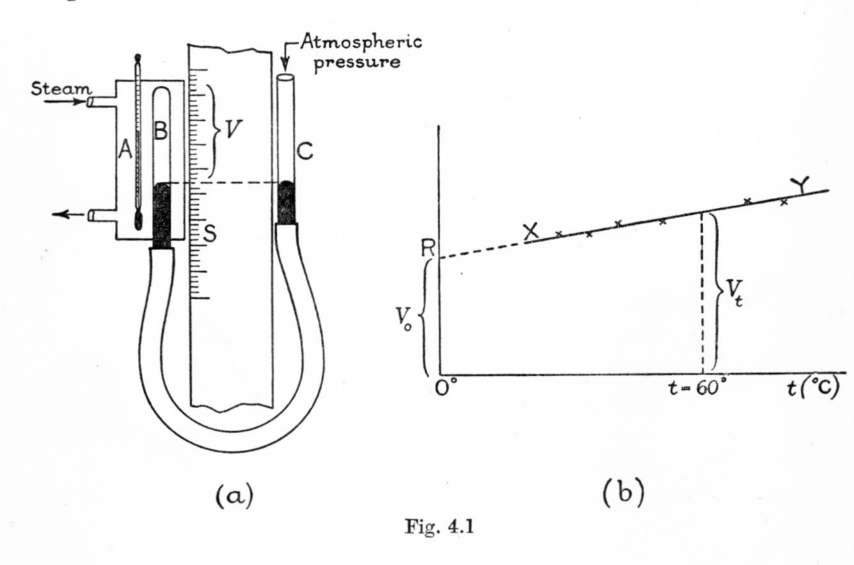

Fig. 4.1

The volume V of the gas in B is proportional to the length of the air-column, and experiments show that the volume-temperature graph is a straight line such as XY (fig. 4.1*b*). Thus the volume of the gas increases at a uniform rate for every degree rise of temperature. The same result is obtained for all other gases, and Charles found that *the volume of a given mass of gas increases by* 1/273 *of its volume at* 0° C. *for every degree centigrade rise in temperature, the pressure being constant.* This is known as *Charles' law.*

2. Volume coefficient of a gas.

The *volume coefficient* of a gas may be defined as *the increase in volume of unit volume of the gas at* 0° C. *when it is heated to* 1° C., *the pressure being kept constant throughout.* Suppose that V_0 is the volume of a given mass of gas at 0° C., V_t its new volume when the gas is heated to t° C., and α_p is the volume coefficient. Then, from the latter's definition,

$$\alpha_p = \frac{\text{increase in volume from } 0^\circ \text{ C.}}{\text{volume at } 0^\circ \text{ C.} \times \text{temp. rise}},$$

i.e.

$$\alpha_p = \frac{V_t - V_0}{V_0 \times t}. \quad . \quad . \quad . \quad . \quad . \quad (16)$$

$$\therefore \; V_t - V_0 = \alpha_p V_0 t.$$

$$\therefore \; V_t = V_0(1 + \alpha_p t). \quad . \quad . \quad . \quad . \quad (17)$$

This is the formula for calculating the volume of a given mass of gas at t° C. when its volume at 0° C. and its volume coefficient α_p are both known.

The volume coefficient of a gas can be found from the results of the experiment described on p. 56. The volume V_0 of the gas at 0° C. is obtained by producing the straight line XY back to cut the volume axis at R, and the volume V_t at any other temperature t° C., e.g. 60° C., is then taken. The volume coefficient α_p is calculated from the relation (16), and is about 1/273, or 0·003 66, per °C. for all gases. Thus, from (17), the volume V_t of the gas at a temperature at t° C. is given by

$$V_t = V_0\left(1 + \frac{t}{273}\right), \quad . \quad . \quad . \quad . \quad (18)$$

or

$$V_t = V_0(1 + \alpha t),$$

where $\alpha_p = \alpha = 1/273$.

3. Absolute temperature, *T*.

If a given mass of gas at constant pressure is slowly cooled, its volume decreases uniformly with the temperature, as shown by the straight line YX in fig. 4.1*b*. As the gas is cooled below 0° C. its volume shrinks further and, theoretically, there is a definite temperature at which the volume of the gas would become zero.

This temperature is known as the *absolute zero*, because it is impossible to obtain any lower temperature, and it can be found from the relation $V_t = V_0(1 + t/273)$ for the volume V_t of a gas at a temperature t° C. When $V_t = 0$, then $(1 + t/273) = 0$;

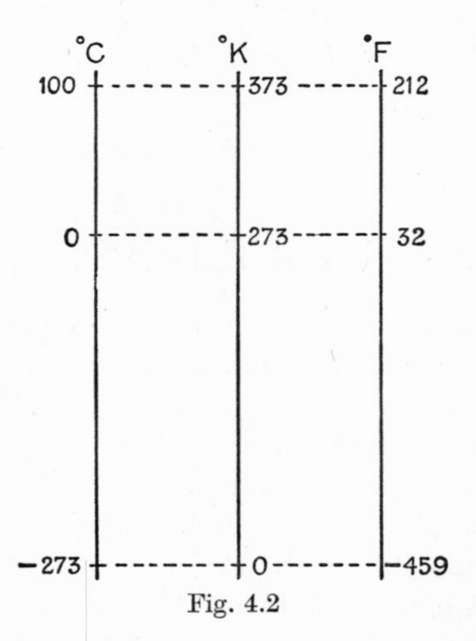

Fig. 4.2

from which it follows that $t = -273$. Thus *the absolute zero is* −273° C., or −459° F. Thus 0° C. is 273 degrees above the absolute zero, and 100° C. is 373 degrees above the absolute zero. When temperatures are measured from the absolute zero they are said to be *absolute temperatures*, and are expressed in " degrees Kelvin " (°K) after Lord Kelvin. It can be seen that the absolute temperature T° K. corresponding to a temperature t° C. is given by

$$T = 273 + t. \qquad (19)$$

Thus 0° C. = 273° K., and 100° C. = 373° K. See fig. 4.2.

4. The relation between volume and absolute temperature, at constant pressure.

The volume V_t of a given mass of gas is given by $V_t = V_0(1 + t/273)$.

$$\therefore\ V_t = V_0\left(\frac{273 + t}{273}\right) = \frac{V_0}{273}T,$$

where T is the absolute temperature corresponding to $t°$ C. But the volume V_0 at 0° C. of a given mass of gas is a constant quantity, and 273 is a constant. Consequently

$$V_t \propto T, \quad . \quad . \quad . \quad . \quad . \quad . \quad . \quad . \quad (20)$$

so that *the volume is proportional to the absolute temperature.* This result is known as *Gay Lussac's law.* Thus if the volume of a given mass of oxygen is 200 c.c. at 15° C., its volume V at 100° C., when the pressure is kept constant, is given by

$$\frac{V}{200} = \frac{273 + 100}{273 + 15} = \frac{373}{288}.$$

$$\therefore\ V = \frac{373}{288} \times 200 = 259 \text{ c.c.}$$

It can now be seen that the concept of absolute temperature enables the new volume of a given mass of gas to be easily calculated when its temperature is altered, the pressure being constant. The relation $V_t = V_0(1 + t/273)$ could also be used for finding the volume of a gas at 100° C. when its volume is 200 c.c. at 15° C., but the volume V_0 at 0° C. would first have to be calculated.

5. The pressure variation of a gas at constant volume.

We have now to turn our attention to the changes of pressure with temperature of a given mass of gas *when its volume is kept constant.* Fig. 4.3*a* illustrates a simple form of apparatus for this purpose. The gas is contained in a bulb B which is connected by narrow tubing to a mercury pressure-gauge, and the volume of the gas is kept constant by moving the open tube M until the mercury on the other side reaches a fixed mark A. The bulb is surrounded by a vessel containing water, and when the latter is heated to different constant temperatures, indicated on the thermometer D, the respective difference in levels h of the mercury is read after the volume of the gas is adjusted to be constant. If the mercury level in M is higher than the level at A, the pressure p of the gas $= (H + h)$ cm., where H is the

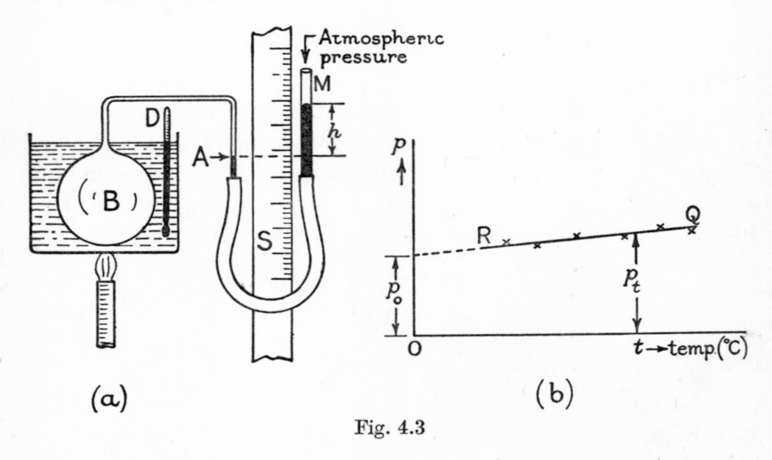

Fig. 4.3

barometric height and h is the difference in levels (fig. 4.3*a*). If the mercury level in M is lower than the level at A, the difference in levels is *subtracted* from the barometric height to find the corresponding pressure of the gas.

When the pressure p is plotted against the temperature t a straight-line graph RQ is obtained (fig. 4.3*b*). Thus experiment shows that the pressure of a given mass of gas at constant volume increases uniformly with the temperature.

6. The pressure coefficient of a gas.

The *pressure coefficient* α_V *of a given mass of gas at constant volume* is defined as *the ratio of its increase in pressure to its pressure at* 0° C. *when the temperature increases by* 1° C. Thus if p_0 is the pressure at 0° C., and p_t the increased pressure at t° C., the pressure coefficient α_V is given by

$$\alpha_V = \frac{\text{increase in pressure}}{\text{pressure at } 0° \text{ C.} \times \text{temp. rise}},$$

i.e.

$$\alpha_V = \frac{p_t - p_0}{p_0 \times t}. \quad . \quad . \quad . \quad . \quad . \quad . \quad (21)$$

The pressure coefficient can be calculated from the results shown in fig. 4.3*b*. The pressure p_0 at 0° C. is obtained by producing the line QR to intersect the pressure axis, and the pressure p_t at any other temperature t° C. is then taken. The pressure coefficient is then calculated from the relation $\frac{p_t - p_0}{p_0 \times t}$, and is found to be about 1/273 per °C. for any gas, which is the same numerical value as the volume coefficient (p. 57). See also p. 64.

From (21), it follows that the pressure p_t is given by

$$p_t = p_0(1 + \alpha_V t) = p_0\left(1 + \frac{t}{273}\right).$$

Thus

$$p_t = p_0\left(\frac{273 + t}{273}\right) = \frac{p_0}{273}\,T,$$

where $T = 273 + t$ is the absolute temperature corresponding to t° C. Since the pressure at 0° C. of a given mass of gas at constant volume is a constant quantity, and 273 is a constant, it follows that

$$p_t \propto T. \quad . \quad . \quad . \quad . \quad . \quad . \quad . \quad . \quad (22)$$

Thus *the pressure is proportional to the absolute temperature.*

It should be carefully noted that, in the definition of the pressure coefficient, we always refer to the pressure *at* 0° C. If a gas is heated from 40° C. to 100° C. at constant volume, and expands from a pressure p_1 to a pressure p_2, we cannot say that $p_2 = p_1[1 + (100 - 40)\alpha]$, where α is 0·003 66, because the pressure coefficient α is defined with reference to the pressure at 0° C. The correct relation between p_2 and p_1 is deduced by noting that

$$p_2 = p_0(1 + \alpha t) = p_0(1 + 100\alpha),$$

and

$$p_1 = p_0(1 + \alpha t) = p_0(1 + 40\alpha),$$

from which, by division,

$$\frac{p_2}{p_1} = \frac{1 + 100\alpha}{1 + 40\alpha}.$$

Thus knowing α (0·003 66), p_2/p_1 can be evaluated. The ratio p_2/p_1 is also given, from (22), by

$$\frac{p_2}{p_1} = \frac{273 + 100}{273 + 40} = \frac{373}{313}.$$

The same remarks apply to changes in volume of a gas at constant pressure. When a gas at a temperature of t_1° C. and volume V_1 is heated at constant pressure to a temperature t_2° C., its new volume V_2 can be evaluated from the relation

$$\frac{V_2}{V_1} = \frac{1 + \alpha t_2}{1 + \alpha t_1},$$

where α is 0·003 66.

7. Boyle's law.

In the seventeenth century Boyle discovered by experiment that *the pressure of a fixed mass of gas at constant temperature is inversely proportional to the volume.* This is known as *Boyle's law.* Thus if p is the pressure and V is the volume, Boyle's law states that

$$p \propto \frac{1}{V},$$

or

$$p = \frac{k}{V},$$

where k is a constant which depends on the mass of the gas, its nature, and its temperature. Consequently *the product* $pV = k$, *a constant.*

A simple apparatus to verify Boyle's law is shown in fig. 4.1*a* on p. 56. The pressure p of the gas is varied by raising or lowering the open tube C, and the corresponding volume V of the gas is proportional to the length of B, which is read from the scale S. The temperature is kept constant during the experiment. The pressure of the gas $p = (H \pm h)$ cm. of mercury, where H is the barometric height and h is the difference in levels of the mercury, the plus or minus being used according as the level of the mercury in the open tube is above or below the level in the other tube. If a graph of $1/V$ is plotted against p, a straight line is obtained passing through the origin, as shown in fig. 4.4a. Thus $p \propto 1/V$, which verifies Boyle's law.

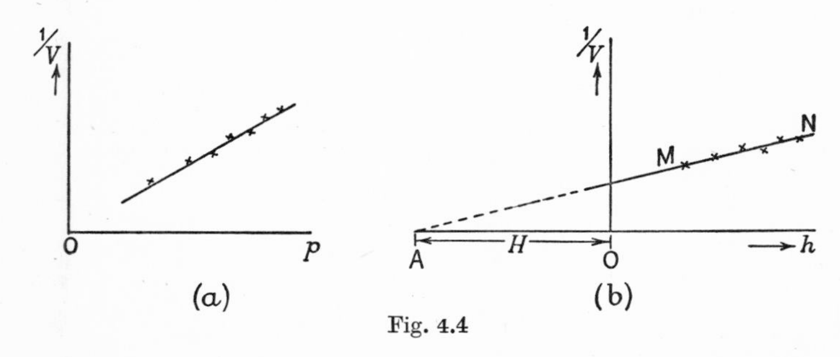

Fig. 4.4

Determining barometric pressure from Boyle's law experiment.

The barometric height H can be determined, if unknown, from a similar experiment to that just described. For this purpose the difference in levels h is plotted against $1/V$, when a straight line NM is obtained (fig. 4.4b).

Now the pressure p of the gas $= k/V$, assuming Boyle's law, and hence $H + h = k/V$, where H is the unknown barometric pressure. Thus when $1/V$ is zero, $H + h = 0$, i.e. $h = -H$. This means that if the line NM is produced to meet the axis of $1/V$ at A (where $1/V$ is zero), the intercept OA $= -H$. Thus the barometric pressure can be read from the horizontal axis, and is in centimetres of mercury if h is in centimetres of mercury.

To show that the volume and pressure coefficients are equal.

We have already mentioned that experiment shows that the volume coefficient α_p of a perfect gas is 1/273, the same value as the pressure coefficient α_V of a perfect gas. The equality of α_p and α_V can also be shown to follow if the gas obeys Boyle's law and Charles' law.

Suppose that a given mass of gas at 0° C. has a pressure p_0 and a volume V_0, and that it is heated to a temperature $t°$ C. This change of temperature can be accomplished *either* at constant volume, when the pressure changes

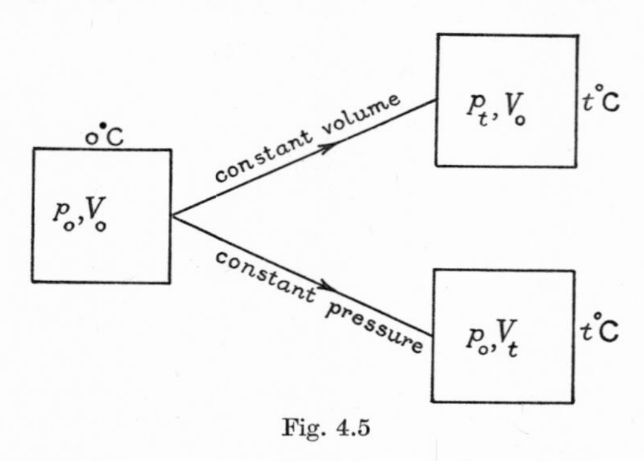

Fig. 4.5

to a value p_t, *or* at constant pressure, when the volume changes to a value V_t (see fig. 4.5). Since the temperature $t°$ C. is the same in either case, it follows from Boyle's law that

$$p_0 V_t = p_t V_0.$$

$$\therefore \frac{p_t}{p_0} = \frac{V_t}{V_0}. \qquad \text{(i)}$$

But $$V_t = V_0\left(1 + \frac{t}{273}\right), \text{ assuming Charles' law.}$$

$$\therefore \frac{V_t}{V_0} = 1 + \frac{t}{273}.$$

Substituting in (i) for V_t/V_0, we have

$$\frac{p_t}{p_0} = 1 + \frac{t}{273}.$$

Thus $$p_t = p_0\left(1 + \frac{t}{273}\right),$$

from which it follows that the pressure coefficient α_V is 1/273. Thus the volume coefficient of the gas is equal to its pressure coefficient if it obeys Boyle's and Charles' laws.

8. Work done by a gas in expansion.

Consider a gas contained in a cylinder XBCY by a piston at BC, and suppose the gas is heated while the pressure is kept constant at a value p and the piston is pushed back a distance x to MN (fig. 4.6*a*). Since work done = force × distance, by definition, the work done by the gas = force on piston × x. But the force on the piston = p × area of piston, since pressure is force per unit area.

$$\therefore \text{ work done} = p \times A \times x,$$

where A is the area of cross-section of the cylinder, supposed uniform.

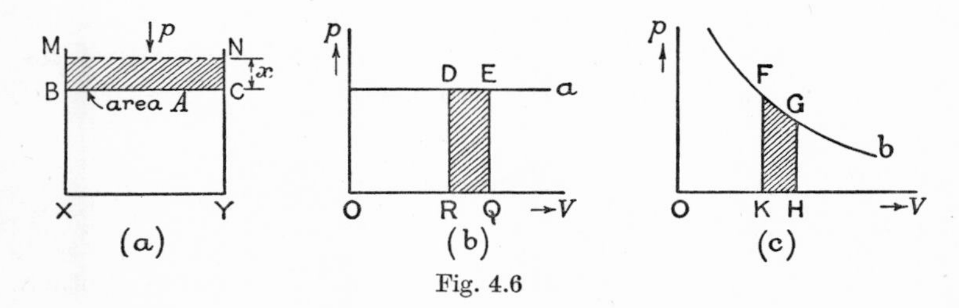

Fig. 4.6

But $A \times x$ = volume BMNC = change in volume of gas (fig. 4.6*a*)

$$\therefore \textit{work done} = p \times \textit{change in volume}. \quad . \quad . \quad (23)$$

The work done by the gas is in ergs if the pressure is in dynes per sq. cm. and the volume change is in c.c.

The work done by a gas can always be found from a graph showing its pressure-volume (p-V) relationship. When the pressure is constant, for example, the p-V graph is the straight line graph indicated by a in fig. 4.6*b*, where the constant pressure = DR, or EQ. If the volume of the gas changes from a value represented by OR to a value represented by OQ, the change in volume = OQ − OR = RQ. Thus work done = p × change in volume = DR × RQ = *area* of DRQE. In fig. 4.6*c* the p-V

graph of a gas is indicated by the curve b, which may correspond to the case when the pressure and volume both change under the condition that Boyle's law is obeyed.

Although the pressure changes from a value represented by KF to a value HG when the volume increases from OK to OH, we can imagine the pressure to be kept *constant* while a very small change of volume is made. In this way a series of very narrow areas are obtained which together make an area represented by KFGH in fig. 4.6*c*; and hence KFGH is a measure of the work done by the gas in expansion from OK to OH. We can thus formulate a general statement:—*The work done by a gas is equal to the area between its pressure-volume graph and the volume axis, taken between the limits corresponding to its initial and final volumes.* Mechanical engineers are thus able to estimate the work done by a gas in an engine by keeping track of its pressure-volume changes. See also p. 171.

Pumps

9. Bicycle pump.

The bicycle pump is one which forces air into a tyre or other empty object connected to it, and is an example of a " compression pump ". Suppose the pump N is connected to a tyre by a connecting tube, Q being the valve leading to the tyre (fig. 4.7). When the piston M is pulled out, the volume of the air contained in the barrel increases, and hence the pressure diminishes. Air then flows past the washer D, and when M is pushed in the air is forced into the tyre through the valve Q, which then opens. As the pump is used the air continues to flow past D and Q into the tyre.

We can obtain an approximate expression for the pressure of the air in the tyre after n repeated strokes of the piston. Suppose that the volume of the air in the tyre is originally V and that the volume of the tyre remains practically constant while the tyre is pumped up. If the volume of the barrel is a, and the piston M is pushed down and lifted up to the limit of the barrel each time, the volume of air forced into the tyre after one complete stroke is a, and after n complete strokes is na. Thus the total volume of the air in the tyre is V, at a pressure of p atmospheres, say. Now the mass of air present in the tyre had a volume $(V + na)$ at atmospheric pressure, i.e. at one atmosphere.

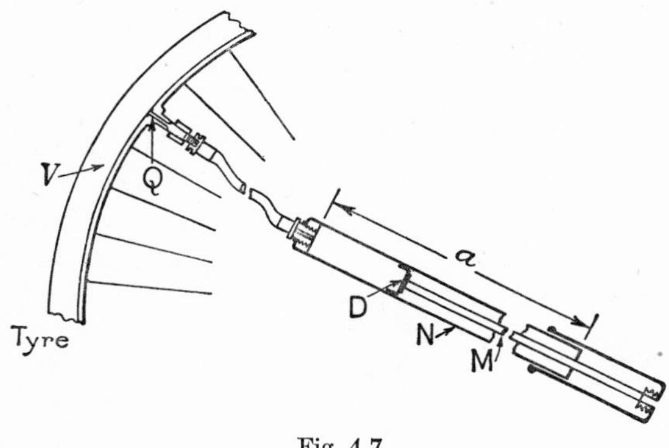

Fig. 4.7

Since we are dealing with a fixed mass of gas we can apply Boyle's law, from which it follows that $pV = 1 \times (V + na)$.

$$\therefore\ p = \frac{V + na}{V} = 1 + \frac{na}{V} \text{ atmospheres.}$$

$$\therefore\ p - 1 = \frac{na}{V}.$$

Since one atmosphere was the original pressure in the tyre, it follows that the increase in pressure $(p - 1)$ is proportional to the number of strokes n.

10. Exhaust pump.

In the case of a bicycle pump, the air always flows through the valves into the tyre. An exhaust (or vacuum) pump, however, is one in which the gas always flows through its valves *away* from the vessel to which it is connected, while the pump is working.

Fig. 4.8 illustrates the principle of a simple exhaust pump, which has a piston N, valves at B and A, and is connected to a vessel R containing air. Suppose the piston is pushed to the end A of the barrel and is then slowly pulled out. The pressure of the air between A and B then decreases, from Boyle's law, and at a certain stage it falls below the pressure of the air in R. The valve A then opens, and air flows out of R through A (fig. 4.8). When the piston is pushed in, the pressure of the air between A and B increases, valve A now closes and, when the pressure exceeds the atmospheric pressure, the valve B opens. The alternate closing and opening of A and B continues as N is pushed in and out, and thus the vessel R is gradually exhausted of air.

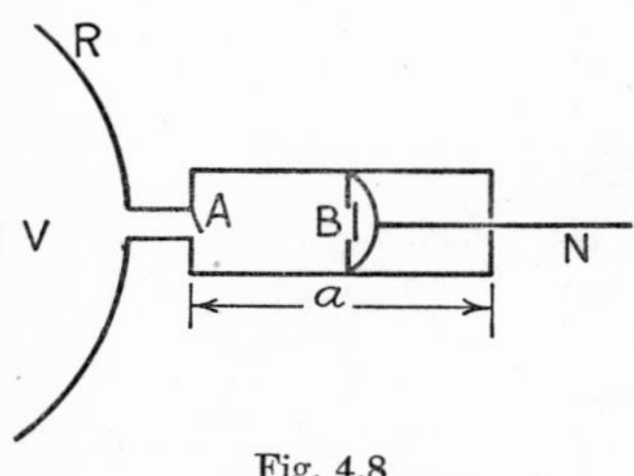

Fig. 4.8

We can obtain an approximate expression for the pressure in the vessel after n strokes of the piston. Suppose p is the initial pressure, V is the volume of the vessel, and imagine the piston to make one complete outward stroke (fig. 4.8). The valve at A then opens, and the gas expands from a volume V to a volume $(V + a)$, where a is the volume of the barrel; and, consequently, for this mass of gas $p_1(V + a) = pV$, where p_1 is the reduced pressure.

$$\therefore\ p_1 = \frac{V}{V + a}p. \qquad \text{(i)}$$

When the piston is pushed in to A, some of the gas is expelled through the valve B, which opens. When the piston is pulled out again, the new pressure p_2 is related to the old pressure p_1 by

$$p_2 = \frac{V}{V + a}p_1,$$

following the same reasoning as before, as the mass of air is constant although it is less than before. From (i), it follows that

$$p_2 = \left(\frac{V}{V+a}\right)\left(\frac{V}{V+a}\right)p = \left(\frac{V}{V+a}\right)^2 p,$$

and by this reasoning, the pressure p_n after n strokes of the piston is given by

$$p_n = \left(\frac{V}{V+a}\right)^n p.$$

There is a limit to the low pressure obtainable with this type of pump, because after a time the pressure in the vessel becomes too small to open the valve A, and the pump then ceases to operate.

11. The Rotary Pump.

Piston pumps have been supplanted by *rotary pumps*, which are simpler, faster, and produce higher vacua. The principle of the *Hyvac* type of rotary pump is illustrated in fig. 4.9. A cylindrical drum D is mounted eccentrically on a shaft S, which lies along the axis of a cylinder C, and the drum and cylinder are accurately machined, so that the surface of the drum just touches the inner surface of the cylinder. Ports P_1, P_2 are cut in the cylinder to allow air to enter and leave it respectively, and the exit port P_2 is provided with a simple valve V. A scraping vane K is pressed on to the drum, between the ports, by a spring P, and the whole arrangement is immersed in oil of low vapour-pressure.

The drum D is rotated clockwise at a few hundred revolutions per minute. At the instant shown in fig. 4.9, the volume on the entrance side of the line of contact L is increasing, and air is therefore flowing through the vacuum connexion into the cylinder. At the same time, the volume on the exit side of L is decreasing, and air is being driven out through the exit valve

V. The scraper K prevents air flowing from the exit side of the pump to the entrance side. As D revolves further, the line of contact passes the exit port, which is then exposed to the vessel to be evacuated, and the atmospheric pressure closes the valve V. Shortly afterwards the line of contact passes the entrance port, and the volume on the entrance side of the drum becomes

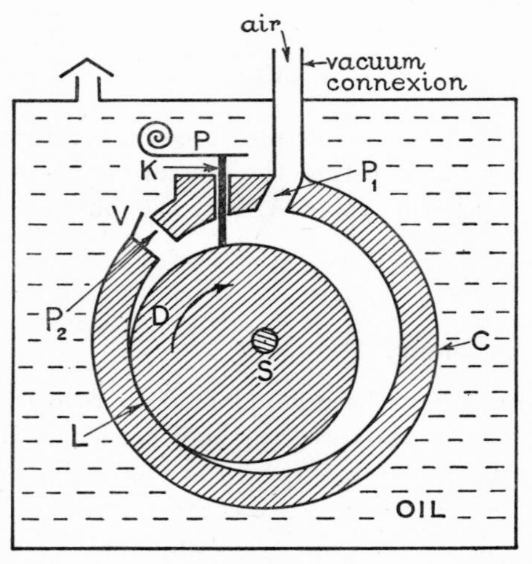

Fig. 4.9

very small. It then increases, air is swept in through the vacuum connexion, and is finally expelled through the exit valve V. The complete *Hyvac* pump comprises two of these units in tandem, in the same oil-filled case, and it can produce a pressure in a vessel as low as one-thousandth of a millimetre of mercury.

12. Measurement of low pressure by a McLeod gauge.

A pressure gauge widely used for measuring low pressures was developed by McLeod. One form of McLeod gauge consists of a main tube T of glass connected to a mercury reservoir R, with a bulb B ending in a closed capillary tube C; a second capillary tube D, of the same bore as C, is sealed on to T (fig. 4.10). C and D are arranged to lie close together, and they are backed by a millimetre scale S.

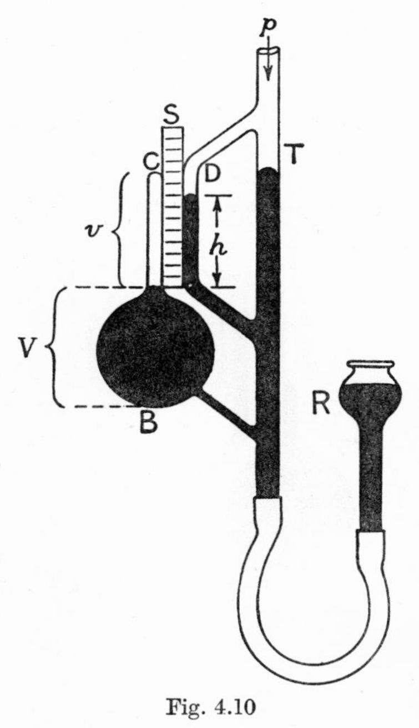

Fig. 4.10

To measure a low pressure p in a vessel, the latter is connected to the top of T, and the reservoir R is gently raised so that mercury flows into the bulb B. The air in B and C is then cut off, and when the mercury rises further, the air here is compressed.

Suppose P is the pressure of the air in the capillary tube C *when the mercury completely fills* B. Then $P = p + h$, where h is the difference in levels of the mercury in C and D, and p is the pressure in the vessel connected to T. But since the mass of air in B and C originally had a volume $(V + v)$, where V is the volume of B and v the volume of C, and the pressure was then p, the pressure in the vessel, it follows from Boyle's law that

$$p(V + v) = Pv.$$

$$\therefore\ p(V + v) = (p + h)v.$$

$$\therefore\ pV = hv.$$

$$\therefore\ p = \frac{v}{V}\,h.$$

Thus *the pressure is proportional to h*, and the scale S can hence be easily calibrated in terms of pressure.

Since $p = hv/V$, it can be seen that low pressures can be measured by making the volume V of the bulb B large and the volume v small. The bores of C and D are made the same to avoid surface tension effects between the mercury and the glass.

An alternative method of using the gauge consists of bringing the mercury in D level with the top of C, and then measuring the difference in levels l of the mercury (fig. 4.11). The volume of the air trapped in C is now al, where a is the cross-section of C; and if its pressure is P, then $P \times al = p(V + v)$, applying Boyle's law, where p is the pressure to be measured. Now $P = p + l$.

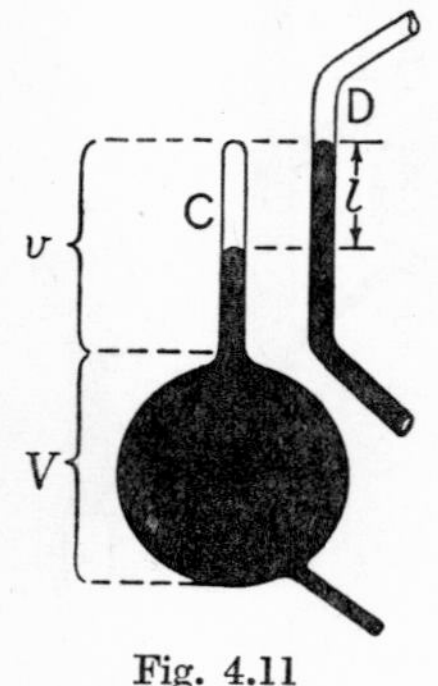

Fig. 4.11

$$\therefore (p + l)al = p(V + v),$$

$$\therefore p = \frac{al^2}{V + v - al}.$$

Since v and al are very small compared with V, it follows that, to a very good approximation,

$$p = \frac{al^2}{V}$$

$$\therefore p \propto l^2,$$

as a and V are constants. A wide range of pressure can hence be measured on a McLeod gauge by bringing the mercury level to the top of C.

The Perfect Gas Equations

Careful experiment shows that gases do not obey exactly Boyle's law and Charles' law. We shall not be concerned much in this book with the deviations from the laws, and shall deal mainly with a *perfect* gas, which may be defined as one which obeys Boyle's and Charles' laws.

13. The perfect gas equation.

Consider a *given mass* of gas with a pressure p_1, a volume V_1, and an absolute temperature T_1, and suppose it is heated so that its pressure changes to p_2, its volume to V_2, and its absolute temperature to T_2. The change from p_1, V_1, T_1 to

p_2, V_2, T_2 can be made in two stages, as represented in fig. 4.12. (i) Keep the pressure constant at the value p_1 and heat the gas until its absolute temperature is T_2; (ii) then keep the temperature constant at the absolute value T_2, and change the pressure from p_1 to p_2, when the volume of the gas changes to a value denoted by V_2. The final condition of the gas is now represented by p_2, V_2, T_2.

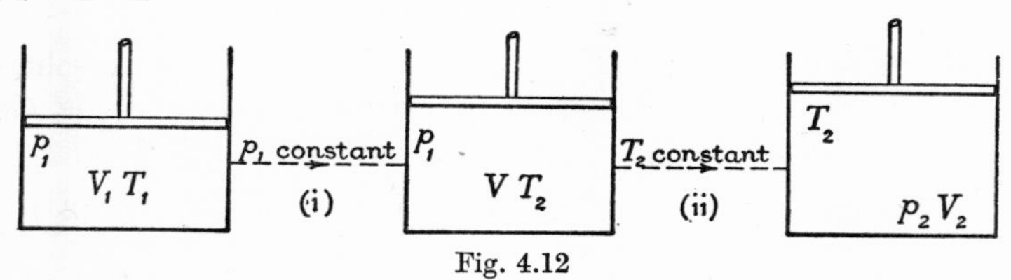

Fig. 4.12

Stage (i).—Let V be the volume of the gas when p_1 is kept constant and the absolute temperature changes from T_1 to T_2. Then, since volume $\propto T$ (p. 59), we have

$$\frac{V}{V_1} = \frac{T_2}{T_1},$$

i.e.

$$V = \frac{T_2 V_1}{T_1}. \quad \ldots \ldots \quad \text{(i)}$$

Stage (ii).—When the temperature is kept constant and the pressure and volume of the gas change, Boyle's law is obeyed,

$$\therefore p_1 V = p_2 V_2,$$

i.e.

$$V = \frac{p_2 V_2}{p_1}. \quad \ldots \ldots \quad \text{(ii)}$$

From (i) and (ii), it follows that

$$\frac{p_2 V_2}{p_1} = \frac{T_2 V_1}{T_1},$$

$$\therefore \frac{p_2 V_2}{T_2} = \frac{p_1 V_1}{T_1}.$$

If the given mass of gas is heated again so that it changes from a condition represented by p_2, V_2, T_2 to a condition represented by p_0, V_0, T_0, then, from the above reasoning, $\frac{p_2V_2}{T_2} = \frac{p_0V_0}{T_0}$. It can now be seen that for a *given mass* of gas,

$$\frac{pV}{T} = K,$$

where p, V, T denote the pressure, volume, and absolute temperature of the gas, and K *is a constant depending on the nature and mass of the gas.* Thus, generally,

$$pV = KT. \quad . \quad . \quad . \quad . \quad . \quad . \quad (24)$$

14. The value of the gas constant.

If we choose to deal with 1 gm. (or 1 lb.) of a given gas, the corresponding gas constant will be denoted by the symbol R.

Thus

$$pV = RT \quad . \quad . \quad . \quad . \quad . \quad . \quad (25)$$

for unit mass of a gas, and this equation is known as the *characteristic equation of a perfect gas.*

The gas constant R for oxygen can be calculated from the observation that the volume of 1 gm. of the gas at N.T.P. is 700 c.c. The pressure p of the gas is 76 cm. of mercury, and since the pressure in dynes per sq. cm. is calculated from the formula $p = hdg$ (p. 42), we have

$$p = 76 \times 13{\cdot}6 \times 980 \text{ dynes per sq. cm.}$$

The temperature of the gas is 0° C., so that its absolute temperature $T = 273°$ K.

$$\therefore\ R = \frac{pV}{T} = \frac{76 \times 13{\cdot}6 \times 980 \times 700}{273} = 2{\cdot}6 \times 10^6 \text{ units.}$$

As we showed before (p. 65), the product pV is a measure of work or energy, and hence R $(= pV/T)$ is expressed in "ergs per degree per gram " in the c.g.s. system, or " ft.-lb. per degree per lb." in the f.p.s. system. The gas constant for one gram of oxygen is hence $2 \cdot 6 \times 10^6$ ergs per degree per gram.

The numerical value of R will be different for one gram of different gases. In the case of hydrogen, for example, 1 gm. occupies a volume of 11·2 litres at N.T.P., so that $V = 11{,}200$ c.c., $p = 76 \times 13 \cdot 6 \times 980$ dynes per sq. cm., and $T = 273°$ K. for this gas. The gas constant for hydrogen is thus given by

$$R = \frac{pV}{T} = \frac{76 \times 13 \cdot 6 \times 980 \times 11{,}200}{273}$$

$$= 4 \cdot 15 \times 10^7 \text{ ergs per degree per gram.}$$

15. The general gas equation.

We have now to consider the gas equation for m grams of a given gas. Suppose, for example, that we have 5 gm. of oxygen. At N.T.P. its volume will be 5 times as great as the volume of 1 gm. at N.T.P., so that the volume $= 5 \times 700$ c.c. (p. 74). Now the gas constant K for 5 gm. of oxygen is given by

$$K = \frac{pV}{T},$$

where p is normal atmospheric pressure, $T = 273°$ K., and $V = 5 \times 700$ c.c. Since the same values of p and T are obtained for 1 gm. of oxygen at N.T.P., but the volume is then 700 c.c. instead of 5×700 c.c., it follows that K is five times as large as the gas constant R for 1 gm. of the gas. Hence $K = 5R$, and thus $5R = pV/T$, or $pV = 5RT$ for 5 gm. of oxygen. If there are m grams of a given gas, it can be seen that the gas equation can be written as

$$\boldsymbol{pV = mRT}, \qquad (26)$$

R being the gas constant for one gram.

From this equation, the mass m of a gas is given by

$$m = \frac{pV}{RT}.$$

This equation can be used to find the mass of a volume of gas, provided the gas constant R for one gram is known. As an illustration, suppose that the volume of a quantity of oxygen collected at 15° C. and 75 cm. pressure is 1,200 c.c. Then, using $R = 2{\cdot}6 \times 10^6$ ergs per degree per gram for oxygen, the mass of the gas is given by

$$m = \frac{pV}{RT} = \frac{75 \times 13{\cdot}6 \times 980 \times 1{,}200}{2{\cdot}6 \times 10^6 \times 288} = 1{\cdot}602 \text{ gm.}$$

Universal Gas Constant.

It is a well-known fact that the volume occupied by the gram-molecular weight of *any* gas at N.T.P. is the same and equal to 22·4 litres approximately. From $pV = KT$, it follows that the gas constant K for the gram-molecular weight of any gas is the same, as p, V, T have the same values in this case. On this account the gas constant for the gram-molecular weight of any gas is known as the *universal* gas constant, and we shall denote it by C.

The universal gas constant is given by

$$C = \frac{76 \times 13{\cdot}6 \times 980 \times 22{,}400}{273}$$

$$= 8{\cdot}3 \times 10^7 \text{ ergs per degree per gram.}$$

The corresponding gas equation is $pV = CT$. But the gas equation can also be expressed by $pV = mRT$, where m is the gram-molecular weight and R is the gas constant for one gram. Hence

$$mR = C, \text{ i.e. } m = \frac{C}{R}.$$

The value of R for hydrogen is $4{\cdot}15 \times 10^7$ numerically; thus the molecular weight of hydrogen $= \dfrac{C}{R} = \dfrac{8{\cdot}3 \times 10^7}{4{\cdot}15 \times 10^7} = 2$ gm.

Similarly, the value of R for oxygen is $2{\cdot}6 \times 10^6$ numerically (p. 74), and hence

$$\text{the molecular weight of oxygen} = \frac{C}{R} = \frac{8{\cdot}3 \times 10^7}{2{\cdot}6 \times 10^6} = 32 \text{ gm.}$$

Example 1.—Explain the difference between the centigrade and the absolute scales of temperature.

It is found that the volume of a certain gas increases in the ratio 1·035 : 1 between 15° C. and 25° C. Calculate the absolute zero on the centigrade scale for this gas. (*O. & C.*)

First part.—See text.

Second part.—Suppose the absolute zero is x° C. below 0° C. Then, assuming the change of volume takes place at constant pressure, the volume is proportional to the absolute temperature. Hence

$$\frac{x + 25}{x + 15} = \frac{1{\cdot}035}{1},$$

from which

$$x = -270{\cdot}7° \text{ C.}$$

Example 2.—Explain what is meant by a *coefficient of expansion.* Describe an experiment to determine the coefficient of volume expansion of a fixed mass of air kept at constant pressure.

The density of argon is 1·60 gm. per litre at 27° C. and at a pressure of 75 cm. of mercury. What is the mass of argon in an argon-filled electric lamp bulb of volume 100 c.c. if the pressure inside is 75 cm. of mercury when the average temperature of the gas is 120° C.? (*N.J.M.B.*)

First part.—See text.

Second part.—The volume of a fixed mass of gas at a constant pressure is proportional to its absolute temperature. Thus the volume V at 27° C. of 100 c.c. of argon at 120° C. and 75 cm. pressure is given by

$$\frac{V}{100} = \frac{273 + 27}{273 + 120},$$

$$\text{i.e. } V = \frac{300}{393} \times 100 = 76{\cdot}3 \text{ c.c.,}$$

the pressure being constant at 75 cm. mercury.

But 1000 c.c. of argon at 27° C. and 75 cm. pressure weigh 1·60 gm.

$\therefore$ 76·3 c.c. „ „ 27° C. „ 75 cm. „ „ $\frac{76{\cdot}3}{1000} \times 1{\cdot}60$ gm.

$$= 0{\cdot}122 \text{ gm.}$$

This is the mass of argon in the electric lamp.

Example 3.—Describe how you would determine the temperature of a room by means of a constant-volume air thermometer.

A diving-bell of uniform cross-section and 2 metres high is full of air at 70° C. when the atmospheric pressure is equal to 77 cm. of mercury. It is then sunk into water at 27° C. and the water rises 50 cm. within the bell. Assuming that no air escapes as the bell is sunk, find the depth of the bell below the water surface. [Take the density of mercury as 13·6 gm. per c.c.] (*L.H.S.C.*)

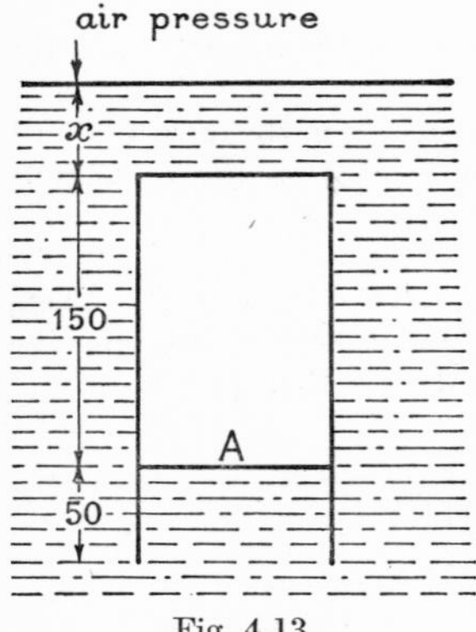

Fig. 4.13

First part.—The temperature of a room in °C. is given by

$$t = \frac{p_t - p_0}{p_{100} - p_0} \times 100,$$

where p_t is the pressure at room temperature, and p_{100}, p_0 are the respective pressures at the temperatures of steam at normal atmospheric pressure and at the melting-point of ice. (See p. 7.)

Second part.—When the level of the water rises 50 cm. to A (fig. 4.13), the volume V_1 of air inside the bell $= 150a$ c.c., where a is the uniform cross-section of the bell in sq. cm.

The pressure p_1 of the air = the pressure at A

$$= 77 \times 13{\cdot}6g + (150 + x)g \text{ dynes per sq. cm.,}$$

where x is the depth of the top of the bell below the surface of the water. The absolute temperature T_1 of the air $= 273 + 27 = 300°$ K.

Now the original pressure p_2 of the air in the bell $= 77 \times 13{\cdot}6g$ dynes per sq. cm., and the original volume V_2 of the air in the bell $= 200a$ c.c. The original absolute temperature $= 273 + 70 = 343°$ K.

Since the mass of the air in the bell is constant,

$$\frac{p_1 V_1}{T_1} = \frac{p_2 V_2}{T_2}.$$

$$\therefore \frac{(77 \times 13{\cdot}6 + 150 + x)g \times 150a}{300} = \frac{77 \times 13{\cdot}6g \times 200a}{343},$$

$$\therefore 77 \times 13{\cdot}6 + 150 + x = \frac{77 \times 13{\cdot}6 \times 200 \times 300}{150 \times 343},$$

$$\therefore x = 24{\cdot}0 \text{ cm.}$$

Example 4.—State the laws showing the relation between pressure, volume, and temperature of a fixed mass of gas. Explain the experimental method of verifying one of the laws.

Two glass bulbs of volume 25 and 35 c.c. are connected by a narrow tube of negligible volume. The apparatus is filled with air at 0° C. and 76 cm. of mercury pressure and sealed off. If the 25 c.c. bulb is maintained at 0° C. and the 35 c.c. bulb at 100° C., what is the new pressure within the apparatus? (*L.H.S.C.*)

First part.—See text.

Second part.—At 0° C. and 76 cm. pressure, the total volume of air $= 25 + 35 = 60$ c.c. Since the mass m of a gas is given by $m = pV/RT$, the total mass of air in the two bulbs $= 76 \times 13{\cdot}6 \times 980 \times 60/(R \times 273)$, where R is the gas constant of one gram of air (see p. 75).

The temperature of the 35 c.c. bulb is changed to 100° C., or 373° K. Hence the mass of air in this bulb $= p \times 35/(R \times 373)$, where p is the new pressure in the apparatus. Similarly, the mass of air now present in the 25 c.c. bulb $= p \times 25/(R \times 273)$. *But the total mass of air is constant.* Hence, from above,

$$\frac{p \times 35}{R \times 373} + \frac{p \times 25}{R \times 273} = \frac{76 \times 13{\cdot}6 \times 980 \times 60}{R \times 273}.$$

Dividing throughout by $1/R$,

$$\therefore \frac{35p}{373} + \frac{25p}{273} = \frac{76 \times 13{\cdot}6 \times 980 \times 60}{273}.$$

from which $$p = 90{\cdot}1 \text{ cm. mercury.}$$

16. Elementary Kinetic Theory of Gases.

In 1860 Clerk Maxwell showed theoretically that the well-known properties of a gas were capable of being explained on the basis of the following assumptions:

(1) The molecules of the gas behaved like elastic spheres.

(2) The time of collision between the molecules was negligible.

(3) The attraction between the molecules was negligible.

(4) The volume of the molecules was negligible compared with the volume occupied by the gas.

Maxwell used advanced mathematics in his statistical treatment of the " Kinetic Theory of Gases ", as the subject is called, and this is beyond the scope of the book; but the following elementary treatment, while not perfectly rigid, will enable us to reach Maxwell's main result.

Consider a cube of length l containing a gas of n molecules each of mass m. The molecules are moving randomly, i.e. in all different directions, but, as a simplification, we can imagine that $\frac{1}{3}n$ molecules are moving in each of three perpendicular directions, Ox, Oy, Oz, which we shall suppose are parallel to the faces of the cube (fig. 4.14). Then the number of molecules moving in *one* direction, e.g. perpendicular to the face A, is $\frac{1}{2}$ of $\frac{1}{3}n$, or $\frac{1}{6}n$.

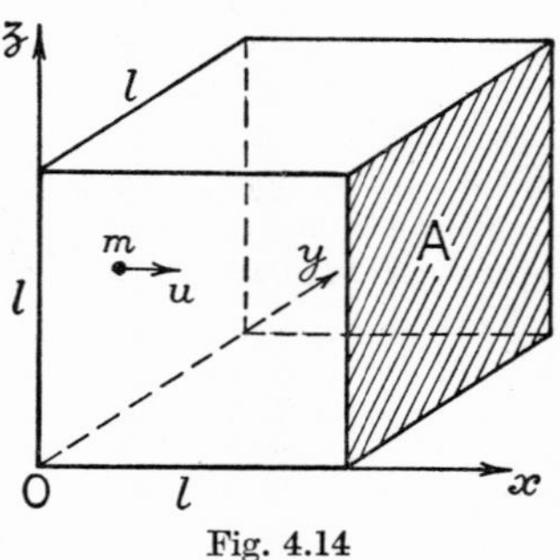

Fig. 4.14

Suppose that a particular molecule moves with a velocity u along Ox towards the face A. The momentum of the molecule is mu, since m is its mass, and the momentum on rebounding from A is $-mu$ if it is perfectly elastic; thus the change in momentum of the molecule $= mu - (-mu) = 2mu$. The molecule takes a time l/u to travel from one side to the other of the cube, and hence the number of impacts *per second* on A of each of the $\frac{1}{6}n$ molecules is u/l.

$$\therefore \text{ total change in momentum per sec.} = \tfrac{1}{6}n \times (u/l) \times 2mu$$
$$= \tfrac{1}{3}nmu^2/l.$$

But force exerted on A = total change in momentum per sec.

$$\therefore \text{ pressure } p \text{ on A} = \frac{\text{force}}{\text{area}} = (\tfrac{1}{3}nmu^2/l) \div l^2 = \tfrac{1}{3}nmu^2/l^3.$$

But volume of the gas $V = l^3$.

$$\therefore \; pV = \tfrac{1}{3}nmu^2.$$

Now we have assumed that all the molecules are moving with the same velocity, which is not true. To correct for this error, we must replace the quantity u^2 by the *average of the squares of the velocities of all the molecules,* which will be denoted by $\overline{c^2}$.

Thus $$pV = \tfrac{1}{3}nm\overline{c^2}, \quad . \quad . \quad . \quad . \quad . \quad . \quad (27)$$

an expression deduced by Maxwell by a more rigid mathematical method.

17. Energy of gas.

Since $nm = M$, where M is the mass of the gas, the average kinetic energy of the gas $E = \tfrac{1}{2}M\overline{c^2} = \tfrac{1}{2}nm\overline{c^2}$. Thus

$$pV = \tfrac{1}{3}nm\overline{c^2} = \tfrac{1}{3}M\overline{c^2} = \tfrac{2}{3}E.$$

If we assume that the energy E of a given mass of gas depends only on its temperature, in accordance with the theory that heat is a form of energy (p. 145), we have *pV is a constant at a given temperature,* which is Boyle's law.

Experiment shows that $pV = KT$, where K is the gas constant for the given mass of gas. Consequently, from above, $\tfrac{2}{3}E = KT$, and hence $E \propto T$. Thus *the energy of a gas is proportional to its absolute temperature.*

18. Root-mean-square (r.m.s.) velocity of a gas.

The quantity $\overline{c^2}$, the " average of the squares of the velocities " of the molecules, can be understood by supposing that we have four molecules with velocities 1100, 1000, 1050, 1070 metres per sec. respectively. The squares of their velocities are then numerically 1100^2, 1000^2, 1050^2, 1070^2, and the average of the squares of the velocities $= \tfrac{1}{4}(1100^2 + 1000^2 + 1050^2 + 1070^2)$. The square root of this average is known as the *root-mean-square (r.m.s.)* value of the four velocities, the term " root " implying " square root " and the term " mean " implying " average ".

If we consider n molecules of the gas, with respective velocities $u_1, u_2, u_3, \ldots, u_n$,

the root-mean-square velocity

$$= \sqrt{\frac{1}{n}(u_1^2 + u_2^2 + u_3^2 + \ldots + u_n^2)},$$

and this should not be confused with the *average velocity* of the molecules which is given by

$$\frac{1}{n}(u_1 + u_2 + u_3 + \ldots + u_n).$$

The average velocity has not the same value as the r.m.s. velocity, as the reader can test by taking four numbers and calculating the two quantities.

As we have used the symbol $\overline{c^2}$ for the average value of the squares of the velocities, the r.m.s. value of the velocities is denoted by $\sqrt{\overline{c^2}}$. The r.m.s. value can be calculated from the relation

$$pV = \tfrac{1}{3}nm\overline{c^2} = \tfrac{1}{3}M\overline{c^2},$$

from which $$\overline{c^2} = \frac{3pV}{M} = \frac{3p}{\rho},$$

where $\rho = \dfrac{M}{V} =$ the density of the gas.

$$\therefore \textbf{r.m.s. value} = \sqrt{\overline{c^2}} = \sqrt{\frac{3p}{\rho}}. \quad . \quad . \quad . \quad (28)$$

If the pressure p of the gas is expressed in *dynes per sq. cm.* and the density ρ in *gm. per c.c.*, the r.m.s. velocity is expressed in *cm. per sec.*

19. Van der Waals' Equation.

The equation $pV = RT$ is the relation between the pressure, volume, and absolute temperature of one gram of an *ideal* gas, i.e. one in which the attraction between the molecules, the volume occupied by the molecules, and the time of collision are all assumed to be zero. These are some of the assumptions which form the basis of the simple kinetic theory of gases (p. 79). VAN DER WAALS proposed a gas equation in 1877 which applies better to real gases than the equation $pV = RT$, and we shall consider briefly how this equation is derived.

If the molecules in one gram of a gas occupy a volume represented by b, a constant for this mass of gas, the "effective" volume of the gas is $(V - b)$. In place of V in the perfect gas equation $pV = RT$, we must hence write $(V - b)$.

To take into account the effect of the attraction between the molecules of a real gas, consider the molecules striking the face of a piston containing the gas. The molecules inside the gas attract these molecules with a force directed inwards, and hence the pressure p on the piston is less than the pressure inside the gas. The true pressure is thus $p + p_1$, where p_1 is due to the attractive force of the molecules. Now if we imagine the same number of molecules of the gas to occupy a larger volume, i.e. the density of the gas decreases, it can be seen that the force of attraction between the molecules decreases because they are then farther apart. If the density of the gas increases, the force of attraction increases. Since the force is proportional to the *product* of the number of molecules striking the piston and the number inside the gas, it follows that the force is proportional to the *square* of the density ρ of the gas. Thus $p_1 \propto \rho^2$. But the density of a given mass of gas is inversely proportional to its volume V. Hence p_1 varies as $\frac{1}{V^2}$, or $p_1 = a/V^2$, where a is a constant for a given mass of gas.

The equation for one gram of actual gas can thus be written as

$$\left(p + \frac{a}{V^2}\right)(V - b) = RT, \quad . \quad . \quad . \quad (29)$$

an equation first derived by Van der Waals and associated with his name. It represents approximately the behaviour of real gases at temperatures well above the critical temperature. Equation (29) is a *cubic* equation in V for a given value of p and T; the p-V curve has then an S-shape, like the isothermals for carbon dioxide gas obtained from Andrews' experiments (see fig. 8.7*b*, p. 182). Many other gas equations, besides Van der Waals' equation, have been proposed for actual gases, but no gas equation has yet been found to represent the behaviour of an actual gas over the *whole range* of its volume, pressure, and temperature.

Example 5.—Distinguish between the "average velocity" and the "root-mean-square velocity" of the molecules of a gas. From considerations of kinetic theory obtain an expression for the pressure of a gas in terms of the root-mean-square velocity of the molecules.

Determine the root-mean-square velocity of hydrogen molecules at N.T.P. (Density of hydrogen at N.T.P. is 0·09 gm. per litre; density of mercury is 13·6 gm. per c.c.; g may be taken as 981 cm./sec.^{2}.) (*C.H.S.C.*)

First part.—See text.

Second part.—The root-mean-square velocity, $\sqrt{\overline{c^2}}$, is given by

$$\sqrt{\overline{c^2}} = \sqrt{\frac{3p}{\rho}},$$

where p is in dynes/sq. cm., ρ in gm. per c.c., $\sqrt{\overline{c^2}}$ is in cm./sec.

Now $$\rho = \frac{0{\cdot}09}{1000}\text{ gm./c.c.} = 0{\cdot}000\,09\text{ gm./c.c.},$$

and $$p = 76 \times 13{\cdot}6 \times 981\text{ dynes/sq. cm.},$$

since normal pressure = pressure at bottom of column of mercury 76 cm. high.

$$\therefore\ \sqrt{\overline{c^2}} = \sqrt{\frac{3p}{\rho}} = \sqrt{\frac{3 \times 76 \times 13{\cdot}6 \times 981}{0{\cdot}000\,09}}$$
$$= 18{\cdot}4 \times 10^4\text{ cm./sec.}$$

Example 6.—Discuss the assumptions which form the basis of the simple kinetic theory of gases and explain under what circumstances the simple laws require modification.

Calculate the root-mean-square velocity of molecules of a gas for which the specific heat at constant pressure is 6·84 cal. per gm.-mol. per deg. C.; the velocity of sound in the gas being 1,300 metres per second. Gas constant $R = 8{\cdot}31 \times 10^7$ ergs per gm.-mol. per deg. C.) (*N.J.M.B.*)

First part.—See text.

Second part.—The velocity, v, of sound in a gas is given by $\sqrt{(\gamma p/\rho)}$, where γ is the ratio C_p/C_V of the two specific heats of the gas, p is the pressure, and ρ is the density of the gas. See also p. 172.

$$\therefore \sqrt{\overline{c^2}} : v = \sqrt{\frac{3p}{\rho}} : \sqrt{\frac{\gamma p}{\rho}} = \sqrt{3} : \sqrt{\gamma}.$$

$$\therefore \sqrt{\overline{c^2}} : 1300 = \sqrt{3} : \sqrt{\gamma}, \quad \ldots \ldots \quad \text{(i)}$$

where $\sqrt{\overline{c^2}}$ is in metres per second.

Since $$C_p - C_V = \frac{R}{J} \text{ (see p. 165),}$$

$$6{\cdot}84 - C_V = \frac{8{\cdot}31 \times 10^7}{4{\cdot}18 \times 10^7} = 1{\cdot}99,$$

as $J = 4{\cdot}18 \times 10^7$ ergs per calorie (p. 146).

$$\therefore C_V = 6{\cdot}84 - 1{\cdot}99 = 4{\cdot}85 \text{ cal. per gm. per °C.}$$

$$\therefore \gamma = \frac{C_p}{C_V} = \frac{6{\cdot}84}{4{\cdot}85} = 1{\cdot}41.$$

Substituting in (i), $\sqrt{\overline{c^2}} : 1300 = \sqrt{3} : \sqrt{1{\cdot}41}$,

$$\therefore \sqrt{\overline{c^2}} = 1300 \times \sqrt{\frac{3}{1{\cdot}41}} = 1898 \text{ metres per sec.}$$

Examples on Chapter IV

1. Define the *volume coefficient* of a gas. At constant pressure, a fixed mass of gas increases from a volume of 350 c.c. at 0° C. to 360·25 c.c. at 8° C. Calculate the volume coefficient of the gas, and its volume at 100° C.

2. The volume coefficient of a gas is 1/273 per °C.; calculate the volume coefficient per °F. What is the absolute zero in °C. and °F.?

3. What is the absolute temperature corresponding to 100° C.? A fixed mass of air has a pressure of 100 cm. of mercury at 100° C. Find its pressure (i) at 20° C., (ii) at 0° C., if the volume of the gas remains constant.

4. The volume of a fixed mass of gas at 50° C. is 80 c.c. At what temperature does the volume become 100 c.c., the pressure remaining constant.

5. A cylinder open at one end has a length of 8 ft., and is submerged with the open end downwards in water until 3 ft. of water rises inside it. If the height of the water barometer is 34 ft., find the depth of the open end below the water surface.

6. What is the relation between the pressure, volume, and temperature of a fixed mass of gas? A quantity of oxygen gas has a volume of 250 c.c. at 15° C. and 77·4 cm. mercury pressure. Calculate its volume at N.T.P. (0° C. and 76 cm. pressure).

7. The density of air is 1·29 gm. per litre at N.T.P. Calculate the gas constant of air for a mass of (i) 1 gram, (ii) 10 grams. What mass of air has a volume of 850 c.c. at 27° C. and 75 cm. mercury pressure? (*Hint*: Use $m = pV/RT$ or reduce to N.T.P.)

8. A gas has a volume of 80 c.c., and expands to 200 c.c. under a constant external pressure of one atmosphere (76 cm. of mercury, density 13·6 gm. per c.c.). Find the work done by the gas against the external pressure in ergs and in joules.

9. The volume of hydrogen collected at N.T.P. in an experiment is 890 c.c. If the gas constant for one gram of hydrogen is $4{\cdot}15 \times 10^7$ ergs per degree, calculate the mass of hydrogen.

10. Boyle's law is expressed by the equation $pV =$ constant; upon what quantities does the constant depend? An expansible balloon filled with air floats on the surface of a lake with two-thirds of its volume submerged. How deep must it be sunk in the water so that it is just in equilibrium, neither sinking further, nor rising? It is assumed that the temperature of the water is constant and that the height of the water barometer is 30 ft. (*L.H.S.C.*)

11. State Charles' law. Assuming the truth of Boyle's law and Charles' law, derive the characteristic equation of a perfect gas. Describe how you would employ Charles' law to determine the temperature of the laboratory without the use of an ordinary thermometer. (*L. Inter.*)

12. State the laws connecting the pressure, volume, and temperature of gases. A barometer tube 90 cm. long contains some air above the mercury. The reading is 74·5 cm. when the true pressure is 76 cm. and the temperature 15° C. If the reading is observed to be 75·8 cm. on a day when the temperature is 5° C., what is the true pressure? (*O. & C.*)

13. Describe an experiment in which Boyle's law is used to determine the atmospheric pressure in the laboratory. A column of air in a uniform tube, closed at one end, occupies 26·4 cm. at atmos-

pheric pressure. When subjected to the pressure of the water supply, the column of air occupies 20·4 cm. Calculate the pressure of the water supply, the atmospheric pressure being 76·5 cm. of mercury. (The density of mercury = 13·6 gm. per c.c.) How would you confirm the result with an open mercury manometer? (*N.J.M.B.*)

14. If a gas obeys Boyle's law rigorously, and if temperature is measured by assuming that the gas obeys Charles' law, prove that the coefficient of expansion of the gas at constant pressure is equal to its coefficient of increase of pressure at constant volume. Describe the constant-volume gas thermometer, and explain how it may be applied to determine the steady temperature of an oil bath. What difficulties are encountered if an accurate value of this temperature is required? (*C.W.B.*)

15. Ice and steam are provided at normal pressure. Explain how you would determine the temperature of a room with a constant-volume air thermometer, no other thermometer being available. The pressures, volumes, and temperatures of two samples of a gas are p_1, v_1, T_1 and p_2, v_2, T_2 respectively. Deduce the pressure of the gases when brought together in a volume V at a temperature T, assuming that no chemical action takes place in the process. (*L.H.S.C.*)

16. State the laws of gases usually associated with the names of Boyle, Charles, Dalton, and Graham. Two gas containers with volumes of 100 c.c. and 1000 c.c. respectively are connected by a tube of negligible volume, and contain air at a pressure of 1000 mm. of mercury. If the temperature of both vessels is originally 0° C., how much air will pass through the connecting tube when the temperature of the smaller is raised to 100° C.? Give your answer in c.c. measured at 0° C. and 760 mm. of mercury. (*L.H.S.C.*)

17. Describe, with diagrams, the construction and mode of action of a pump that will reduce the pressure of the air in a vessel to 0·001 mm. of mercury. How are pressures of this order of magnitude measured? A piston pump of effective volume 200 c.c. is used to exhaust a vessel of volume one litre. How many complete strokes will be required to reduce the pressure of the air in the vessel to one-hundredth of its initial value? (Neglect the volume of the connecting tubes, etc., and assume that the temperature remains constant.) (*O. & C.*)

18. Explain, with the aid of suitable diagrams, the construction and principle of action of a bicycle pump and a tyre valve. The bottom of a bicycle pump was closed and the pump was lowered into deep water. The pump handle moved in so that, at the deepest

point reached, the length of the enclosed air column was reduced to three-eighths of its former value. To what depth was the pump lowered into the water? Assume that the barometric pressure was 29·7 in. of mercury, and that the specific gravity of mercury is 13·6. (*N.J.M.B.*)

19. Show how the elementary kinetic theory of gases accounts for Boyle's law. Calculate the root-mean-square velocity of the molecules of hydrogen at 0° C. and at 100° C. [Density of hydrogen at 0° C. and 76 cm. mercury pressure = 0·000 09 gm. cm.$^{-3}$] (*L. Inter.*)

20. Without deriving any formulæ, use the kinetic theory of gases to explain (*a*) how a gas exerts a pressure, (*b*) why the temperature of a gas rises when the gas is compressed, (*c*) what happens when a quantity of liquid is introduced into a closed vessel. How are the differences in the behaviour of real and ideal gases explained by the kinetic theory? If there are $2{\cdot}7 \times 10^{19}$ molecules in a cubic centimetre of gas at 0° C. and 76 cm. of mercury pressure, what is the number per cubic centimetre (i) at 0° C. and 10^{-6} mm. pressure, (ii) at 39° C. and 10^{-6} mm. pressure. (*N.J.M.B.*)

21. What are the properties of an ideal gas? Show how these properties can be used to establish a scale of temperature.

Describe in detail how the temperature coefficient of increase of pressure for air at constant volume may be determined without the use of a thermometer. How could the apparatus be used to find the boiling-point of a saturated solution of common salt? (*N.J.M.B.*)

22. Outline the kinetic theory of gases. State clearly the assumptions made concerning the properties of the molecules of a perfect gas, and show how the theory accounts for the perfect gas laws. Indicate how the theory would suggest that a non-perfect gas would depart from these laws. (*C.H.S.C.*)

CHAPTER V

Specific Heats of Solids and Liquids. Latent Heat

1. Quantity of heat.

The quantity of heat absorbed or lost by a body may be expressed in terms of the **calorie,** the **British Thermal Unit,** the **therm,** or the **Centigrade Heat Unit.**

The *calorie* (cal.) is defined as the amount of heat required to raise the temperature of one gram of water by 1° C. (strictly, from 14·5° C. to 15·5° C., p. 155), and is the scientific unit of quantity of heat. The *British Thermal Unit* (B.Th.U.) is used in this country, and is the amount of heat required to raise the temperature of 1 lb. of water 1° F. The commercial gas companies base their charges on the *therm,* which is defined as 100,000 B.Th.U. The *Centigrade Heat Unit* (C.H.U.), sometimes used by engineers, is defined as the amount of heat required to raise the temperature of 1 lb. of water by 1° C.

2. Specific heat.

Experiment shows that 10 calories of heat raise the temperature of 1 gm. of copper about 100° C., 1 gm. of aluminium about 42° C., and 1 gm. of paraffin about 20° C. Thus the temperatures of the same mass of different substances are raised by different amounts when they absorb the same amount of heat.

The *specific heat* of a substance is defined as the amount of heat required to raise the temperature of *unit mass* of it *one degree.* If the mass of a substance is m, its specific heat is s, and its rise in temperature t, then, from the definition of specific heat, the quantity of heat Q supplied is given by

$$Q = mst. \quad \quad (30)$$

Thus $s = Q/mt$, and hence the units of s are " calories per gram per °C.", or " B.Th.U. per lb. per °F."

From the definition of the calorie, it can be seen that the specific heat of water is numerically 1. The specific heat of copper, a common material for making calorimeters, is 0·095 cal. per gm. per °C. The liquid aniline has a specific heat s of 0·62 cal. per gm. per °C. Since the rise in temperature t is given by $t = Q/ms$ from (30), it follows that a given quantity of heat would cause a greater rise in temperature in 50 gm. of aniline than in 50 gm. of water. For this reason aniline is preferred to water when a liquid is required in certain calorimetric experiments; greater accuracy of measurement is then possible.

3. Thermal capacity. Water equivalent.

The heat required to raise the temperature of a body 1° C. is known as the body's *thermal capacity*. Now the specific heat s of the body is defined as the heat required to raise the temperature of one gram of it 1° C. Hence the thermal capacity of the body = mass × specific heat, and may be expressed in " calories per °C."

In many experiments water is contained inside a calorimeter, and a change in temperature occurs. As an illustration, suppose that a copper calorimeter has a mass of 120 gm. and the temperature increases from 16° C. to 21° C. The quantity of heat gained by the calorimeter, of numerical specific heat 0·1, say, is then given by $Q = mst = 120 \times 0{\cdot}1 \times (21 - 16) = 60$ cal. Since 12 gm. of *water* absorbs 60 cal. when its temperature rises from 16° C. to 21° C., we may imagine the copper calorimeter to be replaced by 12 gm. of water in calculations concerning the heat gained or lost by the calorimeter. Thus if the calorimeter contained 80 gm. of water, the heat gained or lost by the water and the calorimeter would be effectively that gained or lost by 92 gm. of water.

The mass of 12 gm. of water in the above case is known as the **water equivalent** of the calorimeter. It can easily be checked that the water equivalent W of a calorimeter of mass m grams and specific heat s is always given by

$$W = m \times s, \quad \ldots \ldots \quad (31)$$

and W is in grams in this case. If M grams of water be contained in this calorimeter and a rise in temperature t occur, the total heat gained is given by $(M + W)t$, or $(M + ms)t$.

Methods of Determining Specific Heats

4. Method of mixtures.

The specific heat of a *solid* can be found by heating it in a steam chamber or a vessel of water, then quickly transferring it to a calorimeter containing water, and measuring the final temperature of the mixture. Suppose that

m, s = mass and sp. ht. of the solid,
m_1, s_1 = mass and sp. ht. of the calorimeter,
M = mass of the water,
t_1, t = initial and final temps. of the water,
t_2 = initial temp. of the hot solid.

Then, since heat lost by solid = heat gained by water and calorimeter, assuming no heat loss to the outside,

$$ms(t_2 - t) = (M + m_1s_1)(t - t_1),$$

as m_1s_1 is the water equivalent of the calorimeter. In this equation s is the only unknown quantity, and can hence be evaluated.

Provided no heat of solution occurs, or chemical action with the water takes place, the method of mixtures can be used for a *liquid*. Other methods for the specific heat of a liquid are discussed on p. 95 and p. 97.

5. The cooling correction.

As the result of certain experiments he made, Newton stated in 1701 that *the rate of loss of heat of a body by cooling is proportional to its excess temperature over the temperature of the surroundings.* This is known as *Newton's law of cooling.* Later experiments have shown that this law is an approximate one when the cooling body is surrounded by still air, but it holds at all temperatures when a draught is set up near the cooling body, i.e. under conditions of "forced convection" of the air. In the case of still air, Newton's law is fairly true for excess temperatures over the surroundings of not more than about 30°, a condition usually obtained in the method of mixtures as the final temperature of the mixture is frequently less than 30° above the temperature of the surroundings.

When a hot substance is dropped into water inside a calorimeter, as in the method of mixtures, the temperature of the water begins to rise above that of the surroundings, and the water and calorimeter then lose heat to the surroundings. It therefore follows that the *observed* final temperature is less than the final temperature had no heat been lost, and the number of degrees to be added to the observed reading to compensate for loss of heat is known as the "cooling correction". A cooling correction is necessary for accuracy in the method of mixtures, and it is proposed to give three methods for obtaining it.

Method 1.

As soon as the hot solid is placed inside the water and calorimeter, the temperature of the water is taken at regular intervals, e.g. every 15 seconds to start with, and then every minute later on. The temperature is then plotted against the time in minutes, and a curve NPQ (fig. 5.1) is obtained, where ON is the initial temperature and P corresponds to the observed final temperature.

Suppose y is the excess temperature over the surroundings at one point on the curve when the temperature is falling, and m is the loss in temperature per minute at this temperature excess given by the gradient to the curve (fig. 5.1). The time is now divided into intervals of one minute from the time observations were begun, and we shall suppose that the growing average temperature excess over the surroundings is a, b, c, etc., for each minute. From Newton's law of cooling, the loss in temperature a_1 in the first minute is given by ma/y; hence the "corrected" excess temperature in the first minute $= a + a_1$, and is denoted in fig. 5.1 by the point A. Similarly, the loss in

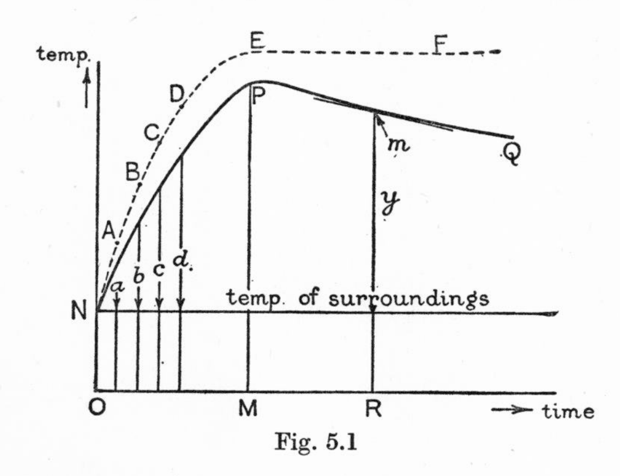

Fig. 5.1

temperature b_1, when the average temperature excess is b, is mb/y; thus the "corrected" excess temperature at the end of the second minute $= b + b_1 + a_1$, and is denoted in fig. 5.1 by B. As the temperature is "corrected", points such as C, D, E are obtained, where E is the corrected temperature to the observed maximum temperature P. Beyond E, the corrected temperature curve follows a fairly horizontal line EF. Thus EF corresponds to the maximum temperature corrected for cooling.

Method 2.

The cooling correction can be found more quickly by finding the average temperature excess, d say, during the time OM minutes (fig. 5.1). Then, since md/y is the average loss in temperature per minute during this time, $(md/y) \times$ OM is the approximate cooling correction in degrees to the observed maximum temperature MP.

Method 3.

Another method of making a cooling correction consists of using "areas" after the temperature-time graph is plotted. The horizontal line NT corresponding to the temperature of the surroundings is first drawn, the vertical line PR from the peak P of the curve is next drawn, and finally a vertical line ST is

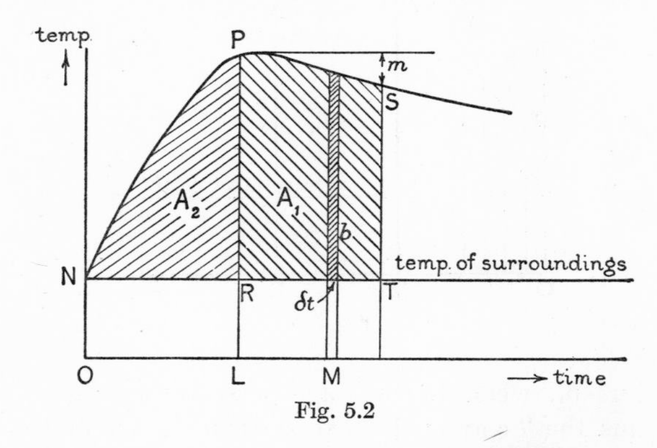

Fig. 5.2

drawn from any point S on the falling part of the curve (fig. 5.2). If m is the difference in temperature between the points corresponding to P and S, the cooling correction c is given by $c/A_2 = m/A_1$, where A_2, A_1 are the respective areas of NPR and RPST, which may be obtained easily in terms of the "boxes" on graph paper. Thus $c = mA_2/A_1$ and hence c can be found. The maximum temperature, corrected for cooling, is thus (c + temperature at P).

The proof of the formula $c/A_2 = m/A_1$ depends on Newton's law of cooling. Consider a temperature excess b over the surroundings, corresponding to a time M. By Newton's law of cooling, the heat lost per sec. is kb, where k is a constant, and hence the heat lost in a further small time δt is $kb \,.\, \delta t$. But $b \,.\, \delta t =$ the small area δA shown shaded in fig. 5.2. Thus the heat lost $= k \,.\, \delta A$. If the water equivalent of the water and calorimeter is denoted by W, and $\delta\theta$ is the small decrease in temperature in the time δt, the heat lost $= W \,.\, \delta\theta$. Hence $W \,.\, \delta\theta = k \,.\, \delta A$. Integrating both sides, from the time corresponding to P to that corresponding to S, we obtain

$$W \,.\, m = k \,.\, A_1. \quad \ldots \ldots \quad \text{(i)}$$

For the period of time between O and L, it can be similarly shown that $W \,.\, c = k \,.\, A_2$, as c is the temperature change due to *cooling* in this time. Thus, with (i),

$$\frac{W \,.\, c}{W \,.\, m} = \frac{k \,.\, A_2}{k \,.\, A_1}, \text{ or } \frac{c}{m} = \frac{A_2}{A_1}. \quad \text{Hence } c = \frac{mA_2}{A_1}.$$

6. Specific heat of a liquid by the method of cooling.

When a hot body is placed inside an enclosure at a lower constant temperature, the heat lost per second by the hot body depends on

(i) *the excess temperature over the enclosure at the instant considered*, and
(ii) *the nature and area of the exposed surface of the body.*

It should be noted by the reader that this statement is true whatever the temperature and the hot body may be, and it should be carefully distinguished from Newton's law of cooling (p. 92).

Suppose that a known volume of hot liquid is placed inside a blackened calorimeter C, which is suspended in a constant temperature enclosure E (fig. 5.3a). To prevent loss of heat by evaporation a lid is placed on the top, and the temperature of the liquid is noted at equal intervals of time while it cools. A cooling curve is then plotted. The experiment is now repeated with the same calorimeter containing an *equal volume* of hot water, and a cooling curve is plotted (fig. 5.3b). Now at the same temperature, the heat lost per minute by the calorimeter and water is equal to the heat lost per minute by the calorimeter and liquid, since the nature and area of the cooling bodies are the same in each case, and so are the respective temperatures. Thus

$$(m_2 + W)g_2 = (m_1 s + W)g_1, \quad . \quad . \quad . \quad . \quad \text{(i)}$$

where m_2, m_1 are the masses of the water and liquid respectively, W is the water equivalent of the calorimeter, and g_2, g_1 are the respective losses in temperature per minute of the water and

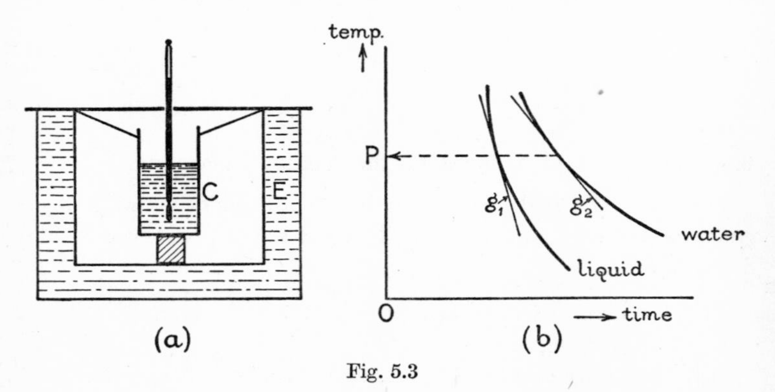

Fig. 5.3

liquid at the temperature P under consideration. The values of g_2, g_1 are found from the *slopes of the tangents* to the cooling curves corresponding to the temperature P, as shown in fig. 5.3*b*. Since m_2, W, m_1, g_1, g_2 are known, the unknown specific heat s of the liquid can be calculated from (i).

Another method can be used to calculate the specific heat s of the liquid from the two cooling curves. In this method the respective times t_1, t_2 to cool from a temperature θ_1(A) to a temperature θ_2(B) are noted from the liquid and water cooling curves (see fig. 5.4). Since the temperatures θ_1, θ_2 are the same in both cases, and the same calorimeter and volumes of water and liquid are used, the average heat lost per minute is the same. Thus

$$\frac{(m_2 + W)(\theta_1 - \theta_2)}{t_2} = \frac{(m_1 s + W)(\theta_1 - \theta_2)}{t_1}.$$

$$\therefore \frac{m_2 + W}{t_2} = \frac{m_1 s + W}{t_1}. \quad . \quad . \quad . \quad . \quad (32)$$

Since m_2, W, m_1, t_2, t_1 are all known, then s can be calculated.

The reader should carefully note that the *volumes* of the liquid and water used in the experiment are the same; thus leading to similar conditions in the two cases.

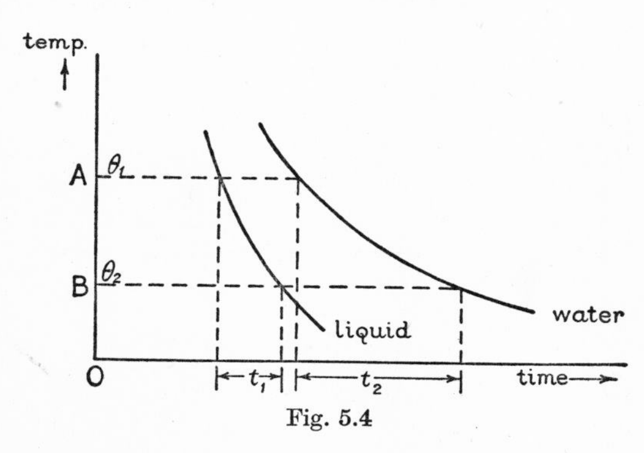

Fig. 5.4

7. Specific heat of water and liquids by electrical methods. " Continuous-flow " calorimetry.

From about the end of the nineteenth century, scientists began to use electrical methods for investigating phenomena in Heat. The advantages in such methods are

(i) the increasing accuracy of electrical instruments,
(ii) the control which could be exercised over the experiment.

Electrical methods are among the most accurate methods of determining the specific heats of solids and liquids, and we shall now consider the determination of the specific heat of liquids.

The essential features of the apparatus are shown in fig. 5.5. The liquid whose specific heat is required flows steadily through a glass tube AB from A to B, and during its passage it is heated electrically by a wire placed along the length of the tube. After a time the inlet and outlet temperatures of the water become constant, and *under these steady conditions*, the difference in temperature is measured by means of platinum resistance thermometers P, Q.

Suppose I is the current in amperes in this wire, V is the potential difference in volts between A and B, m is the mass of liquid flowing steadily along the tube per second, and t is the

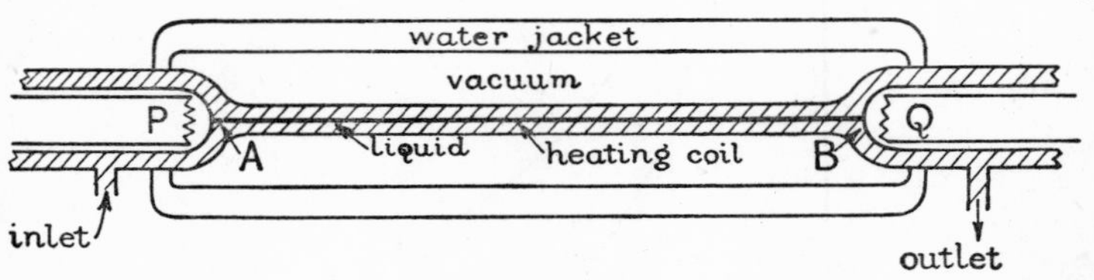

Fig. 5.5

steady difference in temperature of the water at A and B. When conditions are steady, no heat is expended on the calorimeter since its temperature is constant, and *all* the heat produced by the electric current is then used in heating the liquid as it flows from A to B. Now the electrical energy expended per second is IV joules, a formula derived from the definition of potential difference. Further, 4·18 joules of energy produce 1 calorie of heat (p. 146); hence the heat produced per second is $IV/4{\cdot}18$ calories. Thus if s is the specific heat of the liquid,

$$\frac{IV}{4{\cdot}18} = mst, \quad . \quad . \quad . \quad . \quad . \quad . \quad (33)$$

and hence s can be calculated as I, V, m, t are known.

The vacuum jacket (fig. 5.5) is used to eliminate loss of heat to the surroundings. In practice a little heat is lost by radiation but, if extreme accuracy is required, it is possible to eliminate the effect due to the loss of heat (see below). The advantages of the method and the "continuous-flow" calorimeter, as it is called, are:

(i) the water equivalent of the calorimeter, a doubtful quantity, does not need to be considered;

(ii) the difference in temperature between A and B can be measured very accurately because conditions are steady;

(iii) the cooling correction is negligible except for very accurate work;

(iv) *the method can be used for investigating the variation of the specific heat of a liquid with temperature.* In the latter case the difference in temperature is made small, e.g. the temperature at A may be 32° C. and that at B 34° C., in which case the specific heat s is determined at the average temperature 33° C. The electrical method has been used to determine the variation of the specific heat of water with temperature, a point of considerable importance as the calorie is defined with reference to the heat absorbed by water (see p. 154).

8. Elimination of heat lost in continuous-flow method.

Suppose h is the heat lost per second by radiation in the continuous-flow method. Then, instead of (33), we write,

$$\frac{IV}{4\cdot18} = mst + h. \qquad \text{(i)}$$

The steady flow of water is now decreased to a new value, and the current is also diminished until the same liquid temperatures are obtained at A and B. The heat lost by radiation is then the same (the surrounding water-jacket (fig. 5.5) is maintained at the same temperature), and if I_1, V_1, m_1 denote the new magnitudes of current, p.d., and mass of liquid per second, we have

$$\frac{I_1V_1}{4.18} = m_1st + h. \qquad \text{(ii)}$$

Subtracting (i) from (ii),

$$\therefore \frac{I_1V_1}{4{\cdot}18} - \frac{IV}{4{\cdot}18} = (m_1 - m)st,$$

so that h the heat lost is eliminated. From this equation s can be found.

9. Verification of Newton's law of cooling.

We have already mentioned the law of cooling proposed by Newton, which states that the heat lost per second by a cooling body is proportional to the excess temperature over the surroundings at the instant considered (p. 92). Since the heat

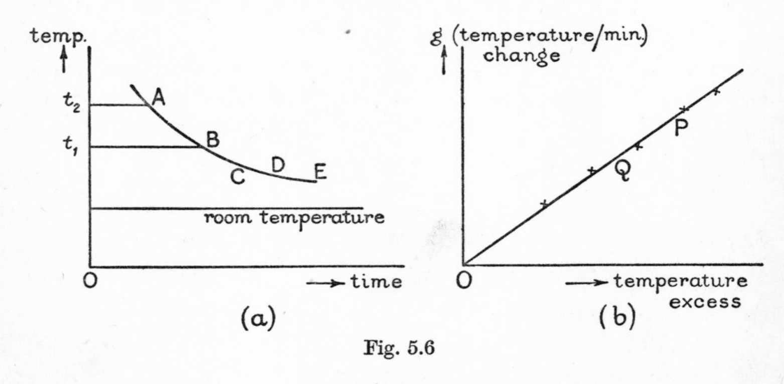

Fig. 5.6

lost by a body = mass × specific heat × temperature change, the heat lost per second is proportional to the temperature change per second for a given body. Thus, from Newton's law, the temperature change per second is proportional to the excess temperature at the instant considered.

It has already been pointed out that Newton's law is approximate when the body cools in still air, but that it holds when the body cools under conditions of forced convection, i.e. when a draught is set up (p. 92). The law can thus be verified by placing a hot liquid in a calorimeter near an open window and noting the temperature every half-minute as the cooling occurs. The cooling curve is then plotted (fig. 5.6*a*). To find the temperature change per minute at a temperature t_2, for example, the *gradient* (g) at the corresponding point A on the curve is found by drawing the tangent to the curve at A. The temperature change per minute at other points B, C, D, E of the curve are found in the same way, and the values of the temperature change/min. are plotted against the excess temperature over the surroundings (fig. 5.6*b*). It will then be found that the points so plotted lie on a straight line passing through the origin, verifying Newton's law.

Example 1.—State Newton's law of cooling. Distinguish clearly between the " rate of cooling " and the " rate of loss of heat " of a vessel containing a liquid at a temperature higher than that of its surroundings.

200 gm. of water, and an equal volume of another liquid of mass 250 gm., are placed in turn in the same calorimeter of mass 100 gm. and specific heat 0·1. The liquids, which are constantly stirred, are found to cool from 60° C. to 40° C. in 180 sec. and in 140 sec. respectively. Find the specific heat of the liquid. (*C.W.B.*)

First part.—For Newton's law, see text. The " rate of cooling " is the fall of *temperature* per second or per minute, and is thus expressed in " °C. per sec. or per min." The " rate of loss of heat " is the loss of heat per second or per minute, and is thus expressed in " calories per sec. or per min." In the latter case, then, the water equivalent of the liquid and vessel is concerned.

Second part.—The average heat lost per second by the liquid and calorimeter while the temperature falls from 60° C. to 40° C. is equal to the average heat lost per second by the water and calorimeter from 60° C. to 40° C., since the excess temperature over the surroundings, and the nature and area of the cooling surfaces, are the same in both cases. As pointed out on p. 95, it should be noted that we are not using Newton's law of cooling.

The average rate of loss of heat of the liquid and calorimeter in cal. per sec. $= (250s + 100 \times 0{\cdot}1)(60 - 40)/140$, and that of the water and calorimeter $= (200 + 100 \times 0{\cdot}1)(60 - 40)/180$.

$$\therefore \frac{(250s + 10)20}{140} = \frac{210 \times 20}{180},$$

$$\therefore s = 0{\cdot}61 \text{ cal./gm./°C.}$$

Example 2.—State Newton's law of cooling, and explain how you would test it experimentally.

A copper calorimeter of mass 100 gm., containing 150 c.c. of a liquid of specific heat 0·6 and specific gravity 1·2, is found to cool at the rate of 2° C. per minute when its temperature is 50° above that of its surroundings. If the liquid is emptied out, and 150 c.c. of a liquid of specific heat 0·4 and specific gravity 0·9 are substituted, what will be the rate of cooling when the temperature is 40° above that of the surroundings? (Specific heat of copper = 0·1.) (*O. & C.*)

First part.—See text.

Second part.—The mass of the first liquid = 150 × 1·2 = 180 gm.

$\therefore$ heat lost per min. at 50° C. above surroundings =

$$(180 \times 0{\cdot}6 + 100 \times 0{\cdot}1)2 \text{ cal.}$$

The mass of the second liquid = 150 × 0·9 = 135 gm.

$\therefore$ heat lost per min. at 40° C. above surroundings =

$$(135 \times 0{\cdot}4 + 100 \times 0{\cdot}1)x \text{ cal.},$$

where x is the rate of cooling. *Assuming Newton's law of cooling*, the rate of loss of heat is proportional to the excess temperature over the surroundings.

$$\therefore \frac{(135 \times 0{\cdot}4 + 100 \times 0{\cdot}1)x}{(180 \times 0{\cdot}6 + 100 \times 0{\cdot}1)2} = \frac{40}{50},$$

$$\therefore 64x = \frac{40 \times 118 \times 2}{50},$$

$$\therefore x = 2{\cdot}95^\circ \text{ C. per min.}$$

Latent Heat

10. Fusion.

If some ice in a calorimeter is gently warmed and stirred, and the temperature is noted throughout, the thermometer will remain steady at 0° C. until *all* the ice has melted to water. As further heat is supplied the thermometer indicates an increased reading, so that the temperature of the water formed now rises.

While the temperature was constant at 0° C., the heat supplied was melting, or *fusing*, the ice. In fact, as we shall see later (p. 145), heat is a form of energy, and energy is needed to change a substance from the solid to the liquid state, where the arrangement of molecules is different. Usually, the application of heat to a body results in a rise of its temperature; but there is no such effect when a solid melts, and the heat supplied was given the name of "hidden" or *latent* heat years ago when the phenomenon was not understood.

11. Latent heat of fusion.

The *latent heat of fusion* of a substance is defined as *the amount of heat required to change one gram of the substance from a solid to a liquid at the melting-point.* The latent heat of fusion will be denoted by L, and the units are "calories per gram". The latent heat of fusion of ice is about 79 calories per gram, so that 79 calories of heat are given out when 1 gm. of water at 0° C. changes to ice at 0° C., and 79 calories of heat are absorbed when 1 gm. of ice at 0° C. changes to water at 0° C. The latent heat of fusion of aluminium is 107 cal. per gm., and its melting-point is 658° C.

If m gm. of ice at 0° C. are converted to water *at* 0° C., it follows from the definition of latent heat of fusion (L) that mL calories are required. If m gm. of ice at 0° C. are converted to water *at* 15° C., an additional amount of heat is required which is $m \times 1 \times (15 - 0)$ calories, from $Q = mst$ (p. 90). The total heat supplied to the ice in this case is hence $(mL + 15m)$ calories.

12. Determination of latent heat of fusion of ice.

The latent heat of fusion of ice can be simply and accurately found from the method of mixtures. Pieces of ice are dried and dropped into a calorimeter containing water, and the final temperature is noted after all the ice has melted. The cooling correction can be eliminated by using warm water whose temperature is as much above the room temperature as the final temperature is below.

The following measurements, taken in an actual experiment, illustrate how the latent heat L is calculated:

Mass of copper calorimeter = 47·3 gm., sp. ht. = 0·095 cal./gm./°C.;
Mass of calorimeter + water = 123·01 gm.;
Mass of calorimeter + water + ice = 134·01 gm.;
Initial temp. of water = 18·4° C., final temp. = 6·4° C.

Since the heat required to convert the ice to water at 6·4° C. = the heat lost by the water and calorimeter, we have

$$11{\cdot}0L + 11{\cdot}0 \times (6{\cdot}4 - 0) = (47{\cdot}3 \times 0{\cdot}095 + 75{\cdot}71)(18{\cdot}4 - 6{\cdot}4).$$

In this expression 11·0 gm. is the mass of ice used, 75·71 gm. is the mass of water originally in the calorimeter, and L can be calculated. Its value in this case is 81 cal. per gm.

13. Determination of specific heat of liquid by using ice.

We have already mentioned that the specific heat of a liquid can be found by a method of mixtures (p. 91). A method which is particularly useful for inflammable liquids is one in which ice is dropped into the liquid, and the final temperature is observed after melting. Thus, if m is the mass of liquid, s its unknown specific heat, W the water equivalent of the calorimeter, t_1 and t the initial and final temperatures of the liquid, then the heat lost $= (ms + W)(t_1 - t)$. If m' gm. of ice be used, the heat required to change the ice to water at t° C. $= m'L + m'(t - 0) = 79m' + m't$, using the value of 79 cal. per gm. for L the latent heat of fusion of ice. Thus

$$(ms + W)(t_1 - t) = 79m' + m't,$$

and hence s can be found as m, W, t, t', and m' are all known.

14. Bunsen's Ice Calorimeter.

In 1871 Bunsen invented a calorimeter for measuring specific heats which used ice in a rather ingenious manner. Bunsen's *ice calorimeter* is illustrated in fig. 5.7, and consists essentially of a tube B containing air-free water to a level C; mercury fills the lower portion, which leads to a horizontal capillary tube D. A tube A is fixed inside B, and the whole arrangement (except D) is placed inside a vessel containing ice. Some ether (not shown) is placed inside A, and air is bubbled through the ether, which then evaporates. The heat absorbed from the surrounding water results in a coating of ice all round the end of A, and the apparatus is then placed inside a double-walled container of melting ice (fig. 5.7), so that the space all round A and B is at a temperature of 0° C.

Theory.—Experiment shows that 1 gm. of ice at 0° C. has a volume of 1·090 8 c.c., while 1 gm. of water at 0° C. occupies a volume of 1·000 1 c.c. *Thus a contraction of* 0·090 7 *c.c. occurs*

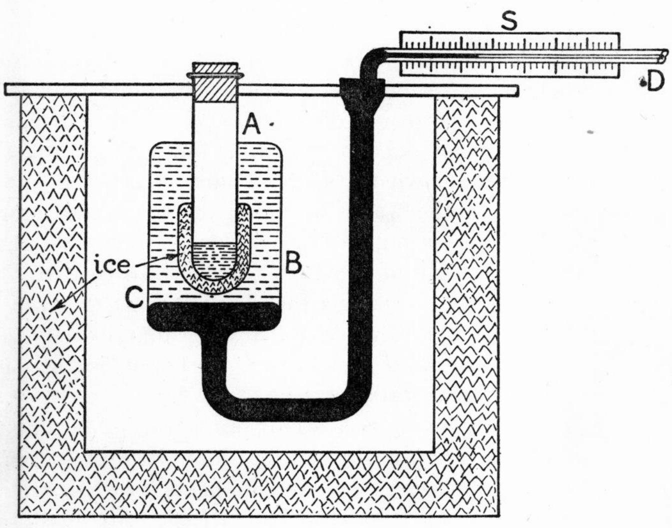

Fig. 5.7

when 1 *gm. of ice is melted.* In an experiment to find the specific heat of a solid, a little pure water is placed in A and the hot solid, at a known temperature t° C., is dropped gently into it. The heat given out by the solid when its temperature falls to 0° C. causes a little ice to melt, and the mercury column in D contracts by an amount which is measured by the scale S.

Suppose v is the contraction in volume in c.c.; m and s are the mass and specific heat of the solid; L is the latent heat of fusion of ice. Since a contraction of 0·090 7 c.c. indicates that 1 gm. of ice has melted, it follows that $v/0{\cdot}090\,7$ gm. of ice has been melted. The heat required for this purpose is $vL/0\cdot090\,7$ calories, and this is the heat given out by the solid when its temperature falls from t° C. to 0° C. It follows that

$$mst = \frac{vL}{0\cdot090\,7},$$

$$\therefore\ s = \frac{vL}{0\cdot090\,7mt}.$$

Thus knowing m, t, v, L, the specific heat s can be calculated.

This method of measuring specific heat depends on a knowledge of L the latent heat of fusion of ice. Another method can be adopted which does not depend on a knowledge of L, and this consists of adding a known mass M of pure water at a known temperature t_1° C. to the water originally in A. The mercury column then recedes by a number of divisions, n say, which thus corresponds to a quantity of heat Mt_1 calories. In this way the number of calories per division is found. The heat Q given up by a hot solid when placed in A can now be found easily, and its specific heat is obtained from $s = Q/(mt)$ if m is the mass and t is the original temperature.

As the mercury column recedes by an appreciable amount for small quantities of heat, Bunsen and later experimenters in 1947 were able to measure the specific heats of rare metals, which were available only in small quantities. An advantage of his calorimeter is that no cooling correction is required, as the surroundings are at 0° C., the same temperature as the calorimeter A. On the other hand, the ice round A may be below the assumed temperature 0° C. as a result of the pressure exerted on it by the surrounding water and mercury, because the melting-point of ice decreases with pressure, and this is a serious disadvantage of the ice calorimeter for very accurate work.

15. Vaporization.

When water is heated, its temperature rises until it begins to boil. At this stage the water changes from the liquid to the vapour state. Steam is obtained, and the temperature of the water remains constant at about 100° C. The heat now supplied is called " latent heat ", and it is used to change the water from the liquid to the vapour state, in which the molecules are farther apart than before.

The *latent heat of vaporization* (L) of a substance is defined as *the quantity of heat required to change one gram of it from a liquid to a vapour at the boiling-point.* The units of L are *calories per gram.* The latent heat of vaporization of water (latent heat of steam) is about 540 calories per gm. If m gm. of steam at 100° C. are condensed to water *at* 100° C., the heat given out is mL calories, where L is the latent heat of steam. If m gm. of steam at 100° C. are condensed to water *at* 35° C. an additional quantity of heat, $m \times 1 \times (100 - 35)$ cal., is liberated. The total heat given out in this case is hence $(mL + 65m)$ calories.

16. Determination of latent heat of steam.

The latent heat of steam can be obtained by the method of mixtures. Some water is boiled in a flask, and using a " trap " for drops of water, steam alone is obtained issuing from the trap. The steam is passed into water placed inside a calorimeter, and the final temperature of water is observed. The mass of steam condensed is obtained by re-weighing the calorimeter and its contents, and the following measurements, taken in an actual experiment, illustrate how the latent heat value is calculated:

Mass of calorimeter = 47·45 gm.,
Sp. ht. of calorimeter = 0·095 cal./gm./°C.
" " + water = 108·73 gm.
" " + water + steam = 112·80 gm.
Initial temp. of water = 18·0° C.; final temp. of water = 54·0° C.
Temp. of steam, at pressure of 77 cm. of mercury = 100·37° C.

Now heat given out by steam in condensing to water at 54° C. = heat gained by calorimeter and water. Hence

$$4{\cdot}07L + 4{\cdot}07 \times 1 \times (100{\cdot}37 - 54)$$
$$= (47{\cdot}45 \times 0{\cdot}095 + 61{\cdot}28)(54 - 18),$$

where L is the latent heat of steam, as 4·07 gm. is the mass of steam condensed and 61·28 gm. is the mass of the water originally in the calorimeter. From this equation L can be calculated, and the result is 538 cal. per gm. A cooling correction should also be carried out during the experiment, and the final temperature of the water must not be more than about 30° C. above the temperature of the surroundings.

17. Berthelot's method for latent heat of vaporization.

In 1877 BERTHELOT carried out a series of fairly accurate experiments on the latent heat of vaporization of substances. He used a flask B containing the liquid whose latent heat is required, and heat is supplied by a gas-ring D (fig. 5.8). A is a condenser of known water equivalent W_1, and it is placed in a vessel V containing water at a known temperature t_1. A wooden cover C prevents the heat from the burners passing to V. The condenser A is connected to a tube T by means of a spiral tube, and when vapour is produced in B it passes into A and condenses there. The temperature of the water and vessel V is now increased, and after several degrees rise in temperature is obtained, the supply of vapour is cut off and the final temperature is noted.

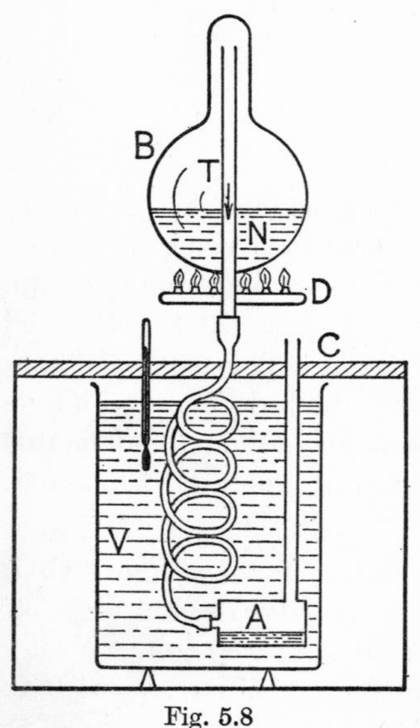

Fig. 5.8

Suppose m_1 is the mass of liquid obtained in A, s is its specific heat, t_2 is the boiling-point of the liquid, t_1 is the initial temperature of V, and W is the total water equivalent of the calorimeter V and the water. Then, if t is the final temperature and L is the latent heat value,

$$m_1L + m_1s(t_2 - t) = (W + W_1)(t - t_1),$$

since the heat given out by the condensed vapour and the liquid formed is equal to the heat gained by the calorimeter V, the vessel in it, and the water. Thus L can be calculated if all the other quantities are known.

The use of the tube T enabled Berthelot to ensure that no drops of liquid were carried over into the condenser, but there is the risk that the temperature of the vapour may be above the boiling-point.

18. Electrical method for latent heat of vaporization.

One of the most accurate methods of measuring the latent heat of vaporization is by an electrical method whose *principle* is illustrated in fig. 5.9. D is an air-tight vessel containing the liquid, which is electrically heated by a current passing through S into a heater coil A. T is a platinum resistance thermometer for measuring the temperature of the vapour obtained, which passes down a tube E into a vessel B where it may be collected. After a time, when conditions are steady, the vapour is obtained at a steady rate and the mass of liquid per second collected in B is measured. Suppose it is m gm. per sec. Then the heat supplied per second is mL calories, where L is the latent heat of vaporization, as the liquid in D is at the boiling-point when vapour is obtained. But the heat supplied per second is $IV/4{\cdot}18$ cal., where I is the current in A in amperes, and V is the p.d. across A in volts (p. 98).

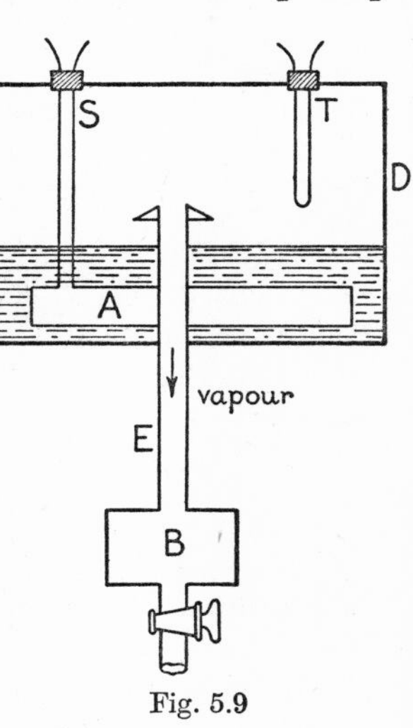

Fig. 5.9

$$\therefore mL = \frac{IV}{4{\cdot}18}, \quad \text{i.e. } L = \frac{IV}{4{\cdot}18m}.$$

Some of the advantages of an electrical method have been noted on p. 99. This method for L has also the advantage that the variation of L with temperature can be measured by altering the pressure in D (see p. 124). It should be noted that Berthelot's method (p. 108) is a method of mixtures utilizing the heat obtained when the vapour condenses, whereas the electrical method measures the heat required to vaporize the liquid at its boiling-point.

Example 3.—Describe and explain the method you would use to find the latent heat of evaporation of alcohol.

A copper calorimeter of mass 120 gm. contains 150 gm. of a liquid at 26° C. 25 gm. of ice at 0° C. are added, and the minimum temperature of the mixture is recorded. At this temperature, vapour from the same boiling liquid is introduced into the mixture until the final temperature of the calorimeter and new content is 30° C. What mass of vapour is condensed? Take the specific heat of copper as 0·1 cal. per gm. per degree C., the specific heat of the liquid as 0·6 cal. per gm. per degree C., the boiling-point of the liquid as 64·7° C., the latent heat of evaporation of the liquid as 267 cal. per gm., the latent heat of fusion of ice as 80 cal. per gm. (*L.H.S.C.*)

First part.—Berthelot's method can be used (p. 108).

Second part.—Let t° C. = the minimum temp. of the mixture.

Since heat lost by liquid and calorimeter = heat gained by ice and water formed,

$$(150 \times 0{\cdot}6 + 120 \times 0{\cdot}1)(26 - t) = 25 \times 80 + 25 \times (t - 0),$$

from which $t = 5{\cdot}1°$ C. (approx.)

Let m = mass in gm. of vapour condensed. Since heat given out by condensed vapour and liquid formed = heat gained by liquid, water, and calorimeter,

$$\therefore\ 267m + m \times 0{\cdot}6 \times (64{\cdot}7 - 30{\cdot}0)$$
$$= (150 \times 0{\cdot}6 + 25 + 120 \times 0{\cdot}1)(30 - 5{\cdot}1).$$
$$\therefore\ 287{\cdot}82m = 3162{\cdot}3.$$
$$\therefore\ m = 10{\cdot}99 \text{ gm.}$$

Example 4.—" Bismuth melts at 271° C." Describe an experiment to verify this statement.

When a quantity of liquid bismuth at its melting-point is transferred to a calorimeter containing oil, the temperature of the oil rises from 12·5° C.

to 27·6° C. When the experiment is repeated with all the circumstances the same except that the hot bismuth is solid, the temperature of the oil rises to 18·1° C. The specific heat of bismuth is 0·032 cal. per gm. per °C. What is its latent heat of fusion? (*N.J.M.B.*)

First part.—In brief, the melting-point of bismuth can be found by using a copper-iron thermocouple connected to a sensitive galvanometer, and placing one junction in the bismuth as its temperature is gradually raised to 320° C., for example. The melting-point corresponds to the temperature at which the reading on the galvanometer becomes constant as the bismuth cools, and this temperature can be found by previously calibrating the galvanometer.

Second part.—Let W be the water equivalent of the calorimeter in grams, m_1 m_2 the respective masses in grams of the bismuth and oil, and s the specific heat of the oil. When the *liquid* bismuth is transferred, it solidifies inside the oil, because the temperature is lower than the melting-point. Since the heat given out by the bismuth on solidification plus that given out by the solid bismuth when its temperature falls from 271° C. to 27·6° C. is equal to the heat absorbed by the calorimeter and contents,

$$\therefore\ m_1L + m_1 \times 0{\cdot}032 \times (271 - 27{\cdot}6) = (m_2s + W)(27{\cdot}6 - 12{\cdot}5).$$

$$\therefore\ m_1(L + 0{\cdot}032 \times 243{\cdot}4) = (m_2s + W)15{\cdot}1. \quad . \quad . \quad \text{(i)}$$

When the *solid* bismuth at 271° C. is transferred, no change of state occurs. Since the heat given out by the solid = the heat absorbed by the calorimeter and contents,

$$\therefore\ m_1 \times 0{\cdot}032 \times (271 - 18{\cdot}1) = (m_2s + W)(18{\cdot}1 - 12{\cdot}5).$$

$$\therefore\ m_1 \times 0{\cdot}032 \times 252{\cdot}9 = (m_2s + W)5{\cdot}6. \quad . \quad . \quad . \quad \text{(ii)}$$

Dividing (i) by (ii) to eliminate all the unknown quantities except L,

$$\therefore\ \frac{L + 0{\cdot}032 \times 243{\cdot}4}{0{\cdot}032 \times 252{\cdot}9} = \frac{15{\cdot}1}{5{\cdot}6},$$

$$\therefore\ 0{\cdot}032 \times 243{\cdot}4 \times 5{\cdot}6 + 5{\cdot}6L = 0{\cdot}032 \times 252{\cdot}9 \times 15{\cdot}1,$$

$$\therefore\ L = 14{\cdot}0 \text{ cal. per gm.}$$

Example 5.—Describe the Bunsen ice-calorimeter and discuss its merits.

The capillary tube of such a calorimeter has an internal diameter of 0·4 mm. When a piece of metal of mass 0·5 gm. heated to 100° C. is dropped into the calorimeter, the mercury meniscus moves 4 cm. What is the specific heat of the metal? (Specific gravity of water at 0° C. = 1·000, that of ice at 0° C. = 0·917; latent heat of fusion of ice = 80 calories per gram.) (*O. & C.*)

First part.—See text.

Second part.—1 gm. of water has a volume of 1·000 c.c.; 1 gm. of ice has a volume of 1/0·917 c.c., or 1·091 c.c. Thus a contraction of 0·091 c.c. occurs when 1 gm. of ice melts. Since the contraction $= \pi r^2 l = \pi \times 0{\cdot}02^2 \times 4 = 0{\cdot}0016\pi$ c.c., the mass of ice melted $= 0{\cdot}0016\pi/0{\cdot}091$ gm.

$$\therefore \text{ heat given out by metal} = \frac{0{\cdot}0016\pi \times 80}{0{\cdot}091} \text{ cal.}$$

$$\therefore \text{ specific heat of metal} = \frac{Q}{mt} = \frac{0{\cdot}0016\pi \times 80}{0{\cdot}091 \times 0{\cdot}5 \times 100}$$

$$= 0{\cdot}088 \text{ cal./gm./°C.}$$

Example 6.—Draw a labelled diagram to illustrate an experiment for determining the latent heat of vaporization of water. Do *not* describe the experiment, but state how the result would be calculated from the experimental data.

Water in a vacuum flask is boiled steadily by passing an electric current through a coil of wire immersed in the water. When the potential difference across the coil is 5·25 volts and the current through it is 2·58 amp., 6·85 gm. of water evaporate in 20 min. When the potential difference and the current are maintained at 3·20 volts and 1·57 amp. respectively, 2·38 gm. of water evaporate in 20 min., all the other conditions being the same. Calculate the latent heat of vaporization of water in joules per gm. (*N.J.M.B.*)

First part.—See text.

Second part.—If I is the current in amperes in a coil of wire and V is the potential difference in volts across the coil, the heat produced *per second* in the coil is IV joules (p. 98). This heat is expended in evaporating the water and in making up the heat losses. Thus, firstly,

$$2{\cdot}58 \times 5{\cdot}25 = \frac{6{\cdot}85L}{20 \times 60} + h, \quad . \quad . \quad . \quad . \quad . \quad \text{(i)}$$

where L is the latent heat of vaporization in *joules* per gm., and h is the heat lost per sec. in *joules*, and 20 min. = 20 × 60 sec. In the second case,

$$1{\cdot}57 \times 3{\cdot}20 = \frac{2{\cdot}38L}{20 \times 60} + h, \quad . \quad . \quad . \quad . \quad . \quad \text{(ii)}$$

as the conditions of cooling are the same. Subtracting (ii) from (i) to eliminate h, we have

$$(2{\cdot}58 \times 5{\cdot}25 - 1{\cdot}57 \times 3{\cdot}20) = \frac{6{\cdot}85 - 2{\cdot}38}{20 \times 60} L.$$

$$\therefore L = \frac{1200(2{\cdot}58 \times 5{\cdot}25 - 1{\cdot}57 \times 3{\cdot}20)}{4{\cdot}47}$$

$$= 2290 \text{ joules per gm.}$$

Examples on Chapter V

1. Name two different units of *specific heat.* Calculate the rise in temperature of 5 lb. of aluminium, specific heat = 0·24 numerically, when 20 B.Th.U. are supplied to it.

2. A calorimeter has a mass of 120 gm. and specific heat 0·1 numerically. What is its water equivalent? If the calorimeter contains 100 gm. of water at 10° C., find the new temperature when 7840 calories are supplied.

3. Name two different units of *latent heat.* (i) 250 gm. of water at 15° C. is heated until it all evaporates, the atmospheric pressure being 76 cm. mercury. Calculate the heat supplied. (ii) 3 gm. of steam at 100° C. are condensed, and the final temperature of the water formed is 35° C. Find the total heat given up. (Latent heat of steam = 540 cal. per gm.)

4. (i) In melting to water at 8° C., 5 gm. of ice at 0° C. give up 435 calories. Calculate the latent heat of fusion of ice. (ii) What mass of iron at 17° C. dropped into liquid oxygen at its boiling-point (−183° C.) will cause 2 gm. of oxygen to evaporate? (Latent heat of oxygen = 51 cal./gm.; sp. ht. of iron = 0·09 cal./gm./°C.)

5. What "correction" must normally be applied in the method of mixtures when specific heats or latent heats are measured? Describe how you would carry out such a correction.

6. 5·8 gm. of steam at 100° C. are passed into a copper calorimeter containing 85 gm. of water at 16° C. If the final temperature is 50° C., calculate the mass of the calorimeter. (Latent heat of steam = 540 cal./gm.; sp. ht. of copper = 0·1 cal. per gm. per °C.)

7. What method would you adopt to find the specific heat of a liquid which reacts with water? 100 c.c. of alcohol takes 6 min. to cool in a draught from 60° C. to 20° C. An equal volume of water

in the same calorimeter takes 18 min. to cool from 60° C. to 20° C. in a draught. If the water equivalent of the calorimeter is 10 gm., calculate a value for the specific heat of alcohol. (Density of alcohol = 0·8 gm./c.c.)

8. The density of ice is 0·89 gm. per c.c. What change in volume occurs when 3 gm. of ice melts to water at 0° C.? If the ice was melted by 8 gm. of a metal initially at 100° C., what is the specific heat of the metal? (L for ice = 80 cal. per gm.)

9. How would you find by experiment the latent heat of evaporation of alcohol?

A copper calorimeter of mass 150 gm. contains 250 gm. of alcohol at 25° C., and 20 gm. of steam at 100° C. are condensed in the alcohol. Assuming that no heat is lost to the surroundings, and neglecting heat effects resulting from mixing the steam and alcohol, find the amount of alcohol evaporated. The following data may be assumed: specific heat of copper = 0·1, specific heat of alcohol = 0·55, latent heat of evaporation of water = 540 cal./gm., latent heat of evaporation of alcohol = 260 cal./gm., boiling-point of alcohol = 78° C. (*L.H.S.C.*)

10. State *Newton's Law of Cooling* and explain how it may be used to correct for heat losses from a calorimeter. Describe in detail how you would find the specific heat of a liquid by the method of cooling. (*L.H.S.C.*)

11. Give a sketch of Bunsen's ice calorimeter explaining how you would use it to find the specific heat of a solid. If a solid of mass 3 gm., specific heat 0·095 cal. gm.$^{-1}$ deg. C.$^{-1}$ and temperature 105° C., is dropped into the ice calorimeter, find the travel of mercury produced in the capillary tube of diameter 1·6 mm., if the latent heat of melting of ice is 80 cal. gm.$^{-1}$ and the density of ice 0·917 gm. cm.$^{-3}$ (*L.U.Inter.*)

12. Describe an experiment to determine the specific heat of a solid which is soluble in water, carefully explaining how you would calculate your result. A piece of aluminium of mass 0·5 lb. and specific heat 0·25 is left for a time in a gas oven heated by a steady burner. The aluminium is then taken out and immediately dropped into 5 lb. of water contained in a copper can of water equivalent 0·05 lb. The temperature of the water rises from 59° F. to 81·5° F. Neglecting any steam produced at first, calculate the approximate temperature of the gas oven. (*N.J.M.B.*)

13. What are (*a*) the advantages, and (*b*) the difficulties of the continuous-flow method of calorimetry? Describe in some detail

how this method may be used to determine the latent heat of steam at atmospheric pressure. (*N.J.M.B.*)

14. State Newton's law of cooling, and describe an experiment by which you would verify it. A calorimeter containing first 40 and then 100 grams of water is heated and suspended in the same constant-temperature enclosure. It is found that the times taken to cool from 50 to 40° C. in the two cases are 15 and 33 minutes respectively. Calculate the water equivalent of the calorimeter. (*O. & C.*)

15. What is meant by the latent heat of vaporization of a substance? 2 gm. of iron wire at 15° C. are dropped into liquid oxygen maintained at its boiling-point in a thermos flask. The volume of oxygen driven off, measured at 16° C. and 80 cm. of mercury pressure, is 432 c.c. Find the latent heat of vaporization of oxygen. The specific heat of iron may be taken as 0·09, the boiling-point of oxygen as −184° C., and the density of oxygen at normal temperature and pressure 0·001 4 gm. per c.c. (*O. & C.*)

16. What are the principal sources of error in the determination of specific heat by the method of mixtures? Explain briefly how the errors are minimized. Equal volumes of water and paraffin are allowed to cool under the same conditions in the same calorimeter, and the time-temperature readings are given in the following table:

Time, min.	0	1	2	3	4	5
Temp. of water, °C. ..	60·4	57·6	55·3	53·4	51·8	50·5
Temp. of paraffin, °C. ..	60·2	55·9	52·2	49·1	46·2	43·6

Draw graphs of temperature (ordinates) and time (abscissæ) for both liquids. If the thermal capacity of the calorimeter is 10·5 cal. deg. C.$^{-1}$., the mass of the water 85·5 gm., and that of the paraffin 68·4 gm., calculate the mean specific heat of paraffin between 51° C. and 57° C. (*N.J.M.B.*)

17. A cylinder of copper has an electric heating filament inside it, so that it may be heated by passing a current. After the temperature had been raised, the current was switched off and the copper allowed to cool. The following observations were made of the temperature at 20-second intervals:

86·0, 70·0, 60·0, 51·7, 44·5, 38·5° C.

The current was again switched on and adjusted to 3·5 amperes in order to keep the cylinder at a constant temperature of 53° C. If the specific heat of copper is 0·095 cal. per gm. per deg. C., and the mass of the cylinder 200 gm., what is the resistance of the heating filament? [Take the value of J as 4·2 joules per calorie.] (*L.H.S.C.*)

18. Describe an experimental determination of specific heat which enabled the variation of this quantity with temperature to be measured. Explain the advantages of the method you describe. (*L.H.S.C.*)

19. Sketch apparatus suitable for determining the latent heat of vaporization of water boiling under atmospheric pressure. Do *not* describe the experiment but (*a*) show how the result would be calculated, (*b*) state the most likely sources of error, and point out any steps you would take to diminish their effects. Deal with each error in a separate short paragraph.

A piece of copper, mass 0·495 gm., at 15·0° C. dropped into liquid oxygen at its boiling-point −183° C., causes some of the liquid to vaporize. The gas formed has a volume of 123 c.c. at 15·0° C. and 75·5 cm. of mercury pressure. If the density of oxygen at S.T.P. is 1·43 gm. per litre and its latent heat of vaporization is 51 cal. per gm., what is the mean specific heat of copper between 15° C. and −183° C.? (*N.J.M.B.*)

20. What is meant by the specific heat of a substance? Describe how you would determine the specific heat of a solid such as copper (*a*) at room temperature, (*b*) at a temperature between 0° C. and −20° C., discussing possible errors and corrections. (*O. & C.*)

21. Define latent heat of change of state. Describe how you would determine experimentally the latent heat of fusion of ice.

A calorimeter of weight 100 gm. and of specific heat 0·1, contains 50 gm. of ice and 50 gm. of water. Steam at 100° C. is passed through at a constant rate until the total weight is 210 gm. Determine the final temperature of the system and draw a rough graph showing the change of temperature with time. Heat losses may be neglected. [Latent heat of fusion of ice = 80 cal. per gm. Latent heat of vaporization of water = 540 cal. per gm.] (*C.H.S.C.*)

22. Discuss the chief sources of error in the determination of specific heats by the method of mixtures. Explain the continuous-flow method of measuring the specific heat of a liquid, and point out its advantages over the method of mixtures. (*C.H.S.C.*)

23. Describe a method of measuring the change in volume of water when it freezes.

m gm. of metal at a temperature t° C. are dropped into a Bunsen ice calorimeter, and the mercury moves a distance x cm. Taking the diameter of the tube to be d cm., the density of ice to be ρ gm. per c.c., and the latent heat of fusion of ice to be L calories per gm., find an expression for the specific heat of the substance. (*C.H.S.C.*)

CHAPTER VI

Change of State. Properties of Vapours. Hygrometry

Change of State

1. Fusion, or Solid to Liquid change.

When a solid is heated its temperature rises until the solid begins to melt, and observation shows that the temperature-time curve follows a path similar to AB (fig. 6.1). At this stage, corresponding to B, the temperature remains constant, and the

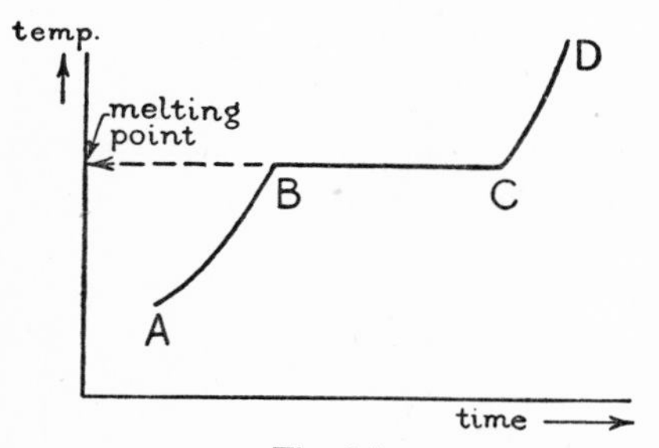

Fig. 6.1

further (latent) heat supplied is utilized in changing the substance from a solid to a liquid state (p. 102). After all the solid has been melted, corresponding to C, the temperature of the liquid formed begins to rise as more heat is supplied, and the temperature-time curve follows a path similar to CD.

If the hot liquid were allowed to cool from the temperature corresponding to D, the temperature-time graph would have the same variation as DCBA, but would be drawn the other way round. Thus the temperature remains constant until all the liquid has changed to solid, during which time heat (latent heat) is given out; after that time the temperature of the solid formed decreases. It can hence be seen that the changes from solid to liquid, and from liquid to solid, are reversible processes.

2. The melting-point of a substance can be deduced from its temperature-time curve as it changes from the liquid to the solid state or from the solid to the liquid state, since it is the temperature which corresponds to the flat portion of the curve. Fig. 6.1 is the curve obtained for *pure* substances, in which case there is a definite melting-point and BC is horizontal. In the case of substances with high melting-points, such as metals, the mercury thermometer is unsuitable, and a thermocouple (p. 11) is used in conjunction with a sensitive galvanometer. The melting-point corresponds to the temperature of the "hot" junction at which the galvanometer readings become constant when the hot junction is placed inside the molten metal.

There is no definite melting-point in the case of *amorphous* or *plastic* substances, such as glass, paraffin wax, and sealing wax, as solidification takes place over a range of temperature. The flat part of the curve is then inclined to the time-axis, unlike the case of the pure substance, shown in fig. 6.1. The melting-point of an *alloy* varies with its composition, and is usually lower than the melting-point of any of its constituents.

3. Effect of pressure on melting-point.

The change from the liquid to the solid state is usually accompanied by a change in volume of the substance. Most substances diminish in volume when they solidify. Water, however, is an exception to the rule as it expands when it changes to ice, 1 c.c. of water forming about 1·09 c.c. of ice (p. 105). The great force exerted in expansion when the water freezes (p. 26) leads to burst pipes in winter.

The melting-point of a substance is affected by changes in pressure, and we can deduce what will happen from elementary considerations. Take the case of ice, for example, which melts at 0° C. under normal atmospheric pressure (76 cm. of mercury). If the pressure on the ice increases, the conditions are more favourable to the formation of water because ice contracts when it melts, and 0° C. is now above the new melting-point. For one atmosphere increase in pressure the melting-point of ice is lowered by about 0·0075° C. Thus increased pressure *lowers* the melting-point of all substances which *contract* when they change from the solid to the liquid state. For substances which expand when they change from the solid to the liquid state, increased pressure raises the melting-point.

The formation of a snowball when the snow is compressed is explained by the fact that increased pressure lowers the melting-point of ice. Some of the snow melts because its temperature is now above the melting-point, and when the pressure is diminished, the water formed freezes to ice again and binds the particles of snow together. The bottom of a skate is made like a knife-edge so that the pressure (force/area) exerted on the ice is large. The melting-point is then lowered, water is formed, and the skate makes progress along the thin film of water thus obtained.

Properties of Vapours

4. Saturated Vapours.

Consider a vertical tube T about a metre long, which contains mercury and has a vacuum in the space at the top of the tube (fig. 6.2). When a small amount of water is introduced at B by a bent pipette, the water rises to the top of the mercury, because it is less dense, and then evaporates in the empty space. The water-vapour formed exerts a pressure, and the mercury level is depressed by a height equal to the vapour pressure in millimetres of mercury. As more water is introduced at B and changes to vapour in the space above A, the level of the mercury is depressed further, but this effect ceases as soon as water is observed in the liquid state on the top of the mercury column.

The water-vapour is now said to be *saturated* (fig. 6.2). The introduction of more water into T has no effect on the water-vapour pressure, which is known as the *saturation vapour pressure* (S.V.P.) of the water at the temperature of the surroundings. If T is raised a little out of the trough of mercury, so that the saturated vapour expands, the height of the mercury column above the level of the mercury in the trough remains the same,

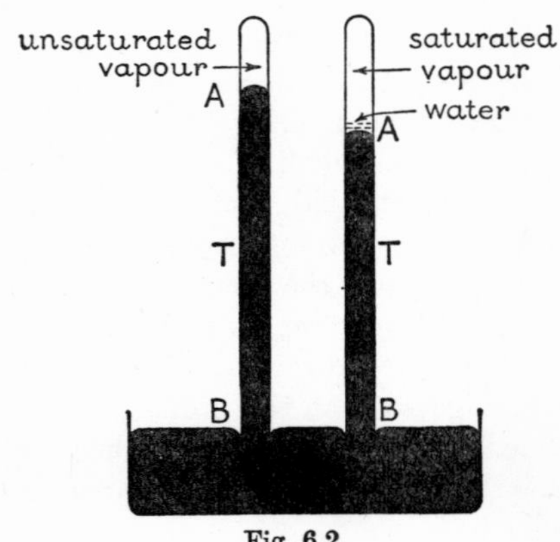

Fig. 6.2

showing that the saturation vapour pressure is unaltered. If T is lowered into the trough so that the volume of the saturated vapour decreases, the mercury height remains unchanged. Thus experiment shows that the saturation vapour pressure is independent of the volume occupied by the vapour.

5. Differences between unsaturated and saturated vapours.

Before water is formed at the top of the mercury column in T, the water-vapour in the space there is said to be *unsaturated vapour* (fig. 6.2). When the volume is increased, observation shows that the pressure of the vapour is decreased, and experiment shows that Boyle's law is approximately obeyed when the pressure values are not near the saturation vapour pressure value for the given temperature. Thus unsaturated and saturated vapours of the same substance have different properties, and the following summary should assist the student to distinguish between them:

(1) A *saturated vapour* is one which is in contact with its liquid in a closed space. The pressure exerted by a saturated vapour is always constant for a given temperature of the liquid, even though the vapour undergoes changes in volume. Experiment shows that the saturation vapour pressure of a liquid varies with its temperature (p. 126).

(2) An *unsaturated vapour* at a given temperature is one which exerts less than the saturation vapour pressure for that temperature, and is obtained when no liquid is in contact with it in a closed space. The pressure of a given mass of unsaturated vapour depends on its volume as well as its temperature, and experiment shows that it obeys Boyle's law approximately.

6. The Kinetic Theory of Matter. Gaseous, Liquid, and Solid states.

Every substance, whether solid, liquid, or gaseous, is made up of many millions of elementary particles known as molecules of the substance. JOHN DALTON, in 1803, was the first person to make use of this conception of matter. Later, it was realized that the molecules of a substance had some form of movement, and there developed the *Kinetic Theory of Matter*, which, in the hands of CLERK MAXWELL, enabled the properties of a gas to be explained (see p. 79).

According to the kinetic theory, the molecules of a **gas** move about in all different directions, making collisions for a short time with each other and with the walls of the containing vessel, and rebounding from them. The motion of the molecules is a random or haphazard one, and the average of the impacts per second of the molecules on one side of the container creates a certain pressure there, which is the pressure of the gas. When the gas is heated the molecules move faster, and hence the average kinetic energy of the gas increases.

Particles of matter have an attraction for each other which decreases as their distance apart increases. In the case of a gas, the molecules are so far apart from each other on the average that there is little inter-molecular attraction. The cohesive force between the particles of matter which constitute a gas is thus extremely small, and this can be seen by the fact that a gas will automatically fill any space into which it is led. The inter-molecular attraction between the particles of a **liquid** is greater than that which exists between the molecules of a gas because they are closer together on the average. Thus, although a liquid always assumes the shape of the vessel in which it is placed, a given amount of it occupies a definite volume, unlike a gas. The cohesive force between the particles of a **solid** is greater than that which exists between the particles of a liquid, as the molecules are relatively closer.

As in the case of a gas, the movement of the molecules inside a liquid is a random one, and in general the speed of the molecules increases as the temperature of the liquid increases. Although the temperature of the liquid may be constant, showing that the average energy of the liquid molecules is constant, the *individual* molecules are moving with different speeds. When a molecule near the liquid surface has a sufficient amount of kinetic energy, it is able to overcome the attraction of the molecules of the liquid round it and escape through the surface of the liquid to the outside, where it constitutes a molecule of vapour. This is the process which takes place continuously when liquid such as a pool of water evaporates in an open space; the molecules which escape from the liquid are carried away by the wind, which thus assists further evaporation.

7. How the kinetic theory explains unsaturated and saturated vapours and their pressures.

When a small quantity of liquid at a given temperature is introduced into a closed space at the top of a barometer tube, all the liquid evaporates and the vapour exerts a pressure (p. 120).

On the kinetic theory, this phenomenon is explained by assuming that, to start with, more molecules per second leave the liquid and become gaseous in the closed space than return to the liquid from the closed space. This process goes on until no more liquid remains, and an *unsaturated vapour* is obtained.

As more liquid is introduced into the closed space, however, a point is reached when liquid remains there, and the vapour is now in contact with the liquid. The pressure exerted by the vapour is then constant no matter how much liquid is introduced into the closed space, and we speak of the " saturation vapour pressure " of the liquid at the given temperature (p. 120). The density of the vapour has increased to such a value that the same number of molecules of the gas now return to the liquid per second from the closed space as escape from the liquid in that time. A state of *dynamic equilibrium* exists in this case between the molecules which constitute the vapour and those which constitute the liquid. The introduction of further liquid into the tube causes no more molecules per second to leave the liquid, because the speed of the molecules depends only on the temperature of the liquid, and dynamic equilibrium is thus maintained with the same average number of molecules of vapour above the liquid. The vapour is therefore saturated, i.e. it has reached the maximum density possible at the given temperature, and has the maximum possible pressure. If the volume of the space above the liquid decreases, more molecules of vapour enter the liquid per second than previously; but as the number of molecules leaving the liquid per second remains constant, some of the vapour condenses until dynamic equilibrium is again restored. Conversely, if the volume of the space above the liquid increases, the density of the vapour again reaches its maximum value by evaporation of some of the liquid, and dynamic equilibrium is once more obtained. Thus the saturation vapour pressure remains constant at a given temperature of the liquid.

When the temperature is increased the speed of the molecules inside the liquid is increased, and the average number of molecules in the space above the liquid increases. Dynamic equilibrium again exists if some liquid is present at this higher temperature, but the saturation vapour pressure is higher as the density of the vapour molecules in the space above the liquid is now greater.

8. Vaporization. Change from state of Liquid to Vapour.

When water is heated in an open vessel its temperature increases, and after a time, observation shows that some bubbles appear inside the liquid, rise to the surface, and then burst and give off vapour. If the external pressure is one atmosphere (76 cm. of mercury), and the temperature of the water reaches 100° C., the whole of the surface of the liquid is filled with bursting bubbles and steam is obtained. *Boiling* is now said to take place, and the temperature of the water remains constant at 100° C. as long as the water changes to vapour.

It is possible for vapour to be given off from water at temperatures well below 100° C. Thus a puddle of water disappears gradually, even though the average temperature of the water may be about 10° C. This process, which is essentially different from boiling, is known as *evaporation*, and is due to the escape from the liquid of some of the faster molecules near the surface. The vapour is swept away continually by the wind, and as other molecules then escape from the liquid, more and more of the water is converted to vapour. The water thus gradually disappears.

9. The effect of pressure on the boiling-point.

Observation shows that water boils at a much lower temperature than 100° C. at the top of a mountain; at 15,000 ft., for example, water boils at 84° C. In the past, mountaineers deduced the height they had ascended by finding the boiling-point of water at this height, and then consulting tables showing the variation of the boiling-point with height. (The apparatus shown in fig. 1.2*a* on p. 3 was called a "hypsometer", or "height-measurer", on this account.) It thus appears that reduced external pressure on a liquid leads to a reduction in the boiling-point. FRANKLIN demonstrated this phenomenon by boiling water in a flask, then waiting until the boiling had ceased, and inverting the flask after sealing the top. When water was poured over the top of the flask (fig. 6.3), it was observed that the water in the flask began suddenly to boil again, and this is due to the condensation of some of the vapour in the flask, which reduces the external pressure on the water. An experiment to find the variation of the boiling-point of water with pressure is described on p. 127.

Fig. 6.3

10. How the kinetic theory explains the effect of pressure on the boiling-point.

Suppose that some water is heated in a vessel, and a bubble, A, is formed in the liquid (fig. 6.4). The external pressure on the bubble is equal to the atmospheric pressure plus the pressure due to the small head of water above A. Inside the bubble the pressure is equal to the saturation vapour pressure of water at the temperature of the liquid, assuming there is only water vapour inside A, and if the saturation vapour pressure is less than the external pressure the bubble cannot grow. As the water is heated, the saturation vapour pressure, which increases with temperature, reaches a value when it just exceeds the pressure outside the bubble. The bubble then grows and rises quickly to the surface of the water, where it bursts. Vapour is now given off, and the liquid is said to be boiling. Thus *boiling occurs when the temperature of the liquid is such that its saturation vapour*

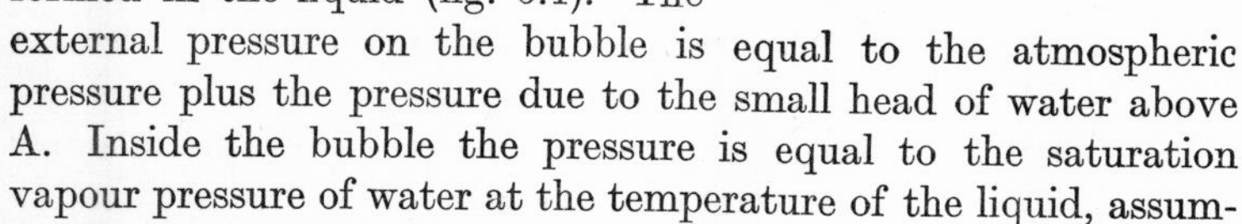

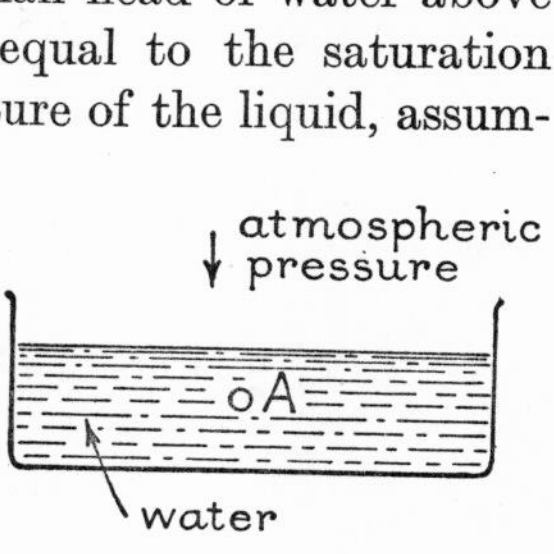

Fig. 6.4

pressure is equal to the external atmospheric pressure. If the atmospheric pressure decreases, the liquid boils at a lower temperature because the saturation vapour pressure necessary for boiling is now less. Similarly, increased pressure raises the boiling-point.

11. The boiling-point of a liquid is influenced by impurities in it, as well as by the external pressure. The boiling-point of water *increases* when salt is added to it, for example, and the boiling-points of other liquids are also increased when impurities are added. There is no simple relation between the elevation of the boiling-point of a liquid and the impurities dissolved in it, but when the mass w of impurity is small, the elevation of the boiling-point is approximately proportional to w.

12. Measurement of saturation vapour pressure (S.V.P.).

We have now to consider methods of measuring the S.V.P. of water, which vary according to the temperature. The magnitude of the S.V.P. of water is required in the design of efficient steam engines, and also in meteorology.

(*a*) *From* 0–50° C. For this range of temperature, the method illustrated in fig. 6.5 can be used. Two long vertical tubes, M, N, filled with mercury, are placed in a trough, and the mercury levels in both tubes are originally at the same level corresponding to A, with a vacuum above each. Water is now continually introduced into M by means of a bent pipette, and the level of mercury is depressed until some water, W, remains on the mercury at B. The difference in height h between A and B is then noted, and corresponds to the S.V.P. at the temperature of the surroundings after correction is made for the small amount of water W and the surface tension effect. A liquid bath D surrounds the upper part of both tubes, and an electrical heating coil H in the liquid enables the temperature to be varied. The temperature is read from thermometers P. D has plane glass windows to enable accurate observations to be made on the mercury levels by a travelling microscope. In this experiment, it should be noted, the level of A acts only as a reference line and remains constant.

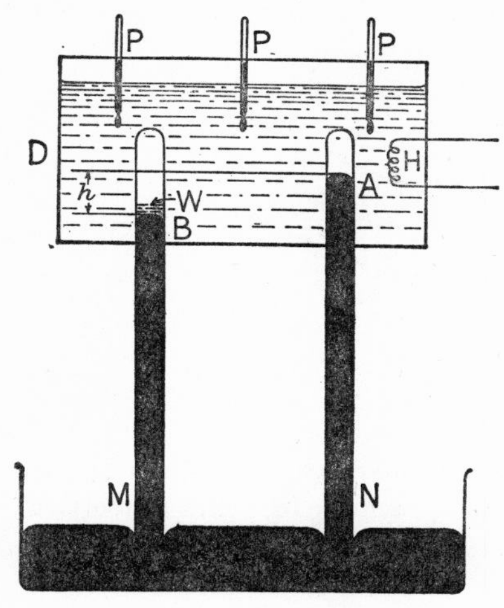

Fig. 6.5

(*b*) *Above* 50° C. We have already seen that a liquid boils when its saturation vapour pressure is just equal to the pressure of the atmosphere outside the liquid (p. 125). Thus if a liquid boils at t° C., the S.V.P. at this temperature is the same as the external pressure.

This principle is utilized in the measurement of saturation vapour pressures at different temperatures. The liquid A is contained in a vessel connected through a sloping tube B to a bulb C and a manometer M (fig. 6.6). B is surrounded by water flowing through a condenser, so that the vapour formed is condensed and the liquid obtained is used again, while the bulb C helps to prevent large fluctuations of pressure in the apparatus. The pressure of the air in the system is first fixed at some value by connecting a pump at E and then closing this tap, and the liquid A is now heated. After a time the liquid boils at a temperature indicated by the thermometer above A, and the corresponding pressure obtained from the manometer M is the S.V.P. of the liquid at this temperature. By varying the pressure, the variation of S.V.P. with temperature is obtained.

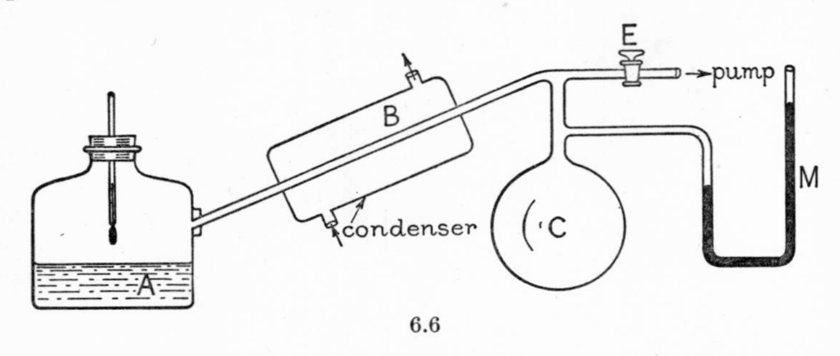

6.6

In contrast to the method described on p. 126, it should be noted that the external pressure (S.V.P.) is settled first, and the corresponding temperature of the liquid is then obtained.

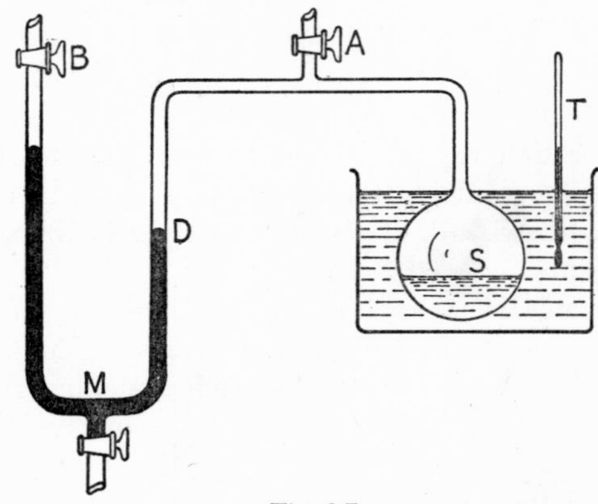

Fig. 6.7

(*c*) *Below* 0° C., the S.V.P. of a liquid can be found by means of the apparatus shown in fig. 6.7. A bulb S is connected to a manometer M, and S is surrounded by a freezing mixture whose temperature is measured by means of a thermometer T. The space between S and M is first exhausted of air, and some vapour of the substance investigated is introduced through A until liquid is formed in S. The mercury level on the right side of M, which had been depressed as soon as the vapour was introduced, now remains constant, and if the space below B is a vacuum, the difference in levels of the mercury column is equal to the S.V.P. at the temperature registered on T.

Although the vapour at D is not at the temperature of the freezing mixture, the pressure measured by M does correspond to this temperature. To prove this, suppose that the pressure of the vapour at D is higher than that above the liquid in S. Vapour then flows from D to S to equalize the pressure, and some condenses to liquid. Similarly, if the vapour pressure at D is less than that above the liquid in S, some of the liquid evaporates to equalize the pressure. Thus the vapour pressure in D is always equal to the S.V.P. of the liquid in S.

13. The variation of the S.V.P. of a liquid with temperature.

In general, the S.V.P. of a liquid increases as the temperature increases, but there is no simple relationship between the two

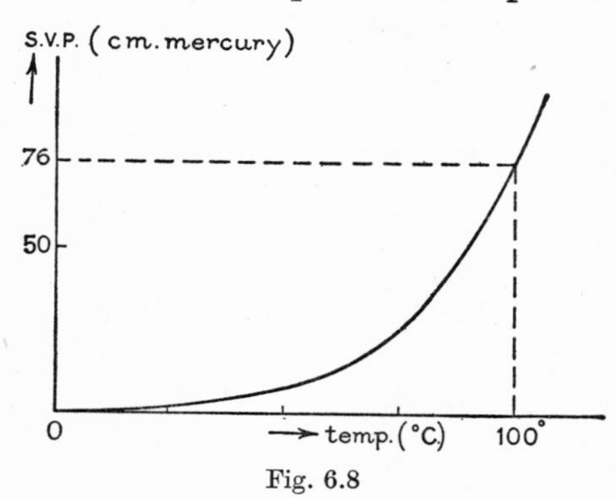

Fig. 6.8

quantities. Fig. 6.8 illustrates roughly the variation of the S.V.P. of water in cm. of mercury with temperature in °C.; at 100° C. the S.V.P. is 76 cm. of mercury.

14. Dalton's Law of Partial Pressures.

DALTON put forward a law, known by his name, relating to the pressure of gases in a mixture. The law states:

In a mixture of gases, each gas exerts a pressure which is the same as if it were alone and occupying the volume of the mixture.

The pressure of a particular gas in the mixture is known as a "partial" pressure because other gases are present, and the *total* pressure of the gases is the sum of all the partial pressures. Thus if the total pressure in a mixture of two gases is 74 cm. of mercury and the pressure of one gas is 1·8 cm., the pressure of the other gas is 74 — 1·8, or 72·2 cm. The volume occupied by either gas is the volume of the mixture, and we can understand this to be the case because the molecules of either gas move about in the whole of the space occupied by the mixture.

15. Mixture of gas and saturated water-vapour.

Suppose that some water and air are present in the closed space at the top of a column of mercury, the temperature being 10° C. If the S.V.P. of water at 10° C. is 0·8 cm. of mercury, and the total pressure of the water-vapour and air is 70 cm. of mercury, the pressure of the air $= 70 - 0{\cdot}8 = 69{\cdot}2$ cm., from Dalton's law. Suppose that the volume of the mixture is 30 c.c., and that the volume is reduced to 25 c.c., the temperature remaining constant. Then if p is the new total pressure of the mixture, the pressure of the air is now $(p - 0{\cdot}8)$ cm., as the S.V.P. of water depends only on its temperature. Further, the volume originally occupied by the air was 30 c.c., and 25 c.c. when the volume is altered.

To find the magnitude of p, we apply Boyle's law to the given mass of *air* in the mixture, since the temperature is unchanged. As pressure × volume is constant,

$$\therefore\ (p - 0{\cdot}8)25 = 69{\cdot}2 \times 30,$$

$$\therefore\ p = 83{\cdot}84 \text{ cm.}$$

It will be noted that any of the gas laws, such as Boyle's or Charles' law, for example, can be applied to a particular gas in a mixture, provided that the mass of this gas remains constant. The choice of the gas to which a gas law can be applied is limited to air in the case of an air and water-vapour mixture, as some of the water-vapour may condense, or some of the water present may vaporize, when the pressure, volume, or temperature is altered. This results in a change in the mass of water-vapour present in the mixture, so that the gas laws, which apply to a *constant* mass of gas, cannot be applied to water-vapour in contact with water.

16. The measurement of the S.V.P. of water, using Dalton's law.

Dalton's law can be used as the basis of a simple method of determining the variation of the S.V.P. of water with temperature, when the S.V.P. at one temperature is known. A pellet of water W is contained in a uniform capillary tube, T, open at one end so that a mixture of air and saturated water-vapour is obtained in a closed space below the pellet (fig. 6.9). The tube is placed inside a liquid bath, and the length of the capillary tube containing the mixture of gases is measured as the temperature is varied.

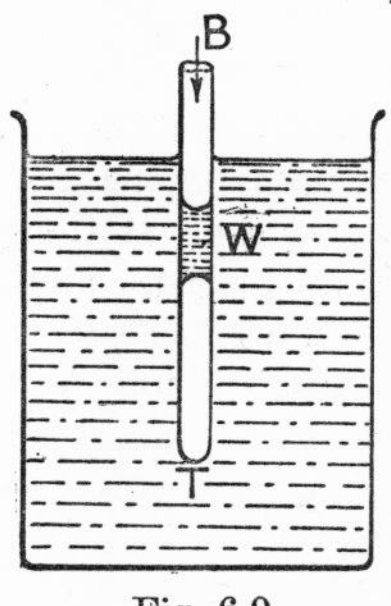

Fig. 6.9

Suppose B is the atmospheric pressure, a the uniform cross-sectional area of the tube, l and l_1 the lengths of the tube containing the mixture at temperatures t, t_1° C. respectively. Then the pressure of the air in the closed space at t° C. is $B - p$, where p is the S.V.P. of water at t° C., as the total pressure of the gases in the closed space is always equal to the external (atmospheric) pressure, if we neglect the weight of W. Similarly, the pressure of the same mass of air at t_1° C. is $B - p_1$, where p_1 is the S.V.P. of water at t_1° C. The volume of the air at t_1° C. $= l_1 a$, and the volume at t° C. $= la$. Hence, since pV/T is constant for a given mass of air, we have

$$\frac{(B - p_1)l_1 a}{273 + t_1} = \frac{(B - p)la}{273 + t}.$$

$$\therefore \frac{(B - p_1)l_1}{273 + t_1} = \frac{(B - p)l}{273 + t}.$$

Knowing B, l_1, l, t_1, t and the S.V.P. p at temperature t° C., the S.V.P. p_1 at the temperature t_1° C. can be calculated from this relation. The S.V.P. at other temperatures is calculated from similar relations.

Example 1.—A vessel contains a mixture of air and water-vapour in contact with excess of the liquid. How will the pressure in the vessel change, (*a*) if the volume is changed at constant temperature, (*b*) if the temperature changes at constant volume?

A closed vessel contains a mixture of air and water-vapour in contact with excess of water. The pressures in the vessel at 27° C. and 60° C. are respectively 77·7 cm. and 98·1 cm. of mercury. If the vapour pressure of water at 27° C. is 2·7 cm. of mercury, what is the vapour pressure at 60° C. (*O. & C.*)

First part.—(*a*) If the volume is reduced at constant temperature, the pressure of the air increases, by Boyle's law. The S.V.P. of the water remains unchanged, however, and the total pressure of the mixture thus increases. If the volume is increased, similar reasoning shows that the total pressure diminishes. (*b*) If the temperature is increased at constant volume, the pressure of the air and the S.V.P. of water both increase; hence the total pressure increases. Similar reasoning shows that the total pressure diminishes if the temperature diminishes.

Second part.—The pressure of the air at 27° C. = 77·7 − 2·7 = 75·0 cm.
 „ „ „ „ 60° C. = 98·1 − p,

where p is the S.V.P. of water at 60° C. Since the pressure of a gas at constant volume is proportional to its absolute temperature (p. 61), we have, for the constant mass of air in the mixture,

$$\frac{98 \cdot 1 - p}{75 \cdot 0} = \frac{273 + 60}{273 + 27}.$$

$$\therefore 98 \cdot 1 - p = \frac{333}{300} \times 75 \cdot 0$$

$$\therefore p = 14 \cdot 85 \text{ cm.}$$

Example 2.—Explain what is meant by the " dew-point ", and describe an accurate method of determining its value. The saturated vapour pressure of water at 11·25° C. is 1 cm. of mercury, the density of dry air at 76 cm. pressure and 25° C. is 0·001 184 gm./cm.^{3}, and the density of water-vapour relative to that of air at the same pressure and temperature is 0·624. Find the weight of a litre of moist air at 25° C., if the barometer stands at 76 cm. and the dew-point is 11·25° C. (*C.W.B.*)

First part.—The " dew-point " is the name given to the temperature at which the air becomes saturated with the water-vapour present in it. An accurate method of determining the dew-point is described later, p. 136.

Second part.—Since the dew-point is 11·25° C., the S.V.P. of the water = 1 cm. of mercury. Hence the pressure of the air at 25° C. = 76 − 1 = 75 cm. The mass of 1000 c.c. of air at 76 cm. pressure and 25° C. is 1·184 gm. At 75 cm. pressure and 25° C. the volume of this air is 1000 × 76/75 c.c., from Boyle's law.

∴ mass of 1 litre of air at 75 cm. pressure and 25° C.

$$= 1{\cdot}184 \times \frac{1000}{1000 \times 76/75} = 1{\cdot}184 \times \frac{75}{76} = 1{\cdot}169 \text{ gm.}$$

We have now to find the mass of 1 litre of water-vapour at 1 cm. pressure and 25° C., since the pressure of the water-vapour in the moist air is 1 cm. As the mass of 1 litre of air at 1 cm. pressure and 25° C. is $\frac{1}{75} \times 1{\cdot}169$ gm., and the density of water-vapour is 0·624 of that of air at the same pressure and temperature, the mass of 1 litre of water-vapour at 1 cm. pressure and 25° C. is

$$0{\cdot}624 \times \frac{1}{75} \times 1{\cdot}169 = 0{\cdot}0097 \text{ gm.}$$

$$\therefore \text{ mass of moist air} = 1{\cdot}169 + 0{\cdot}0097 = 1{\cdot}179 \text{ gm.}$$

Principles of Hygrometry

17. Relative Humidity.

When a person wearing spectacles comes into a warm room after having been outside on a cold night, a mist forms on his glasses, showing that the air in the room contains water-vapour. The atmosphere outside also contains water-vapour, which comes originally from the evaporation of water in seas and lakes, and a scientific study of the degree of humidity or " wetness " of the air is of great service in weather-forecasting. The humidity of the air in refrigerators storing meat must not exceed a definite value, otherwise the meat deteriorates; artificial seasoning of timber takes place under pre-arranged values of air humidity. Tobacco deteriorates unless the air in the store-room has a specified humidity.

On fine days the air feels clear and dry; on "muggy" days the air feels damp and oppressive. Nevertheless there may be much more water-vapour in the air in the former case than on a muggy day, so that our judgment of the degree of humidity of the air cannot be based only on the actual amount of water-vapour in the air. The important point is: *How near to saturation* is the water-vapour in the air? If it is very close to saturation we cannot perspire freely, as the air now contains nearly as much moisture as it can possibly have, and thus we feel uncomfortable. Conversely, we can perspire freely if the water-vapour is not close to the saturation value, and we are correspondingly comfortable. It should now occasion no surprise to learn that scientists define the **relative humidity** (R.H) of the air as a *ratio*, as follows:

$$\mathbf{R.H.} = \frac{m}{M} \times 100\%, \quad \ldots \quad (34)$$

where m is the mass of water-vapour in a given volume of air, and M is the mass of water-vapour required to *saturate* that volume at the same temperature.

An imaginary experiment may assist the reader to understand the definition better. Suppose the water-vapour in the air in a sealed room has a mass of 4·2 gm. If a hole is made in a wall, and steam (water-vapour) is allowed to enter the room slowly, more and more water-vapour enters the air. At some stage, however, the surfaces of polished metal objects in the room will become misty, showing that water has formed on them, and the air in the room is now saturated. If the water-vapour in the air is now 5·0 gm., the relative humidity of the air originally is $(4{\cdot}2/5{\cdot}0) \times 100$ per cent, from (34), or 84 per cent. A high value of relative humidity means that the air is nearly saturated, and a low value means that the air is far from being saturated.

18. The " pressure " definition of relative humidity.

Water-vapour obeys the gas laws fairly well. Suppose the (partial) pressure of water-vapour in a volume V of the air is p, and that the gas constant of 1 gm. of water-vapour is denoted by R. Then, if the absolute temperature of the air is T, the mass m of vapour-water is given in grams by

$$m = \frac{pV}{RT}, \qquad \text{(i)}$$

as shown on p. 75. Suppose P is the *saturation* vapour pressure of water at the same temperature as the air. Then, assuming the same equation is true, the mass M of water-vapour required to saturate the same volume of air is given in grams by

$$M = \frac{PV}{RT}. \qquad \text{(ii)}$$

Dividing (i) by (ii), we have

$$\frac{m}{M} = \frac{p}{P},$$

and since the relative humidity (R.H.) was defined as $(m/M) \times$ 100 per cent, another definition of relative humidity is

$$\textbf{R.H.} = \frac{p}{P} \times \mathbf{100\%}. \qquad (35)$$

In this expression p is the pressure of the water-vapour in a given volume of the air, and P is the saturation vapour pressure of water for the same volume of air at the same temperature.

On a warm fine day, the saturation vapour pressure P of water at the same temperature as the air is well above the vapour pressure p of the water-vapour in the same volume of air. The relative humidity is thus low, from (35).

19. The Dew-point.

In the early morning, when the temperature is low, dew may be observed on grass, showing that the air near the grass has become saturated with water-vapour. The temperature at which the air becomes saturated with the water-vapour present in it is known as the **dew-point,** and the latter can be determined by progressively cooling a bright metal surface in the air. At some point the surface becomes misty, showing that water has condensed on it, and the dew-point is the corresponding temperature of the metal surface (see p. 137).

The dew-point is utilized in one of the standard methods of measuring relative humidity. Suppose that the temperature of the air in a room is 15° C. and that dew is deposited on a metal surface, as it is cooled, when its temperature is 10·8° C. Then the pressure of the water-vapour in the room at 15° C. is equal to the S.V.P. of water at 10·8° C. It follows from the definition of relative humidity given in equation (35), p. 135, that, generally,

$$\textbf{relative humidity} = \frac{\textbf{S.V.P. of water at the dew-point}}{\textbf{S.V.P. of water at the air temperature}} \times 100\%. \quad (36)$$

Thus one method of measuring relative humidity consists basically of (*a*) finding the dew-point, (*b*) then referring to tables giving the S.V.P. values for water at different temperatures, and (*c*) using the relation in (36).

20. Regnault's Dew-point Hygrometer.

A hygrometer is an instrument used for measuring the relative humidity of the air. REGNAULT designed a hygrometer which enables the dew-point to be obtained, and a simple form of the instrument is illustrated in fig. 6.10. Two glass tubes have highly polished silvered thimbles, B, C, attached to their respective ends, and the tubes are connected together, as shown. T_1, T_2 are thermometers inside each tube, and while T_2 measures the temperature of the air, T_1 measures the temperature of a quantity of ether which fills the thimble B.

By means of an aspirator connected to D, bubbles of air are drawn at a steady rate through a tube A dipping into the ether, which has the effect of causing some of the ether to evaporate as well as stirring the ether. The production of ether vapour causes the liquid ether to cool, because the (latent) heat to produce the vapour is taken from the liquid, and hence the silver thimble B is cooled continuously. After a time, moisture is observed on B, and the temperature on T_1 is then recorded.

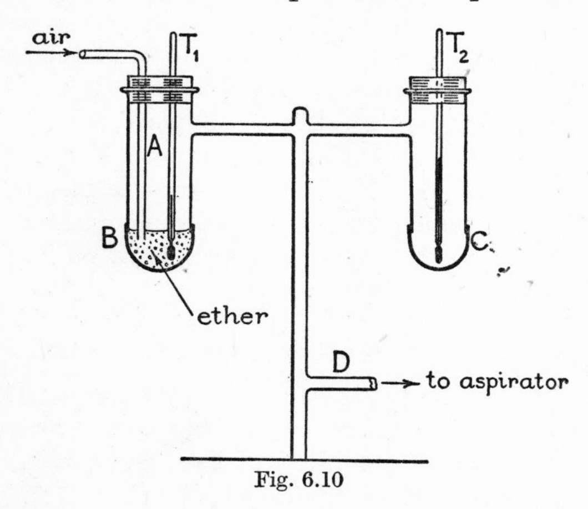

Fig. 6.10

The flow of air is now considerably reduced, with the result that the temperature of the ether begins to rise, and the reading on T_1 is observed when the moisture on B just disappears. The dew-point is taken as the average value of the two temperatures on T_1 thus obtained; suppose it is 9·0° C. The temperature of the air is observed from the thermometer T_2; suppose it is 14·0° C. From tables, the S.V.P. of water at 9·0° C = 8·55 mm., and the S.V.P. at 14·0° C. = 11·88 mm.

$$\therefore \text{ relative humidity} = \frac{\text{S.V.P. at dew-point}}{\text{S.V.P. at air temperature}} \times 100\%$$

$$= \frac{8\cdot55}{11\cdot88} \times 100\% = 72\%.$$

The thimble C is used as a comparison surface to enable the operator to recognize when dew is obtained on the thimble B. As the operator must take care not to breathe on B, a sheet of glass is interposed between him and B, or a telescope is used. Nowadays, in accurate work, a thermocouple is used for measuring directly the temperature of the surface of B, as the surface may not be at the same temperature as that recorded on the thermometer T_1 in the ether.

An improved form of Regnault's hygrometer is used at the National Physical Laboratory, and this form of the hygrometer is accurate. Nevertheless, the instrument has several disadvantages for everyday use. In the first place, a skilled observer is required; then, the instrument is not self-recording and calculations are necessary to find the relative humidity. Other hygrometers have therefore been developed which have neither of these disadvantages.

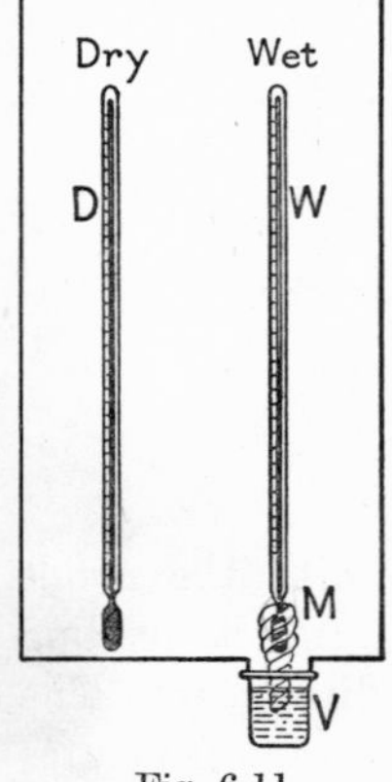

Fig. 6.11

21. Wet-and-dry bulb hygrometer.

The wet-and-dry bulb hygrometer is one which requires no skilled observer to operate it, and consists of two thermometers, D, W, placed beside each other (fig. 6.11). The dry-bulb thermometer D measures the temperature of the air. The wet-bulb thermometer W has muslin M wrapped round its bulb, and the other end of the muslin passes into a vessel V full of water placed beneath the bulb. The muslin round the bulb is thus saturated with water. When the relative humidity of the air is low, evaporation of water from the muslin takes place at a comparatively high rate and heat is therefore abstracted from the bulb. The wet thermometer W thus indicates a lower temperature than the dry thermometer D. If the relative humidity is high, evaporation from the muslin takes place at a slow rate, and the temperature registered on W is hence high, though still lower than the temperature registered on D. If the relative humidity were 100 per cent no evaporation would take place, and the temperatures on W and D would then be the same.

These general arguments indicate that there is some relation between the relative humidity, the difference in temperature between the wet and dry thermometers, and the temperature of the dry thermometer. Regnault provided an empirical formula which forms the basis of tables giving the relative humidity from (i) the observed difference in temperature of the wet and dry thermometers, and (ii) the dry thermometer temperature, with the stipulation that the air draught past the wet bulb must be maintained at a known speed.

22. Hair hygrometer.

When hair becomes moist its length increases slightly, and this is put to practical use in a form of hygrometer known as a *hair hygrometer*. A fine hair is kept taut by fixing one end to A and passing it round a grooved wheel B to a spring S (fig. 6.12).

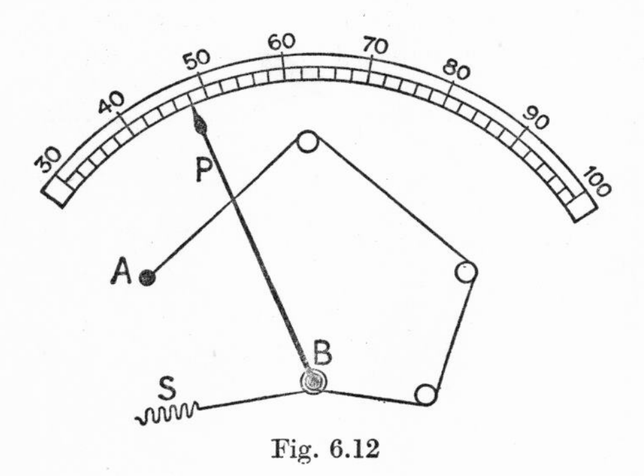

Fig. 6.12

When the length of the hair increases, a pointer attached to B moves over a scale containing relative humidity values, which has been calibrated by comparison with a Regnault hygrometer, for example. The advantage of the instrument is that it is simple to use and is direct-reading.

Accurate weather-forecasting is now made with the aid of a knowledge of the relative humidity of the " upper atmosphere ", situated high above the earth. A small radio transmitter is carried into the air by means of a balloon which rises, and the radio signals received on the earth are modified as the humidity of the atmosphere alters. Previous calibration of the transmitter enables the relative humidity to be deduced. The same arrangement also enables the temperature and pressure of the upper atmosphere to be obtained, and it is known as a **radio sonde.**

Example 3.—What is meant by the hygrometric state of the air? Describe a satisfactory way of finding it. Calculate what fraction of the mass of the water-vapour would condense if the temperature fell from 20° C. to 5° C., and if originally at 20° C. the humidity was 60 per cent.

Saturation pressure of water-vapour at 20° C. = 17·5 mm.; at 5° C. = 6·5 mm. (*N.J.M.B.*)

First part.—The " hygrometric state " of the air is its relative humidity, which is defined on p. 134. The relative humidity can be found by using Regnault's hygrometer, p. 136, or the wet-and-dry bulb hygrometer, p. 138.

Second part.—Suppose m is the mass of water-vapour in 1 litre of air at 20° C., and M is the mass required to saturate the same volume at 20° C.

Then, since relative humidity $= \frac{m}{M} \times 100\% = 60\%$, from data,

$$m = 0{\cdot}6M = \tfrac{3}{5}M. \qquad \text{(i)}$$

Suppose m_1 is the mass of water-vapour required to *saturate* 1 litre of air at 5° C. Then,

$$\frac{m_1}{M} = \frac{\text{S.V.P. at } 5^\circ \text{ C.}}{\text{S.V.P. at } 20^\circ \text{ C.}},$$

i.e.

$$\frac{m_1}{M} = \frac{6{\cdot}5}{17{\cdot}5}.$$

$$\therefore\ m_1 = \tfrac{13}{35}M. \qquad \text{(ii)}$$

Thus the mass of water-vapour in 1 litre which condenses when the temperature changes from 20° C. to 5° C. $= m - m_1 = \frac{3}{5}M - \frac{13}{35}M = \frac{8}{35}M$.

$$\therefore \text{ fraction condensed} = \frac{8/35\,M}{3/5\,M} = \frac{8}{21}.$$

Examples on Chapter VI

1. Draw sketches illustrating the cooling curves of a pure and an impure liquid, and explain the appearance of the curves.

2. What is a *saturated* and an *unsaturated vapour*? Which of them obeys Boyle's law? Explain your answer.

3. What is the effect of a change of (*a*) volume, (*b*) temperature on the pressure of a vapour in contact with its liquid? How is your answer explained by the kinetic theory of gases?

4. Under what conditions of external pressure does a liquid begin to boil? State how the boiling-point of water is affected as one ascends a mountain, and the effect this has on the cooking of meals at high altitudes.

5. Draw a sketch of a method of determining the variation of the saturation vapour pressure of water over a *wide* range of temperature. Explain briefly the principle of the method.

6. Write down two definitions of *relative humidity*. Give three examples in everyday life in which a knowledge of relative humidity is important.

7. What is meant by the "dew-point"? The dew-point of the air is 6° C., and the temperature of the air is 14° C. Calculate the relative humidity (S.V.P. of water at 14° C., 6° C. = 11·9, 7·0 mm.)

8. State *Dalton's law of partial pressures*. A closed vessel contains water at a temperature of 17° C., and the total pressure in the vessel is 77 cm. of mercury. The total pressure increases to 81 cm. when the temperature rises to 27° C., and water is still present in the vessel. Calculate the S.V.P. of water at 27° C., if the S.V.P. at 17° C. is 1·2 cm.

9. Define *relative humidity* or *hygrometric state*. Describe a dew-point hygrometer and explain how you would use it to find the relative humidity of the atmosphere. Give experimental details. How do you account for the fact that a road surface or roof often appears to be "steaming" when sunshine follows soon after rain? (*L.H.S.C.*)

10. What is meant by *saturated vapour pressure*? Explain the experiments you would perform in order to find the saturated vapour pressures of water at temperatures from 0 to 100° C. (*L.H.S.C.*)

11. Distinguish between saturated and unsaturated vapour. Describe a method for determining the saturation pressure of water-vapour at temperatures between 40 and 80° C. and indicate the precautions you would take to ensure accurate results. What atmospheric conditions are most favourable to a high rate of evaporation? (*N.J.M.B.*)

12. Give a brief account of the kinetic theory of matter, referring to the gaseous, liquid, and solid states. Derive a relation between the pressure, density, and mean square velocity of the particles in the gaseous state, pointing out the assumptions on which the calculation is based. Describe an experiment which indicates that these assumptions are not quite true for a real gas. (*N.J.M.B.*)

13. Describe a constant-volume gas thermometer. How would you calibrate such an instrument for use over a range of about −20 to 150° C.? The bulb of a constant-volume gas thermometer contains air and sufficient alcohol to keep the air saturated. The pressure in the bulb is 1168 mm. at 60° C. when the saturated vapour pressure of alcohol is 350 mm. What will be the pressure in the bulb at 20° C. when the saturated vapour pressure of alcohol is 44 mm.? (*C.H.S.C.*)

14. What is meant by the vapour pressure of a liquid? Describe, in general terms, from the view-point of the kinetic theory, why you would expect the temperature of a liquid to fall when it evaporates, and the vapour pressure to increase with temperature. Describe an experiment by which you could investigate the variation of vapour pressure with temperature of a volatile liquid. (*O. & C.*)

15. Define *relative humidity* and *dew-point*. Describe an instrument with which the dew-point can be determined. The relative humidity in a closed room at 15° C. is 60 per cent. If the temperature rises to 20° C., what will the relative humidity become? On what assumptions is your calculation based? [Saturation vapour pressure of water-vapour at 15° C. = 12·67 mm. of mercury, at 20° C. = 17·36 mm.] (*L. Inter.*)

16. Describe an experiment which demonstrates that the pressure of a vapour in equilibrium with its liquid depends on the temperature. A narrow tube of uniform bore closed at one end has some air entrapped by a small quantity of water. If the pressure of the atmosphere is 76 cm. of mercury, the equilibrium vapour pressures of water at 12° C. and at 35° C. are 10·5 mm. of mercury and 42·0 mm. of mercury respectively, and the length of the air column at 12° C. is 10 cm., calculate its length at 35° C. (*L. Inter.*)

17. Describe how you would determine the dew-point, and explain

how you would use its value in order to calculate the relative humidity. Indicate very briefly how you would find by experiment the data (other than the dew-point) required in the calculation. Explain the effect on the dew-point of (*a*) raising the temperature of the air, (*b*) sprinkling water in the air. (*N.J.M.B.*)

18. Explain in general terms the kinetic theory of liquids and gases, and apply it to explain the phenomena of evaporation, boiling, saturated and unsaturated vapours, and the pressure of gases. (*C.H.S.C.*)

19. It is often stated that burning a gas-fire in a room makes the air "dry". How do you interpret this statement, and how would you test its truth experimentally?

A sealed room, 4·5 m. by 4 m. by 3 m., is initially at a temperature of 13° C., the relative humidity being 50 per cent. Calculate the volume of water which must be evaporated in the room in order to maintain the relative humidity at 50 per cent when the temperature is raised to 20° C. [Saturation vapour pressures of water at 13° C. and 20° C. are 11·23 mm. and 17·51 mm. of mercury respectively; density of air at N.T.P. is 1·29 gm. per litre; density of water-vapour relative to air is 0·6.] (*C.W.B.*)

20. Explain what is meant by the statement that the vapour pressure of ether at 20° C. is 44 cm. of mercury. A glass tube closed at one end is completely filled with mercury and inverted in a bowl of mercury, so that the top of the tube is 32 cm. above the level of the mercury in the bowl. Describe and explain what will happen if a little ether is introduced into the tube, the temperature being 15° C. and the barometric height 76 cm. What will happen if the temperature is gradually increased to 40° C.? The boiling-point of ether is 35° C. (*O. & C.*)

21. What are the distinguishing characteristics of *saturated* and *unsaturated* vapours? State Dalton's law of partial pressures. A uniform capillary tube, sealed at one end, contains air enclosed by a water index, which keeps the air saturated with water-vapour. The length of the air column is 17·8 cm. at 20° C. and 29·4 cm. at 70° C. The pressure of saturated water-vapour at 20° C. is 17 mm., and the barometric height at the time of the experiment was 760 mm. Calculate the pressure of saturated water-vapour at 70° C. (*C.H.S.C.*)

22. State Dalton's law of partial pressures; how is it explained on the kinetic theory? A closed vessel contains air, saturated water-vapour, and an excess of water. The total pressure in the vessel is

760 mm. of mercury when the temperature is 25° C.; what will it be when the temperature has been raised to 100° C.? [Saturation vapour pressure of water at 25° C. is 24 mm. of mercury.] (*C.H.S.C.*)

23. Outline the kinetic theory of matter and explain the essential differences between the solid, liquid, and gaseous states. How are evaporation and boiling explained on the kinetic theory? Explain *on the basis of the kinetic theory*: (*a*) Why the temperature of a gas rises when it is compressed, (*b*) why the temperature of an evaporating liquid may be less than that of the atmosphere. (*C.H.S.C.*)

CHAPTER VII

The Mechanical Equivalent of Heat

1. Heat is a form of energy.

The exact nature of heat was a problem which occupied the minds of many early scientists, and until the beginning of the nineteenth century it was considered that heat was a material substance. Thus a body gaining heat was thought to increase its content of " caloric ", as the material substance was called, and an object losing heat lost some " caloric ".

In 1798, however, BENJAMIN THOMPSON, or COUNT RUMFORD as he became known, recorded an observation which foretold the doom of the caloric theory. At that time he was engaged in superintending the boring of a gun barrel at a munitions factory in Bavaria, and he noticed the large amount of heat that was generated, although the quantity of metal chips then obtained from the gun barrel per minute was very small indeed. He reasoned that it was extremely unlikely that such a small quantity of metal could have had such a large quantity of heat (caloric) stored in it, and he then observed that the longer the boring took place, the greater the amount of heat produced. Rumford thus associated the heat produced with the *mechanical energy* expended by the borer. To verify this theory, Rumford bored a gun barrel for some hours in a tank of water, and to the astonishment of observers, who could see that no flame was being used, the water was eventually made to boil.

Rumford communicated his observations to the Royal Society, but little notice was taken of them. In 1842, however, J. P. JOULE of Manchester began a series of famous experiments which proved conclusively that heat is not a material substance but is a form of energy. The principle of Joule's experiments is described later, but it may be noted here that all observations lead to the conclusion that *heat is a form of energy*. It is considered, for example, that the atoms of a solid vibrate faster about their respective " anchored " positions when the solid is heated, so that the energy of the atoms is increased. Also, the molecules of a liquid, and a gas, move faster when the substance is heated, and hence the energy of the molecules is increased (p. 81).

2. Mechanical equivalent of heat, *J*.

Joule's experiments were designed to measure the amount of mechanical energy required to produce one unit of heat. Later and more accurate experiments show that about $4 \cdot 18 \times 10^7$ ergs of mechanical energy produce 1 calorie of heat, and that about 772 ft.-lb. of mechanical energy produce 1 British Thermal Unit of heat.

Joule's mechanical equivalent of heat, denoted by J, is defined as *the mechanical energy required to produce one unit of heat.* Thus if W is the mechanical energy which produces H units of heat,

$$J = \frac{W}{H}. \quad \ldots \ldots \quad (37)$$

The magnitude of J is $4 \cdot 18 \times 10^7$ ergs per calorie, or $4 \cdot 18$ joules per calorie, since 10^7 ergs $= 1$ joule by definition; J is also given by 772 ft.-lb. per B.Th.U. Joule's mechanical equivalent of heat is a constant of nature, and its value is required by mechanical engineers to convert the heat obtainable from fuel to mechanical energy; thereby is gained some knowledge of the distance which an engine with a given supply of fuel, for example, is capable of hauling a train.

3. Joule's experiment on the mechanical equivalent of heat.

Joule spent many years of his life in carrying out experiments to find the mechanical equivalent of heat. The *principle* of his experiments in 1842 is illustrated in fig. 7.1, in which D is a calorimeter containing water, with vanes F. Joule placed two equal weights A and B at the same distance above the ground and, by means of string attached to A and B and then wound doubled round a cylinder C, the latter was rotated when the weights were allowed to fall. Joule attached a paddle P, of the shape shown in fig. 7.1, to an axle passing through C, so that P was rotated when the two weights fell and the water was "churned". Heat was produced by the friction between P and the water, and the temperature of the water and calorimeter thus rose, and was measured by a sensitive thermometer which Joule designed

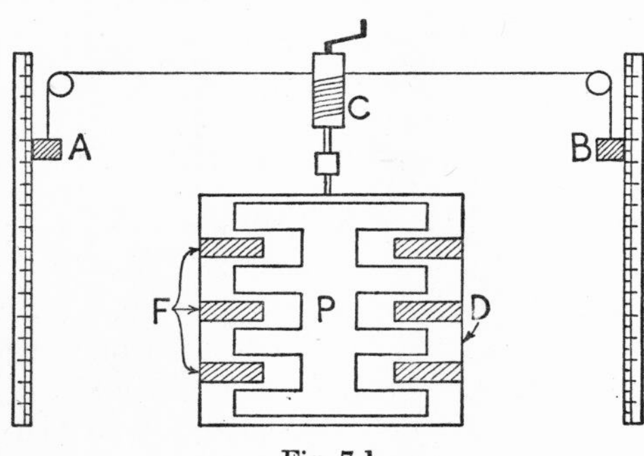

Fig. 7.1

specially. The vanes F projecting from the sides of the calorimeter were used to prevent movement of the water by "breaking" up the liquid, thus diminishing the kinetic (mechanical) energy of the water when P rotated.

Provided the weights A, B reach the ground without any kinetic energy, it can be stated that the total loss of their potential energy is the mechanical energy expended on the water and calorimeter. This condition is arranged by choosing a length of string such that the weights just reach the ground when the whole of the string is unwound round C. The *mechanical energy* expended is thus $2Mh$ ft.-lb. if M is the weight of A or B in lb. wt. and h is the height in feet. The *heat* produced $= Wt$ B.Th.U., where W is the total water equivalent in pounds of the calorimeter and water, and t is the rise in temperature in °F.

The mechanical equivalent of heat J, which is the mechanical energy required to produce one unit of heat, is thus given by

$$J = \frac{2Mh}{Wt} \text{ ft.-lb. per B.Th.U.}$$

If m is the mass of each weight in grams and x is the height above the ground in *centimetres*, the mechanical energy expended when the two weights falls to the ground is $2mgx$ *ergs*, where g, the acceleration due to gravity in cm. per sec.^{2}, is 980. If W_1 represents the total water equivalent of the calorimeter and water in *grams* and t_1 the rise in temperature in °C., the heat produced is W_1t_1 calories. Thus

$$J = \frac{2mgx}{W_1t_1} \text{ ergs per calorie.}$$

By continually winding up the string round C, Joule repeated the experiment a large number of times; he also corrected for the kinetic energy of the weights on reaching the ground. He obtained a small rise in temperature, much less than one degree, and in spite of criticism about the lack of sensitiveness of his thermometer from those scientists of the day who believed in the caloric theory (p. 145), his result for J is not far from the value obtained by later scientists, who used very accurate and sensitive instruments.

Joule performed other experiments on heat; he discovered the laws relating to the heating of an electric current, for example, and he is regarded as one of Britain's outstanding scientists of the nineteenth century.

4. Joule's improved method.

About thirty years after he had carried out his first determination of the mechanical equivalent of heat, Joule was invited by the British Association to repeat the determination, and decided to adopt a new and more accurate method. His results for J were published in 1878, and in 1879 Rowland, an eminent American scientist, repeated Joule's experiment on a larger scale and obtained a much greater rise in temperature.

The principle of Joule's and Rowland's experiment is illustrated in fig. 7.2. The calorimeter D is also fitted with vanes F to diminish the movement of the water when the paddle A is rotated. Rowland used an engine coupled to the axle R to rotate the paddle A, and the number of revolutions was read from a counter.

The paddle A exerts a turning effect on the calorimeter because of the frictional force between A and the water, and

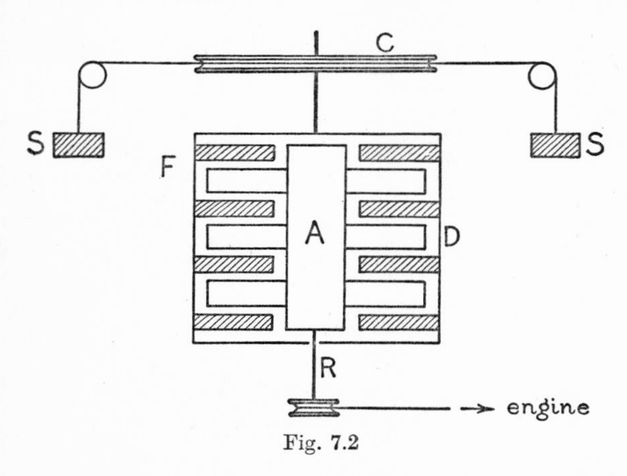

Fig. 7.2

between the water and the vanes, and to prevent the calorimeter from turning, an *opposing* turning-effect must be exerted on it. Rowland did this by attaching two equal weights S to the ends of a string passing round the circumference of a wheel C whose axle was attached to the calorimeter (fig. 7.2), and adjusting the magnitudes of S so that the turning effect of the forces on the wheel was exactly opposite to that of the frictional forces on the calorimeter due to the rotation of A. In this case the two weights remained stationary while A rotated.

Calculation of J.

The tension in the string round the wheel C is mg dynes, where m is the mass of either weight in grams and g is 980 numerically. The two equal forces of mg dynes act tangentially to C, as shown in fig. 7.3, and together they are said to act as a " couple ", whose turning-effect (moment) is defined as the product of *one* of the forces and the perpendicular distance between them. Thus the moment of the couple is mgd dyne-cm., where d is the diameter of C in centimetres.

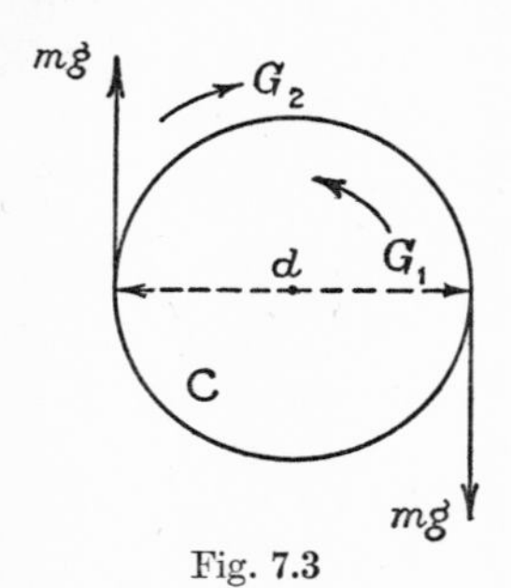

Fig. 7.3

When the paddle A rotates, it does work against the couple just discussed, which acts in an opposite direction. In fig. 7.3, the arrow denoted by G_2 is the direction in which the couple tends to turn the calorimeter, while the arrow G_1 is the direction of rotation of the paddle. The study of mechanics shows that the work done against a couple = moment of couple × angle of rotation in radians. If the paddle makes n revolutions, the angle of rotation is $2\pi n$ radians, as $360° = 2\pi$ radians by definition.

$$\therefore \text{ work done against couple} = mgd \times 2\pi n \text{ ergs.}$$

If the total water equivalent in grams of the calorimeter and water is W_1 and the rise in temperature is $t_1°$ C., the heat H produced $= W_1 t_1$ calories. Thus the mechanical equivalent J is given by

$$J = \frac{mgd \times 2\pi n}{W_1 t_1} \text{ ergs per calorie.}$$

5. Callendar's Rotating Drum method for finding J.

A simple method of measuring J in the laboratory by a mechanical method was devised by CALLENDAR, and the apparatus can be used with fair results by elementary students. In fig. 7.4, D is a section of a brass drum containing water whose temperature is measured by a thermometer A passing through a hole in the middle of D. A silk belt T is wound tightly all round the drum, and a weight W is attached to one end, while the other end of the silk is connected to the hook of a spring balance S. The drum can be rotated by means of the handle H, and the number of revolutions described in a given time is determined from the readings on the revolution-counter C.

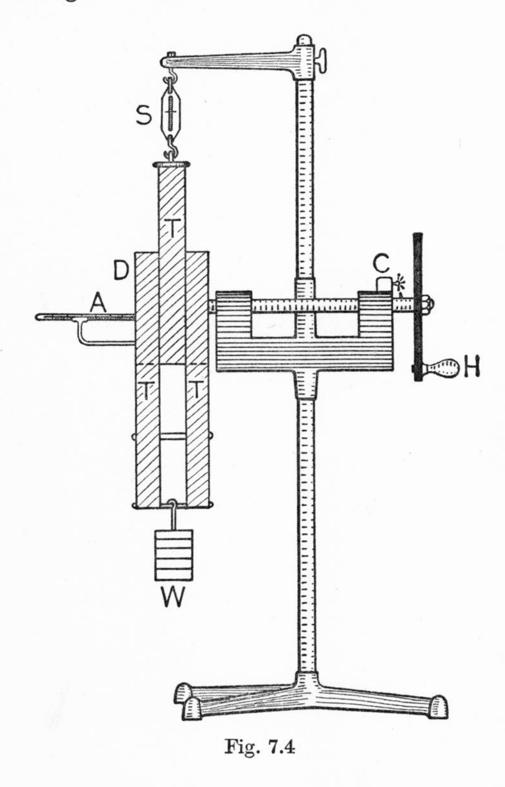

Fig. 7.4

In the experiment to find J, the drum D is rotated at a steady rate, in which case the reading on S is fairly steady and W remains constant in position. The silk belt also remains fixed in position, and work is therefore done against the frictional force F between the belt and the drum by the person turning the handle. When a suitable rise in temperature is obtained the turning is stopped, and the true temperature rise is obtained by making a cooling correction. The following measurements were taken in an actual experiment:

Load on silk band $W = 400$ gm. wt. $= 400 \times 980$ dynes.
Tension in spring balance $T = 80$ gm. wt. $= 80 \times 980$ dynes.
Water equivalent of drum and water $= 85$ gm.
Diameter of drum $= 2r = 7{\cdot}5$ cm.
Rise in temperature $= 2{\cdot}1°$ C., after cooling correction applied.
No. of revolutions $n = 1000$.

The frictional force $F = (400 - 80) \times 980$ dynes, as the weight W acts downwards on the silk belt and the tension T acts upwards on the belt. Since the work done against the friction = force × distance, the work done $= F \times 2\pi rn = (400 - 80) \times 980 \times 2\pi \times (7{\cdot}5 \div 2) \times 1000$ ergs (in one revolution a point on the edge of the drum turns a distance $2\pi r$). The heat produced $= 85 \times 2{\cdot}1$ calories.

$$\therefore J = \frac{320 \times 980 \times 2\pi \times 7{\cdot}5 \times 1000}{85 \times 2{\cdot}1 \times 2}$$

$= 4{\cdot}14 \times 10^7$ ergs per calorie, or $4{\cdot}14$ joules per calorie.

6. Callendar and Barnes' Electrical Method for J.

In 1902, Callendar and Barnes carried out a very accurate determination of the mechanical equivalent of heat by an electrical method. A steady stream of water in a glass tube was heated by a constant current in a coil of wire AB as the water flowed from one end to the other, and the difference between the inlet and outlet temperatures was measured by means of platinum resistance thermometers P and Q *when the temperatures were steady* (fig. 7.5). Under these conditions, *all* the energy supplied by the current was expended in raising the temperature of the water, none being used to raise the temperature of the glass tube, which had settled at some fixed value.

If I amperes is the current in AB and V volts is the potential difference between A and B, then the electrical energy supplied is IV joules per second (see p. 98). The heat produced per second $= mt$ calories, where m is the mass of water in grams flowing along the tube per second, and t is the difference in temperature in centigrade degrees between the inlet and outlet temperatures. The mechanical equivalent of heat is hence given by

$$J = \frac{IV}{mt} \text{ joules per calorie,}$$

or, since 1 joule = 10^7 ergs by definition,

$$J = \frac{IV \times 10^7}{mt} \text{ ergs per calorie.}$$

To eliminate the cooling correction.

If J is required very accurately, a correction must be made for the small amount of heat h lost per second by cooling. Callendar and Barnes reduced the magnitude of h to a very low value by having a vacuum round the flow tube (fig. 7.5), but some heat is still lost by radiation, which takes place across a

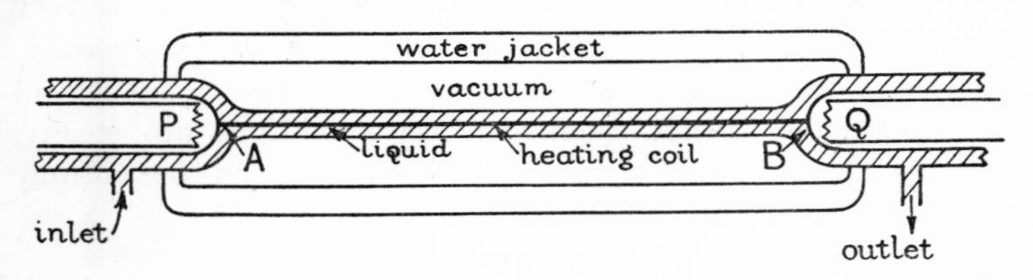

Fig. 7.5.

vacuum (p. 213). To eliminate h entirely, the experiment is repeated with a different steady rate of flow of water, and the current is then adjusted to a new value until the outlet temperature is the same as before. It is then known that the heat lost per second is h, the same as before, since the heat lost by radiation depends on the excess temperature over the surroundings.

Suppose I_1, V_1 are now the respective current in amperes and potential difference in volts. The heat produced per second in calories is given by I_1V_1/J, where J is the mechanical equivalent in joules per calorie, and hence

$$\frac{I_1V_1}{J} = m_1t + h, \quad . \quad . \quad . \quad . \quad . \quad . \quad . \quad \text{(i)}$$

where m_1 is the mass of water in grams flowing along the tube per second and t is the temperature rise. From the first experiment, adopting the notation already used, we have similarly

$$\frac{IV}{J} = mt + h. \quad . \quad . \quad . \quad . \quad . \quad . \quad . \quad \text{(ii)}$$

Subtracting (ii) from (i) to eliminate h,

$$\therefore \frac{I_1V_1 - IV}{J} = (m_1 - m)t,$$

$$\therefore J = \frac{I_1V_1 - IV}{(m_1 - m)t} \text{ joules per calorie.}$$

The *advantages* of the electrical method are (i) that very accurate measurement of the difference in temperature is possible because the temperatures are steady, (ii) the water equivalent of the calorimeter is not required when conditions are steady, (iii) the cooling correction is small, and it can be entirely eliminated, as already explained.

7. The variation of the specific heat of water.

If the inlet temperature of the water is 15° C. and the outlet temperature is 17° C., the average temperature of the water is 16° C. (fig. 7.5). If the inlet temperature of the water is made 19° C. and the outlet temperature is 21° C., the average water temperature is 20° C. When the temperature of the water is varied in this way in the electrical method of determining J, varying values of J are obtained. Now the mechanical equivalent of heat is a constant of nature, and hence some assumption in the theory of the experiment has been made which is not true. The assumption is that the specific heat of water is constant at all temperatures, and this experiment shows that *the specific heat of water varies with temperature.*

The different values of the specific heat are obtained by using s for the specific heat of water in the expression on p. 153, and then substituting the accepted accurate value for J; the results show that the specific heat of water is a minimum at about 35° C. After this discovery, which was first made by Rowland in his experiments on the mechanical equivalent of heat, scientists had to recast the definition of a calorie, because the heat required to raise the temperature of one gram of water by 1° C. depended on the actual temperature of the water. It is now agreed to define a calorie as the heat required to raise the temperature of one gram of water from 14·5° C. to 15·5° C., and this is sometimes known as the " 15° C. calorie ".

8. Some mechanical energy formulæ.

It is advisable for the student to know how mechanical energy is calculated, and in what units the result is expressed. The following formulæ should hence be carefully studied.

Work.—A machine does work if it moves an object, and the work done W is given by

$$W = \textit{force} \times \textit{distance},$$

where the distance moved is in the same direction as the force. If the force is in dynes (980 dynes = 1 gm. wt.) and the distance is in centimetres, the work done is in ergs; if the force is in pounds weight (lb. wt.) and the distance is in feet, the work done is in foot-pounds (ft.-lb.).

Kinetic energy.—The kinetic energy of an object is the energy it possesses by virtue of its motion, and is given by

$$\textit{kinetic energy} = \tfrac{1}{2}mv^2,$$

where m is the mass of the object and v is its velocity. If m is in grams and v is in centimetres per second, the energy is in ergs. If m is in pounds and v is in feet per second, the energy is in foot-poundals; since 32 poundals = 1 pound weight, the energy in foot-poundals must be divided by 32 to change it to foot-pounds.

Potential energy.—An object held stationary at some height above the ground is said to possess " potential " energy, because, if it were released, it could move another object connected to it. Suppose m is the mass of the object in grams, and h is its height above the ground in centimetres. The weight of the object is mg dynes, where g is 980 numerically and, since work = force × distance, the energy obtained when the object just reaches the ground is $mg \times h$ ergs. This is equal to the potential energy of the object, assuming no loss of energy as it falls.

$$\therefore \textit{potential energy} = mgh \textit{ ergs.}$$

If the weight W of the object is in pounds weight and its height h above the earth is in feet, the potential energy is given by

$$\textit{potential energy} = w \times h \textit{ ft.-lb.}$$

Example 1.—Explain briefly the simplest method you know of measuring the mechanical equivalent of heat.

A motor-car weighing 2 tons is brought to rest by its well-adjusted four-wheel brakes from a speed of 90 m.p.h. If the brake mechanism on each wheel weighs 16 lb., calculate the greatest possible rise in temperature. (Specific heat of brake material = 0·140, J = 1400 ft.-lb. per lb. °C.) (*N.J.M.B.*)

First part.—See text.

Second part.—Work done by brakes in bringing car to rest is given by $\frac{1}{2}mv^2$ foot-poundals, as this is the original kinetic energy of the car if m is the mass of the car in pounds and v its original speed in ft. per sec.

Since $m = 2 \times 2240$ lb., $v = 132$ ft. per sec.,

$$\therefore \text{work done} = \tfrac{1}{2} \times 2 \times 2240 \times 132^2 \text{ ft.-poundals}$$
$$= \frac{2 \times 2240 \times 132^2}{2 \times 32} \text{ ft.-lb.}$$

$$\therefore \text{heat produced} = Q = \frac{2 \times 2240 \times 132^2}{1400 \times 2 \times 32} \text{ lb. °C.}$$

(1 lb. °C. is the heat required to raise the temperature of 1 lb. of water 1° C., see p. 89).

But $$Q = mst \text{ (p. 90)},$$

where $m = 4 \times 16$ lb. = total mass of brakes, $s = 0{\cdot}14$ = specific heat of brakes, and t is the rise in temp. in °C.

$$\therefore t = \frac{Q}{ms} = \frac{2 \times 2240 \times 132^2}{1400 \times 2 \times 32 \times 64 \times 0{\cdot}14} = 97{\cdot}3° \text{ C.}$$

Example 2.—Give a *short* account of Joule's classical experiment to determine the mechanical equivalent of heat by the water churning method.

A river, flowing horizontally, reaches a vertical fall of 100 metres. If the temperature of the water at the top is 20° C., what will be the water temperature (*a*) half-way down the fall, (*b*) in the pool at the bottom of the fall? [$J = 4{\cdot}2$ joules per calorie.] (*C.W.B.*)

First part.—See text.

Second part.—Suppose, for convenience, that we consider 1 gm. of water at the top of the waterfall. When it is half-way down the fall, the potential energy lost by this water is completely changed into kinetic energy, i.e. mechanical energy of a different kind to potential energy. But no *loss* of mechanical energy has occurred. Hence no heat is obtained, and the temperature of this water remains at 20° C.

A different state of affairs, however, occurs when the gram of water reaches the bottom of the fall. The water is moving fast just before it reaches the bottom, but when it falls into the pool, its speed changes to practically zero. Mechanical energy has thus been *lost*, and an equivalent amount of heat is produced.

Mechanical energy lost = potential energy at top of fall = mgh

$$= 1 \times 980 \times (100 \times 100) \text{ ergs}$$

$$= \frac{9{,}800{,}000}{10^7} \text{ joules,}$$

since 10^7 ergs = 1 joule.

$$\therefore \text{ heat produced} = \frac{9{,}800{,}000}{4{\cdot}2 \times 10^7} \text{ calories} = 0{\cdot}23 \text{ cal.}$$

$$\therefore \text{ temp. rise in 1 gm.} = 0{\cdot}23^\circ \text{ C.}$$

$$\therefore \text{ temp. of water in pool} = 20{\cdot}23^\circ \text{ C.}$$

(It is of interest to note that Joule, on his honeymoon, attempted to detect such a rise of temperature at the bottom of a waterfall.)

Example 3.—Give a critical account of the methods available for determining the mechanical equivalent of heat.

In the absence of bearing friction a winding engine could raise a cage weighing 1000 kg. at 10 metres per sec., but this is reduced by friction to 9 metres per sec. How much oil, initially at 20° C., is required per second to keep the temperature of the bearings down to 70° C? (Sp. ht. of oil $= 0{\cdot}5$; $g = 981$ cm. per sec. per sec.; $J = 4{\cdot}2 \times 10^7$ ergs per calorie.) (*O. & C.*)

First part.—See text.

Second part.—Since the mass of oil per second is required, it is best to deal with the work done per second.

In 1 sec., work done without friction = force × distance = $10^6 \times 981 \times 1000$ ergs, since 1000 kg. = 10^6 gm. and 10 metres = 1000 cm. Similarly, work done in 1 sec. with friction present = $10^6 \times 981 \times 900$ ergs.

∴ work done in 1 sec. against friction

$$= 10^6 \times 981 \times 1000 - 10^6 \times 981 \times 900$$

$$= 10^6 \times 981 \times 100 \text{ ergs.}$$

$$\therefore \text{ heat produced per second} = \frac{10^6 \times 981 \times 100}{4{\cdot}2 \times 10^7} \text{ calories.}$$

Suppose m is the mass of oil in grams required per second.

The heat given to oil per second = $mst = m \times 0{\cdot}5 \times (70 - 20)$, as the temperature rises from 20° C. to 70° C.

$$\therefore m \times 0{\cdot}5 \times (70 - 20) = \frac{10^6 \times 981 \times 100}{4{\cdot}2 \times 10^7}, \text{ from above.}$$

$$\therefore m = 93{\cdot}5 \text{ gm.}$$

Example 4.—Describe a method that has been used for measuring the mechanical equivalent of heat.

Find how much heat is used in performing external work when 1 gm. of water at 100° C. is boiled away to form steam at 100° C. Take the density of water as 1 gm. cm.$^{-3}$; the density of steam at 100° C. as 0·606 gm. per litre, and atmospheric pressure as 76 cm. of mercury. (*L. Inter.*)

First part.—See text.

Second part.—Since the volume of 1 gm. of water at 100° C. is 1 c.c., and the volume of 1 gm. of steam at 100° C. = 1000/0·606 c.c.,

$$\text{the expansion in volume} = \frac{1000}{0{\cdot}606} - 1 = 1649 \text{ c.c.}$$

The expansion takes place against the constant pressure of the atmosphere, whose magnitude is $76 \times 13{\cdot}6 \times 980$ dynes per sq. cm.

∴ work done = pressure × change in volume (see p. 65),

$$= 76 \times 13{\cdot}6 \times 980 \times 1649 \text{ ergs.}$$

$$\therefore \text{ heat required} = \frac{76 \times 13{\cdot}6 \times 980 \times 1649}{4{\cdot}2 \times 10^7}$$

$$= 39{\cdot}8 \text{ calories.}$$

EXAMPLES ON CHAPTER VII

1. Name two units of *mechanical equivalent of heat* (J). A 200 lb. weight falls from a height of 50 ft. to the ground. Calculate the heat produced at the ground and the rise in temperature of the object if all the heat is given to it, assuming its specific heat is 0·05 cal./gm./°C. [J = 780 ft.-lb./B.Th.U.]

2. A lead bullet of mass 1·5 gm. has a speed of 2000 cm. per sec., and is brought to rest at a target. If all the heat produced is gained by the bullet, calculate its rise in temperature. [Specific heat of lead = 0·03 cal./gm./°C., $J = 4{\cdot}2 \times 10^7$ ergs/cal.]

3. An electric current of 2 amp. is flowing in a wire whose potential difference is 50 volts. Calculate the heat produced in 7 minutes. If the wire is immersed in 200 gm. of water initially at 10° C., how long will the water take to reach boiling-point under normal atmospheric pressure? [J = 4·2 joules/calorie.]

4. The height of the Niagara Falls is about 150 ft. What is the difference in temperature of 1 lb. of water at the top of the waterfall and the same water at the bottom?

5. Draw labelled diagrams of Joule's first and second methods of measuring the mechanical equivalent of heat. What is the essential difference between the methods, and which is the more accurate? Give reasons.

6. Draw a labelled diagram of an electrical method of determining the mechanical equivalent of heat. Write down the advantages of the method.

7. Two similar metal cones are placed in contact inside each other. The inner cone is rotated at a steady rate of 2 rev. per sec., while the outer cone, of diameter 10 cm., is kept stationary by two equal and opposite forces of 1000 gm. wt. acting tangentially to it. What work in ergs is done against the couple in 10 min.? If the inner cone, of water equivalent 40 gm., is filled with 160 gm. of water, and the rise in temperature after 10 min. is 9° C., calculate a value for J in joules per calorie.

8. Explain the term *Joule's equivalent*. Describe a method of determining it involving the use of a friction balance. Compare the cost of energy from gas at 14*d*. per therm and from electricity at ½*d*. per kWh. (*L.H.S.C.*)

9. Give a brief account of the reasons which led to the abandonment of the caloric theory of heat and the adoption of the mechanical theory. Describe a non-electrical method of determining the mechanical equivalent of heat, suitable for use in a school laboratory. What difference would exist between the temperature of the water above and below a fall 100 metres high if the whole of the gravitational energy lost was retained as heat in the water? (*L.H.S.C.*)

10. Describe a non-electrical method of measuring the mechanical equivalent of heat. Explain your calculation. A roller-skater glides 50 times round the floor of a rink, keeping to a circle of average radius 78 feet, only one skate being on the floor at any one instant. If each skate, of mass 1 lb. and specific heat 0·1, is raised in temperature 20° F., calculate the average force applied by the skater in overcoming friction. Assume that 20 per cent of the heat generated is received by the skates. [J = 780 ft.-lb. per B.Th.U.] (*N.J.M.B.*)

11. Describe an electrical method of determining J. In the Callendar-Barnes flow calorimeter, it is found that there is a rise in temperature of 3° C. when the rate of flow is 5 gm. per sec. and a current of 0·75 amp. passes along the heating wire, the difference of potential between its ends being 100 volts. If the rate of flow is reduced to one-third of its former value, a current of 0·5 amp. gives the same rise in temperature. From these data determine the value of Joule's constant. (*O. & C.*)

12. Give an account of the evidence for our belief that heat is a form of energy.

A lead bullet of mass 20 gm. enters a fixed block of wood with a velocity of 10,000 cm. per second, and is brought to rest in the wood. Calculate (*a*) the heat developed in gramme-calories, (*b*) the rise of temperature of the bullet, if it is assumed that two-thirds of the heat produced is absorbed by the bullet. [$J = 4{\cdot}2 \times 10^7$ ergs per gramme-calorie. Specific heat of lead = 0·032.] (*C.W.B.*)

13. Define the *mechanical equivalent of heat* and show how it may be measured experimentally. [Describe the continuous-flow method if possible.] (*L.H.S.C.*)

14. What are the chief reasons for believing that heat is a form of energy? Explain the statement that $4{\cdot}2 \times 10^7$ ergs are equivalent to 1 calorie, and describe an experiment involving the conversion of mechanical energy into heat by which it may be checked. Calculate the number of foot-pounds which are equivalent to the quantity of heat required to raise the temperature of 1 lb. of water 1° F. Assume that 1 ft. = 30·5 cm. and that the acceleration of gravity = 980 cm. sec.$^{-2}$ (*N.J.M.B.*)

15. Describe an experiment to determine the mechanical equivalent of heat. (A method which does not involve heating a wire by an electric current is required.) Show how to calculate the result from the observations. If the latent heat of liquid oxygen is 51 cal. per gm. at its boiling-point, determine the fraction of this energy required to overcome the atmospheric pressure of 76 cm. of mercury. You may assume that the temperature of the liquid oxygen is $-183°$ C. and that its density is 1·1 gm. per c.c. The density of oxygen at S.T.P. is 1·43 gm. per litre, that of mercury 13·6 gm. per c.c., and the mechanical equivalent of heat is $4{\cdot}18 \times 10^7$ ergs per cal. (*N.J.M.B.*)

16. Give a short account of the experimental work that has been done on the relation between heat and work, and describe in detail one accurate method of finding the mechanical equivalent of heat. (*C.H.S.C.*)

CHAPTER VIII

Specific Heats of a Gas. Isothermal and Adiabatic Changes

1. The principal specific heats of a gas.

When a gas is heated, its volume and its pressure may alter considerably. If the piston of a cylinder containing the gas is pushed back, the gas does some mechanical work, and the energy required comes from the source heating the gas. In this case part of the heat supplied to the gas is used to increase its temperature, and the remainder is used to supply the mechanical energy just mentioned. It can now be seen that the conditions of volume and pressure under which a gas is heated require careful consideration when discussing its specific heat. The two most important specific heats are defined as follows:

The *principal specific heat of a gas at constant volume* C_V is the amount of heat required to raise the temperature of 1 gm. of the gas 1° C. when the volume is kept constant throughout.

The *principal specific heat of a gas at constant pressure* C_p is the amount of heat required to raise the temperature of 1 gm. of the gas 1° C. when the pressure is kept constant throughout.

Instead of a mass of 1 gm., it may be necessary to consider the heat gained or lost by a " gram-molecular weight " of a gas. In this case we refer to the " molecular specific heat " of the gas at constant volume and at constant pressure. If the gram-molecular weight is m gm., it can be seen that the molecular specific heats are m times the respective principal specific heats, which refer to one gram of the gas.

2. The relation between C_p and C_v.

Consider one gram of a gas contained in a cylinder by a piston (fig. 8.1*a*). If the piston is kept in position at AB while the gas is heated, the volume, XABY, of the gas remains constant. The heat supplied to the gas when its temperature rises by 1° C. is thus, by definition, C_V, the principal specific heat of the gas at constant volume.

Suppose, however, that the gas is heated while the pressure p exerted by the piston is kept constant. The piston is then

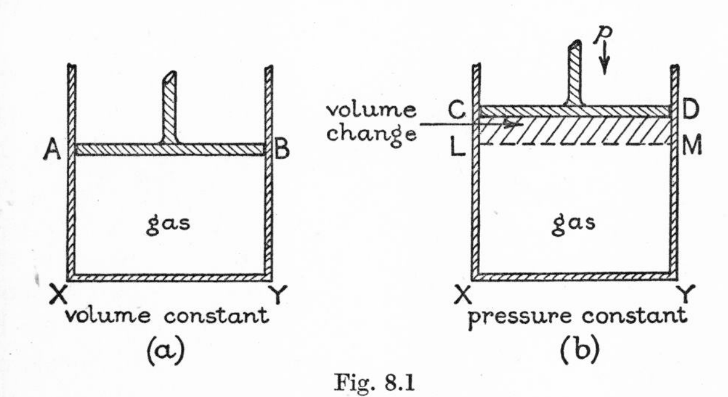

Fig. 8.1

pushed back (fig. 8.1*b*), *and some of the heat supplied is used in doing this mechanical work.* The remainder of the heat is used in raising the temperature of the gas. The mechanical work is often known as the "external" work done by the gas, and the equivalent amount of heat in calories required for the external work = (work done)/J, where the work done is in ergs and J is the mechanical equivalent of heat in ergs per calorie.

Suppose that the piston is pushed back to CD when the temperature of the gas at constant pressure increases by 1° C. The heat supplied to the gas is then, by definition, C_p, the principal specific heat. From what has been stated before, it should be evident that C_p can be analysed into two parts:

(1) The heat required to raise the temperature of one gram of the gas without doing external work, i.e. at *constant volume.*

(2) The equivalent amount of heat required for the external work W done in pushing the piston back from its original position LM to its final position CD (fig. 8.1*b*). Now the heat in (1) is C_V, the principal specific heat at constant volume, and the heat in (2) is W/J if W is in ergs and J is in ergs/calorie. It therefore follows that

$$C_p = C_V + \frac{W}{J}, \quad \ldots\ldots \quad (38)$$

or

$$C_p - C_V = \frac{W}{J}. \quad \ldots\ldots \quad (39)$$

The principal specific heat of a gas at constant pressure C_p is thus always greater than C_V, the principal specific heat of the same gas at constant volume. For hydrogen $C_p = 3{\cdot}40$ cal. per gm. per °C., and $C_V = 2{\cdot}40$ cal. per gm. per °C.; for air, $C_p = 0{\cdot}24$ cal. per gm. per °C., and $C_V = 0{\cdot}17$ cal. per gm. per °C. The difference between C_p and C_V depends on the nature of the gas. If 0·17 calories are supplied to 1 gm. of air at *constant pressure*, the increase in temperature of the gas is less than 1° C., because some of the heat is used up in doing external (mechanical) work against the pressure. A further 0·07 calories are required to raise the temperature of the gas 1° C, as $C_p = 0{\cdot}24$ cal. per gm. per °C.

3. The relation between C_p, C_V, R and J.

The external work W done by a gas in expanding at constant pressure p can easily be evaluated. Suppose that the mass of the gas is 1 gm., its original volume is V_1, and its final volume is V_2 when the temperature of the gas increases by 1° C. Then, since the external work done by the gas = pressure × change in volume (see p. 65),

$$W = p \times (V_2 - V_1). \quad \ldots\ldots \quad \text{(i)}$$

If the initial absolute temperature of the gas is T, and the gas constant for 1 gm. of the gas is R, then $pV_1 = RT$. When the temperature increases by 1° C, the absolute temperature becomes $(T + 1)$; as the new volume is V_2, then $pV_2 = R(T + 1)$. Thus

$$pV_2 - pV_1 = R(T + 1) - RT,$$

and hence $$p(V_2 - V_1) = R.$$

Thus, from (i), $$W = R.$$

But $$C_p - C_V = \frac{W}{J},$$

$$\therefore\ \mathbf{C_p - C_V = \frac{R}{J}}. \quad \ldots \quad (40)$$

In this relation C_p and C_V are in calories, R is expressed in ergs, and J is expressed in ergs per calorie; the dimensions (calories) are then the same on both sides of the equation.

4. Mayer's approximate value of J.

The relation $C_p - C_V = R/J$ was first derived by a German doctor MAYER in 1842, just before Joule began his classical experiments to determine the mechanical equivalent of heat. Mayer proceeded to calculate an approximate value for J from this relation, and as an illustration of the method we shall take the case of oxygen.

From experiments, it is known that, for oxygen, $C_V = 0{\cdot}115$ cal. per gm. per °C., $C_p = 0{\cdot}179$ cal. per gm. per °C., and that the mass of 1 litre of the gas at N.T.P. is 1·433 gm. Thus the volume of 1 gm. at N.T.P. $= 1000/1{\cdot}433$ c.c., and using $pV = RT$, the gas constant for 1 gm. is given in *ergs* per degree by

$$R = \frac{pV}{T} = \frac{76 \times 13{\cdot}6 \times 980 \times 1000}{273 \times 1{\cdot}433}.$$ (See p. 74).

But $C_p - C_V = R/J$, and hence $J = R/(C_p - C_V)$.

$$\therefore\ J = \frac{76 \times 13{\cdot}6 \times 980 \times 1000}{273 \times 1{\cdot}433 \times 0{\cdot}064},$$

since $C_p - C_V = 0{\cdot}064$ calories.

$$\therefore\ J = 4{\cdot}04 \times 10^7 \text{ ergs per calorie.}$$

In deriving the work done by a gas in expanding, we concerned ourselves only with the external work done (p. 163). Now experiment shows that the molecules of a gas have some attraction for each other which is known as an " inter-molecular " attraction (p. 83). When a gas expands, therefore, it does work against this force of attraction, called *internal work*, as well as external work. Now the relation $C_p - C_v = R/J$ has been derived without taking the internal work into account. The relation is thus an approximate one, and the value of J obtained is less than the true value, as shown by the case of oxygen. Nevertheless, Mayer's work is important historically, because it was the first time an attempt was made to determine the mechanical equivalent of heat.

5. Measurement of C_p for a gas. Continuous-flow (electrical) method.

REGNAULT determined the principal specific heat of a gas at constant pressure by allowing it to flow into a vessel where it was heated to a high temperature, and then passing it at constant pressure into another vessel inside a calorimeter and water,

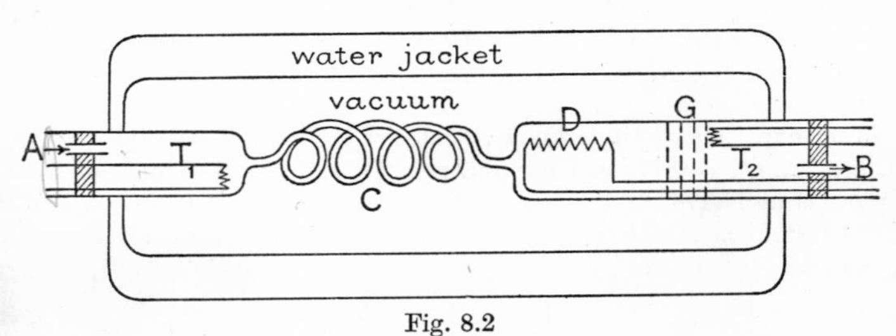

Fig. 8.2

which rose in temperature. A much more accurate method of determining C_p, however, consists of using the same technique with a gas as was used in determining the specific heat of a liquid by the continuous-flow (electrical) method (see p. 98).

The apparatus used is illustrated in fig. 8.2. A steady flow of gas at constant pressure is introduced into the glass tube at

A, and its temperature is measured by the platinum resistance thermometer T_1. The gas then flows through a coiled tube, represented by C, and issues slowly past an electrical heating coil D towards a gauze G, whose purpose is to mix the gas so that the whole of it is at a uniform temperature. This temperature is measured by the platinum resistance thermometer T_2, and the gas issues at B.

Suppose m is the mass of the gas in grams flowing through the tube per second, t is its rise in temperature, and I, V are the current in amperes in the heating coil and the potential difference across it in volts. The heat supplied per second by the current is then $IV/4{\cdot}18$ cal./sec. (p. 98), and, neglecting any heat lost, is equal to the heat per second gained by the gas.

$$\therefore\ mC_p t = \frac{IV}{4{\cdot}18},$$

$$\therefore\ C_p = \frac{IV}{4{\cdot}18mt}.$$

A vacuum jacket serves to diminish loss of heat by cooling (fig. 8.2); the very small amount of heat lost can be found by repeating the experiment, as explained on p. 99. The continuous-flow electrical method of measuring specific heats has the advantages given on p. 97.

6. Measurement of the specific heat C_V of a gas. Joly's differential steam calorimeter.

In 1886 Joly designed a calorimeter for measuring the specific heat of a gas at constant volume, known as a *differential steam calorimeter*. Fig. 8.3 illustrates the principle of the experiment. Two identical copper spheres A and B are suspended in a chamber from the scale-pans of a balance, and while A is filled with the gas whose specific heat is required, B is completely evacuated. P and Q are two pans beneath the respective spheres. Initially a balance is obtained by adding weights to the scale-pan to which B is attached, and when suitable corrections are made, the mass of the gas in A is known.

Steam is now passed into the chamber through a pipe at C, and after a time, when conditions are steady, *more steam is observed to have condensed on* A *than on* B, the scale-pans P and Q collecting the water formed. The balance is then restored, and the extra mass of steam M condensed on A is now known.

Theory.—The temperature, $t°$ C. say, in the chamber is that of the steam. The two spheres A and B, and the gas in A, have thus been raised to a temperature of $t°$ C. from an initial temperature

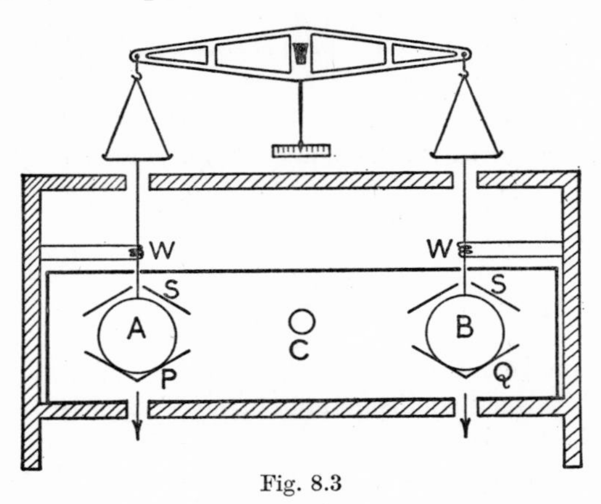

Fig. 8.3

$t_1°$ C. say. Now since A and B are identical spheres, and A contains a gas while B contains a vacuum, more heat is required to raise the temperature of A and its contents to $t°$ C., than to raise the temperature of B to $t°$ C. The difference is the heat required to raise the temperature of m gm. of the gas at constant volume from $t_1°$ C. to $t°$ C. But this is the heat given out by M gm. of steam at $t°$ C. when it condenses to water at the same temperature, which is ML calories, where L is the latent heat of steam. Hence

$$mC_V(t - t_1) = ML.$$

$$\therefore\ C_V = \frac{ML}{m(t - t_1)}.$$

Thus C_V can be calculated from a knowledge of M, m, t, t_1, and L.

In fig. 8.3 SS represent shields which prevent the water condensing on the roof of the chamber from being collected by P and Q. WW represent electrical heaters, which prevent drops forming round the wire attached to the scale-pans; such drops would hinder the free movement of the scale-pans. Corrections are necessary for the small expansion of the copper sphere containing the gas, as its temperature rises, thus altering the volume of the gas slightly; and also for a slight difference in the thermal capacity of the two spheres. It will be noted that the use of the two identical spheres eliminates the necessity of considering the water equivalent of the sphere containing the gas; it is also the reason for the name "differential" steam calorimeter, as the *difference* in the masses of the steam condensed on the two spheres is used.

Example 1.—A quantity of a gas is allowed to expand in a given proportion either (*a*) isothermally, or (*b*) adiabatically. How does the final state of the gas depend on the mode of expansion adopted?

A gas initially at S.T.P. and of volume 1000 c.c. expands to double its volume without change of pressure. Calculate the quantity of heat that must be supplied.

Density of mercury = 13·6 gm./c.c.; specific heat of the gas at constant volume = 0·168 cal./gm.; density of the gas at S.T.P. = 0·001 29 gm./c.c.; $J = 4{\cdot}18 \times 10^7$ ergs/cal.; $g = 981$ cm./sec.^{2}] (*L.H.S.C.*)

First part.—See later text, pp. 70–4.

Second part.—The heat supplied is given by mC_pt, where m is the mass of gas, C_p is its principal specific heat at constant pressure, and t is its rise in temperature.

t.—At constant pressure, the volume of a gas is proportional to the absolute temperature.

$$\therefore \frac{273 + x}{273} = \frac{2}{1},$$

where x is the final temperature of the gas after expansion.

$$\therefore 273 + x = 546, \quad \text{i.e. } x = 273^\circ \text{ C.}$$

$$\therefore t = 273 - 0 = 273^\circ \text{ C.}$$

C_p.—The gas constant for 1 gm. $= R = \dfrac{pV}{T}$

$$= \frac{76 \times 13{\cdot}6 \times 981}{273 \times 0{\cdot}001\,29} \text{ ergs/gm./deg.}$$

$$\therefore C_p = C_v + \frac{R}{J} = 0{\cdot}168 + \frac{76 \times 13{\cdot}6 \times 981}{273 \times 0{\cdot}001\,29 \times 4{\cdot}18 \times 10^7}.$$

$$\therefore C_p = 0{\cdot}237 \text{ cal./gm./°C.}$$

m.—The mass of the gas = 1·29 gm., since 1000 c.c. of the gas at S.T.P. has this mass.

$\therefore$ heat supplied in calories = 1·29 × 0·237 × 273 = 83·5.

Isothermal and Adiabatic Changes

7. Isothermal expansion of a gas.

In a steam engine, the vapour expands at constant temperature in a cylinder during one stage of the action; the same type of gas expansion occurs at stages in other gas engines. Changes of pressure and volume which take place at *constant temperature* are known as *isothermal* changes, and the mechanical engineer requires to study the laws governing the isothermal expansion and contraction of a gas.

We can understand how an isothermal change takes place if we suppose that a quantity of gas is enclosed in a metal cylinder by a piston. If the piston is depressed *very slowly*, mechanical work is done on the gas and a little heat is produced. But the metal cylinder is a good conductor of heat, and the heat has time to escape from the gas through the metal; the gas therefore remains at the same temperature as the cylinder, which may be room temperature, for example, while the gas contracts. This is an example of an isothermal change.

Similarly, suppose that the piston in the cylinder is released very slowly, so that the gas expands. This time the gas does work, and the energy is taken from the gas itself, which therefore decreases slightly in temperature. Heat now flows from the surroundings through the metal cylinder to the gas, however, and the temperature of the gas remains unaltered; an isothermal expansion has thus taken place.

Since an isothermal change is one which takes place at constant temperature, it follows that the pressure-volume changes obey

Boyle's law. Thus $pV = k$, where k is a constant. k is equal to RT, where T is the absolute value of the constant temperature, and R is the gas constant for 1 gm., assuming this is the mass of the gas. If the temperature of the gas is kept constant at 100° C., the curve A is obtained when the values of pressure (p) and volume (V) are plotted (fig. 8.4). Similarly shaped curves, B, C, D, are obtained at other constant temperatures, 80° C., 40° C., 20° C. respectively, and these curves are known as *isothermals* of the gas under investigation.

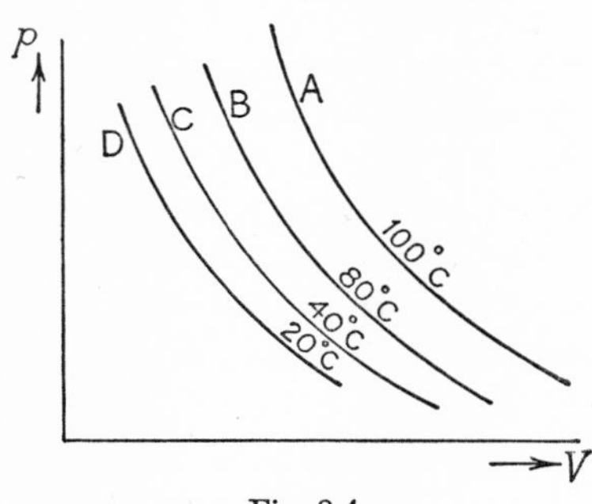

Fig. 8.4

8. Work done by a gas in isothermal expansion.

The work done by a gas in expanding isothermally is easily calculated. Since a small amount δW of work = pressure × small change of volume $= p.\delta V$, it follows that the total work W done is given by

$$W = \int_{V_1}^{V_2} p dV,$$

where V_1 is the initial volume and V_2 is the final volume of the gas. Now $pV = RT$, if we assume that the mass of the gas is 1 gm. and T is its constant absolute temperature, and hence $p = RT/V$.

$$\therefore W = \int_{V_1}^{V_2} p dV = RT \int_{V_1}^{V_2} \frac{dV}{V} = RT \log_e \left[\frac{V_2}{V_1}\right].$$

9. Adiabatic expansion of a gas.

Besides undergoing isothermal changes, the gases in an engine expand and contract under such conditions that *no heat enters or leaves them.* The corresponding pressure-volume changes are said to take place *adiabatically*, and an adiabatic change is defined as one during which no heat enters or leaves the system concerned; in other words, the heat content of the gas remains constant.

We can understand how an adiabatic change can take place if we again consider a gas contained inside a cylinder fitted with a piston; but this time, we shall suppose that the outside of the cylinder has been surrounded by insulating material, such as cotton-wool, and that the piston is also made of insulating material. If the piston is depressed, work is done on the gas, and an equivalent amount of heat is produced. Unlike the case of an isothermal change, however, no heat escapes from the gas because the container and piston are insulated; and the temperature of the gas rises. This is an example of an adiabatic contraction. If the piston is raised, work is done by the gas, and the equivalent of heat is taken from the gas itself, which is therefore cooled. No heat, however, enters or leaves the gas while it expands, and this is an example of an adiabatic expansion.

10. The relation between pressure and volume for an adiabatic change.

When a gas undergoes an adiabatic change, the pressure-volume changes obey the law

$$pV^{\gamma} = \textbf{constant}, \quad . \quad . \quad . \quad . \quad . \quad (41)$$

where γ is the ratio of the specific heat of the gas at constant pressure to the specific heat at constant volume, i.e. $\gamma = C_p/C_V$. This relation between p and V is proved later (see p. 179). Since C_p is always greater than C_V, γ is always greater than 1, and the following values of γ have been obtained: For gases which have one atom in their molecule, e.g. argon, helium, $\gamma = 1{\cdot}66$; for air, and for gases which are diatomic, e.g. oxygen, hydrogen, $\gamma = 1{\cdot}41$; for triatomic gases, such as ozone, $\gamma = 1{\cdot}29$.

Example 2.—Suppose the pressure of 100 c.c. of air is 75 cm. of mercury, and that the gas is compressed adiabatically so that its volume becomes 25 c.c. Then, since pV^{γ} = constant and $\gamma = 1{\cdot}4$ (approx.) for air, we have

$$p \times 25^{1\cdot4} = 75 \times 100^{1\cdot4},$$

where p is the new pressure of the gas.

$$\therefore\ p = \frac{75 \times 100^{1\cdot4}}{25^{1\cdot4}}.$$

Now $\log p = \log 75 + 1{\cdot}4 \log 100 - 1{\cdot}4 \log 25 = 2{\cdot}7180,$

$$\therefore\ p = 522{\cdot}4 \text{ cm. of mercury.}$$

The calculation is slightly more difficult if the new volume of a gas is required. Suppose, for example, that the volume of a given mass of air is 80 c.c. at a pressure of 60 cm. of mercury, and that the gas expands adiabatically to a final pressure of 45 cm. of mercury. The new volume V of the air is then given by

$$45 \times V^{1\cdot4} = 60 \times 80^{1\cdot4},$$

since $pV^{1\cdot4}$ is a constant.

$$\therefore\ V^{1\cdot4} = \frac{60 \times 80^{1\cdot4}}{45}.$$

Taking logs to the base 10 on both sides, we have

$$1{\cdot}4 \log V = \log 60 + 1{\cdot}4 \log 80 - \log 45,$$

$$\therefore\ \log V = (\log 60 + 1{\cdot}4 \log 80 - \log 45)/1{\cdot}4 = 1{\cdot}9924,$$

$$\therefore\ V = 98{\cdot}3 \text{ c.c.}$$

11. Adiabatic curves. Temperature variation in an adiabatic change.

Suppose the pressure p_1 and volume V_1 of a gas are represented by the point Q in fig. 8.5. If the absolute temperature of the gas is T_1, the point Q lies on the isothermal curve corresponding to this temperature. Now suppose that the gas undergoes an adiabatic expansion; the temperature of the gas then decreases to an absolute value, T_2 say, and if pressure and volume reach a point corresponding to S, the latter lies on the isothermal of T_2 (fig. 8.5). OQS is thus the $p - V$ curve obeying the relation pV^{γ} = constant. By similar reasoning DLM is the $p - V$ curve if the pressure and volume of the same mass of gas are originally represented by the point L and an adiabatic change takes place. Thus adiabatics, as the pV^{γ} curves are called, are generally steeper than isothermals of the same mass of gas, and fig. 8.5 illustrates isothermals and adiabatics.

We are now in a position to find how the temperature varies in an adiabatic change. Suppose that 1 gm. of a gas has a pressure p_1, a volume V_1, and an absolute temperature T_1, corresponding

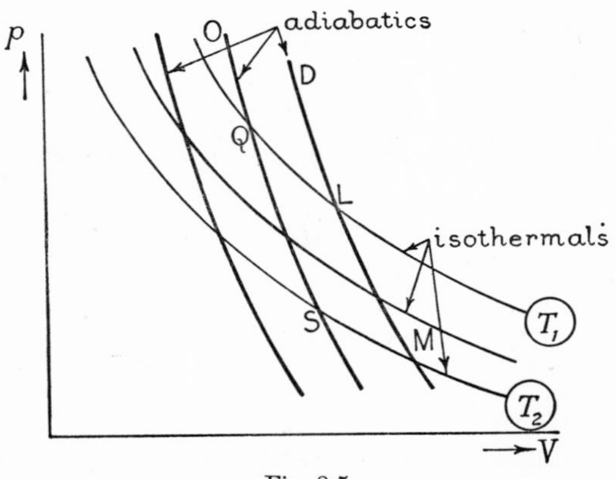

Fig. 8.5

to Q (fig. 8.5); and that after an adiabatic expansion, during which the pressure-volume changes take place along OQS, the gas has a new pressure p_2, a new volume V_2, and a new absolute temperature T_2, corresponding to S. Then, since Q is on the isothermal for T_1, $p_1V_1 = RT_1$; also, since S is on the isothermal for T_2, $p_2V_2 = RT_2$.

$$\therefore \frac{p_1V_1}{T_1} = \frac{p_2V_2}{T_2}. \quad . \quad . \quad . \quad . \quad . \quad . \quad \text{(i)}$$

But Q and S are both on the adiabatic curve OQS, which has the equation $pV^{\gamma} = \text{constant}$.

$$\therefore p_1V_1^{\gamma} = p_2V_2^{\gamma}. \quad . \quad . \quad . \quad . \quad . \quad \text{(ii)}$$

To eliminate p_1 and p_2, we divide (ii) by (i). Hence

$$T_1V_1^{\gamma-1} = T_2V_2^{\gamma-1}.$$

Thus, in general, for an adiabatic change

$$\boldsymbol{TV^{\gamma-1} = \text{constant}.} \quad . \quad . \quad . \quad . \quad (42)$$

This is the relation between volume and temperature. To obtain the relation between pressure and temperature, we first raise both sides of equation (i) to the power γ. Thus

$$\frac{p_1^{\gamma}V_1^{\gamma}}{T_1^{\gamma}} = \frac{p_2^{\gamma}V_2^{\gamma}}{T_2^{\gamma}}, \quad . \quad . \quad . \quad . \quad . \quad \text{(iii)}$$

and dividing (iii) by (ii), we eliminate the volumes. The result is

$$\frac{p_1^{\gamma-1}}{T_1^{\gamma}} = \frac{p_2^{\gamma-1}}{T_2^{\gamma}}.$$

Hence, in general, $$\boldsymbol{\frac{p^{\gamma-1}}{T^{\gamma}} = \text{constant}.} \quad . \quad . \quad . \quad . \quad . \quad (43)$$

Example 3.—Suppose that a mass of air at a temperature of 40° C. and pressure 70 cm. of mercury is compressed adiabatically until its volume is halved. If its original volume is V, its new absolute temperature is given by

$$T \times (\tfrac{1}{2}V)^{\gamma-1} = 313 \times V^{\gamma-1},$$

since 40° C. = 313° K.

$$\therefore \ T = 313 \times \left(\frac{V}{\frac{1}{2}V}\right)^{\gamma-1} = 313 \times 2^{\gamma-1}.$$

Assuming $\gamma = 1{\cdot}4$ for air, $T = 313 \times 2^{0{\cdot}4} = 413°$ K. Hence the new temperature of the gas = 413 − 273 = 140° C.

The new pressure p of the gas is easily obtained, as pV^{γ} = constant.

Thus $$p(\tfrac{1}{2}V)^{1{\cdot}4} = 70(V)^{1{\cdot}4}, \ \text{i.e. } p = 70 \times \left(\frac{V}{\frac{1}{2}V}\right)^{1{\cdot}4} = 70 \times 2^{1{\cdot}4}$$

$$= 184{\cdot}7 \text{ cm. of mercury.}$$

12. Determination of γ. Clément and Desormes' experiment.

In 1819 Clément and Desormes designed a simple method of measuring γ, the ratio of the specific heats of a gas. A lagged large vessel M was fitted with a tap at T and a manometer N, containing oil, and by means of a pump connected to P, the pressure of the air in M was increased until there was an appreciable difference in level between the oil columns in N (fig. 8.6). The pressure p_1 of the air in M is then slightly above atmospheric

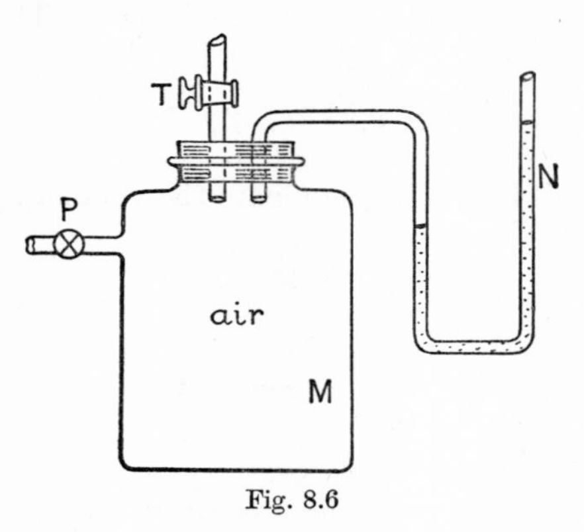

Fig. 8.6

pressure p_0. The tap T is now quickly opened and closed, when some of the air escapes from M, and after conditions are steady, the new pressure p_2 is read from the manometer N.

Consider the mass of air *left* in M, and suppose that it had a volume V_1 before the tap T was opened. When T is opened, the volume of this mass of air increases rapidly to V_0, the volume of the vessel M; and since the expansion takes place rapidly and M is lagged, the change in pressure and volume occur under *adiabatic* conditions. Thus

$$p_1 V_1^{\gamma} = p_0 V_0^{\gamma}. \quad . \quad . \quad . \quad . \quad . \quad . \quad (i)$$

After a time, when the air left in T has completely settled down, the temperature of this air becomes the same as that of the surroundings, and we shall suppose its pressure is then p_2. Since Boyle's law is applicable to this fixed mass of air, which has finally a volume V_0,

$$p_1V_1 = p_2V_0. \quad \ldots \quad \text{(ii)}$$

From (ii), $\dfrac{V_0}{V_1} = \dfrac{p_1}{p_2}$. But, from (i), $\dfrac{V_0{}^\gamma}{V_1{}^\gamma} = \dfrac{p_1}{p_0}$.

$$\therefore \left(\frac{p_1}{p_2}\right)^\gamma = \frac{p_1}{p_0}.$$

$$\therefore \gamma(\log p_1 - \log p_2) = \log p_1 - \log p_0,$$

$$\therefore \gamma = \frac{\log p_1 - \log p_0}{\log p_1 - \log p_2}. \quad \ldots \quad (44)$$

Thus γ can be calculated if p_0, p_1, p_2 are known.

A very convenient approximation can be made if p_1 and p_2 are only slightly greater than p_0, an adjustment easily obtainable by arranging the pressure p_1 in M to be initially slightly greater than the atmospheric pressure p_0. From (44),

$$\gamma = \frac{\log \dfrac{p_1}{p_0}}{\log \dfrac{p_1}{p_2}} = \frac{\log\left(\dfrac{p_0 + h_1}{p_0}\right)}{\log\left(\dfrac{p_0 + h_1}{p_0 + h_2}\right)} = \frac{\log\left(1 + \dfrac{h_1}{p_0}\right)}{\log\left(1 + \dfrac{h_1 - h_2}{p_0 + h_2}\right)},$$

where h_1 is the difference in pressure of p_1 and p_0, and h_2 is the difference in pressure of p_2 and p_0. Now $\log_e(1 + x) = x - \frac{1}{2}x^2 + \frac{1}{3}x^3 - \ldots$, from a well-known formula in mathematics, where x is less than 1,

$$\therefore \gamma = \frac{h_1/p_0}{(h_1 - h_2)/(p_0 + h_2)},$$

if h_1, h_2 are small compared with p_0. Since $(p_0 + h_2)$ is then equal to p_0, to a very good approximation, we have finally

$$\gamma = \frac{h_1}{h_1 - h_2}. \quad \ldots \quad (45)$$

The quantity h_1 is proportional to the difference in levels initially in the manometer N, and h_2 is proportional to the final difference in levels in N, after the adiabatic expansion has taken place. Thus γ can be obtained very easily, from (45). Clément and Desormes' method has the disadvantage, however, that the time of opening and closing the tap affects the result considerably, as oscillations of the air occur in the neck of the vessel when the tap is opened.

13. The First Law of Thermodynamics.

Since the molecules of a gas have kinetic energy and some attraction for each other, a gas is said to possess an amount of *internal energy*, which we shall denote by U. The actual quantity of internal energy can never be measured, but this is no handicap as in practice we are only concerned with *changes* in the internal energy. Thus when a gas expands and does external work W without taking in heat, the internal energy of the gas is diminished by the amount W. Again, if a gas is heated at constant volume, so that it does no external work, the increase in its internal energy is equivalent to the heat given to the gas; thus if C_V is the specific heat of the gas at constant volume and δT its small rise in temperature, the increase in internal energy of one gram is $C_V . \delta T$. This result is generally true, so that $C_V . \delta T$ is the increase in internal energy of one gram of a gas whenever its temperature increases by δT.

When a quantity of heat is supplied to a gas, then, generally, the gas does external work, and its internal energy is increased at the same time. Consequently, it may be stated that

heat supplied = increase of internal energy + external work,

and this statement is known as the *First Law of Thermodynamics.* It will be noted that this law is simply a statement of the law of the Conservation of Energy applied to the case under consideration. If we deal with small changes, and the small quantity of heat supplied is δQ, the small increase in internal energy is

δU, and the small quantity of work done is $p \,.\, \delta V$, then

$$\delta Q = \delta U + p \,.\, \delta V. \quad . \quad . \quad . \quad . \quad . \quad . \qquad (46)$$

This is the mathematical statement of the First Law of Thermodynamics.

14. Proof of $pV^\gamma =$ constant.

Suppose that a gas expands adiabatically. Then no heat enters or leaves the gas, and δQ is thus zero. Hence, from (46) $\delta U + p \,.\, \delta V = 0$. But $\delta U = C_V \,.\, \delta T$, where δT is the small change in temperature of the gas (p. 178).

$$\therefore\ C_V \,.\, \delta T + p \,.\, \delta V = 0.$$

$$\therefore\ \delta T = -\frac{p \,.\, \delta V}{C_V}. \quad . \quad . \quad . \quad . \quad . \quad . \qquad \text{(i)}$$

Now if we deal with 1 gm. of the gas, $pV = RT$ always applies to the pressure, volume, and absolute temperature values of the gas. Taking small changes in both sides of the gas equation, and noting that pV is a product of two variables, we have

$$p \,.\, \delta V + V \,.\, \delta p = R \,.\, \delta T.$$

But $C_p - C_V = R$, assuming R is expressed in the same units as C_p and C_V.

$$\therefore\ p \,.\, \delta V + V \,.\, \delta p = (C_p - C_V)\delta T. \quad . \quad . \quad . \qquad \text{(ii)}$$

Substituting for δT from (i) in (ii),

$$\therefore\ p \,.\, \delta V + V \,.\, \delta p = -\frac{(C_p - C_V) \,.\, p\delta V}{C_V} = -\frac{C_p}{C_V} p \,.\, \delta V + p \,.\, \delta V.$$

$$\therefore\ V \,.\, \delta p = -\frac{C_p}{C_V} p \,.\, \delta V = -\gamma p \,.\, \delta V,$$

where $\gamma = \dfrac{C_p}{C_V}$.

$$\therefore\ \frac{\delta p}{p} = -\gamma \frac{\delta V}{V}.$$

This is the relation which holds between small changes of p and V in an adiabatic change. To find the relation between the actual values of p and V, this relation must be integrated.

$$\therefore \int \frac{dp}{p} = -\gamma \int \frac{dV}{V}.$$

$$\therefore \log_e p = -\gamma \log_e V + a,$$

where a is a constant depending on the initial conditions of pressure and volume.

$$\therefore \log_e p + \gamma \log_e V = a, \quad \text{i.e. } \log_e p + \log_e V^\gamma = a.$$

$$\therefore \log_e (pV^\gamma) = a.$$

$$\therefore pV^\gamma = e^a.$$

But e^a is a constant,

$$\therefore pV^\gamma = \textit{constant}.$$

Example 4.—How are the pressure and volume of a fixed mass of gas related during isothermal expansion and during adiabatic expansion?

22·4 litres of air at 15° C. and 76 cm. of mercury pressure, weighing 27·3 gm., expand adiabatically until the volume has increased by 50 per cent. What will be the final pressure and temperature?

By considering the internal energy of the gas find how much work is done against external pressure during the expansion [$C_V = 0{\cdot}17$; $C_p = 0{\cdot}24$ cal. gm.$^{-1}$ °C.$^{-1}$]. (*L.H.S.C.*)

First part.—In an isothermal expansion, pV = constant; in an adiabatic expansion, pV^γ = constant.

Second part.—As 22·4 litres is the original volume, the final volume is 33·6 litres. Since $\gamma = C_p/C_V$, $\gamma = \frac{0{\cdot}24}{0{\cdot}17} = 1{\cdot}4$ (approx.). Applying pV^γ = constant, we have

$$p \times 33{\cdot}6^\gamma = 76 \times 22{\cdot}4^\gamma,$$

where p is the final pressure.

$$\therefore p = 76\left(\frac{22{\cdot}4}{33{\cdot}6}\right)^{1{\cdot}4} = 76 \times \left(\frac{2}{3}\right)^{1{\cdot}4}$$

$$\therefore \log p = \log 76 + 1{\cdot}4 \log 2 - 1{\cdot}4 \log 3 = 1{\cdot}6343.$$

$$\therefore p = 43{\cdot}1 \text{ cm. of mercury.}$$

Since $TV^{\gamma-1}$ = constant for an adiabatic change (p. 175), and 15° C. = 288° K., we have

$$T(33{\cdot}6)^{1{\cdot}4-1} = 288(22{\cdot}4)^{1{\cdot}4-1},$$

where T is the final temperature.

$$\therefore\ T = 288 \times \left(\frac{22{\cdot}4}{33{\cdot}6}\right)^{0{\cdot}4}$$

$$= 288 \times (\tfrac{2}{3})^{0{\cdot}4}.$$

$$\therefore\ \log T = \log 288 + 0{\cdot}4 \log 2 - 0{\cdot}4 \log 3 = 2{\cdot}3890,$$

$$\therefore\ T = 245^\circ \text{ K.}$$

$$\therefore\ \text{temperature in °C.} = 245 - 273 = -28.$$

Third part.—Since no external heat is supplied to a gas in an adiabatic expansion, the change in the internal energy of the gas = the external work done (p. 178). But the change in the internal energy = mass of gas × C_V × temperature change.

$$\therefore\ \text{internal energy change} = 27{\cdot}3 \times 0{\cdot}17 \times [15 - (-28)]$$

$$= 199{\cdot}6 \text{ calories.}$$

15. Andrews' investigation of the isothermals of carbon dioxide.

In 1869 ANDREWS made an investigation of the isothermals of carbon dioxide, i.e. the relation between the pressure and volume at constant temperatures, and, as we shall see later, his results are of great importance in the liquefaction of gases (p. 183). Andrews subjected carbon dioxide gas to various pressures, and noted the volumes obtained, keeping the temperature constant each time at different values. The principle of the apparatus he used is illustrated by fig. 8.7*a*. Carbon dioxide (CO_2) is contained in a capillary tube A by a mercury pellet, and next to A is another capillary tube B containing air, which is also kept in the tube by a mercury pellet. The open ends of the tubes lead to the same liquid chamber, and by means of the plungers M, M, which can be screwed into the chamber, the carbon dioxide and air are subjected to the same pressures. Andrews had previously determined the volume of the air in B at *known* pressures, and was thus able to find the pressure on the carbon dioxide by noting the corresponding volume of the air in B.

The results obtained are illustrated in fig. 8.7*b*, which represents some of the isothermals ($p - V$ curves at constant temperature) of carbon dioxide. As the carbon dioxide vapour is compressed from a condition represented by A on the

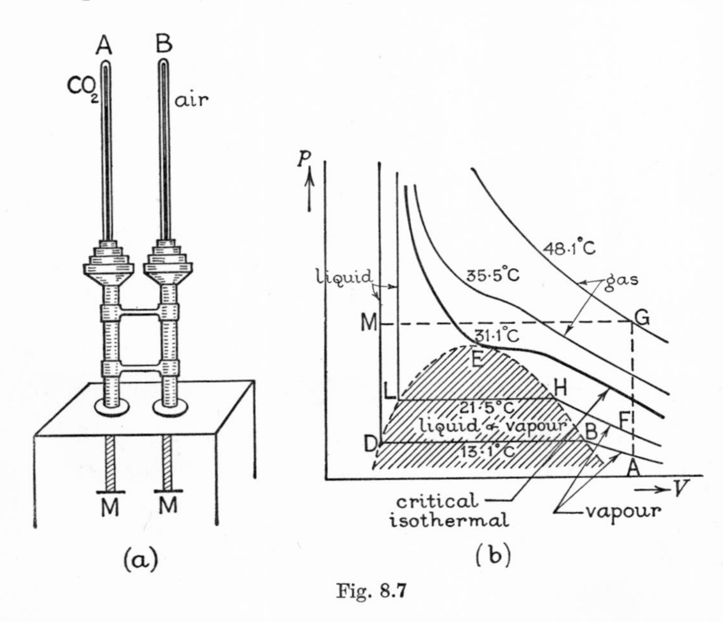

Fig. 8.7

isothermal of 13·1° C., a point is reached at B when liquid carbon dioxide begins to be formed. The vapour is then saturated, and the pressure remains constant while its volume decreases until the point D is reached. The carbon dioxide is now completely liquid, and consequently further pressure decreases the volume only slightly, as shown by the nearly vertical line DM. As shown by the *isothermal of* 21·5° C., the carbon dioxide exhibits the same changes in state as it did at 13·1° C., but the volume change on liquefying is less than before since HL is smaller than BD.

As the temperature is increased further, the decrease in volume, corresponding to the horizontal portion of the isothermal, diminishes, and at 31·1° C. the liquid state is barely obtained, as shown by the *isothermal of* 31·1° C. At the condition represented by E on the isothermal, the meniscus of liquid carbon dioxide will disappear. Above 31·1° C., as shown by the *isothermal of* 35·5° C., no liquid is formed, and the " kink " in the curve becomes less. The *isothermal* of 48·1° C. shows that the gas now obeys Boyle's law, as the curve follows the law $pV =$ constant.

16. Critical temperature and pressure. Continuity of state.

The most important deduction from Andrews' experiments is that carbon dioxide gas cannot be liquefied if its temperature is above 31·1° C., no matter to what degree of pressure the gas is subjected. The temperature of 31·1° C. is accordingly known as the **critical temperature** of carbon dioxide, and the corresponding isothermal is known as the *critical isothermal.* Every gas has a critical temperature which depends on its nature and, generally, *the critical temperature of a substance may be defined as the temperature above which it is impossible to liquefy it.* The pressure of a substance at its critical temperature is known as its **critical pressure,** and the volume of one gram of a substance at its critical temperature and pressure is known as its **critical volume.** The critical pressure of carbon dioxide, corresponding to the point E in fig. 8.7*b*, is about 73 atmospheres. Andrews' experiment has thus an important connexion with the methods of liquefying gases. The critical temperature of nitrogen is —147° C., for example, and the temperature of the gas must hence be lower than —147° C. in order to liquefy it.

Andrews' experiments also illustrate the *continuity* which exists between the liquid and gaseous states of a substance. Above a temperature of 31·1° C., carbon dioxide exists only as a gas; below this temperature it can exist as a liquid or a vapour, or as a mixture of both states. The mixture of vapour and liquid corresponds to the shaded area in fig. 8.7*b*. The change from the vapour to the liquid state, however, can be made without vapour and liquid being both present at some intermediate stage. Thus, suppose the volume of vapour in the condition A is kept constant, and the pressure is increased by heating until the point G is reached (fig. 8.7*b*); the liquid state can then be achieved at once by keeping the pressure constant and decreasing the volume by cooling until M is reached. These arguments show that *one* equation should fit *all* isothermals of a substance, such as those in fig. 8.7*b*. Further discussion is outside the scope of this book.

17. Distinction between a "gas" and a "vapour."

We are now in a position to understand the scientific difference between a gas and a vapour. When a substance is below its critical temperature, e.g. carbon dioxide at room temperature, we refer to the substance as "vapour," thereby implying that the liquid form is easily obtainable. When the substance is *above* its critical temperature, however, we refer to it as a "gas" since it cannot be liquefied. The critical temperatures of hydrogen and nitrogen are respectively —241° C. and —147° C., and hence these substances are normally well above their critical temperatures. Hydrogen and nitrogen are consequently known as "permanent" gases. It can now be seen that the terms "vapour" and "gas" are artificial distinctions; above the critical temperature the substance is termed a "gas", but below the critical temperature it is termed a "vapour".

Liquefaction of Gases

18. Cascade method.

In 1877 Pictet liquefied oxygen by a series or cascade arrangement whose principle is illustrated by fig. 8.8. Methyl chloride is liquefied by compression in A, and is then cooled by a water-bath W. By means of the valve V the substance is allowed to evaporate into a vessel under normal atmospheric pressure, and since methyl chloride boils at — 24° C. at this pressure, the temperature is sufficiently low to liquefy ethylene, whose critical temperature is 10° C., by compression. This substance is contained in the pipes B, and when liquid ethylene evaporates under reduced pressure, a temperature of about —150° C. can be obtained. Oxygen, whose critical temperature is —118° C., can thus be liquefied in the pipes C by compression. By adding another stage, as illustrated by fig. 8.8, DEWAR liquefied air by the cascade method in 1898.

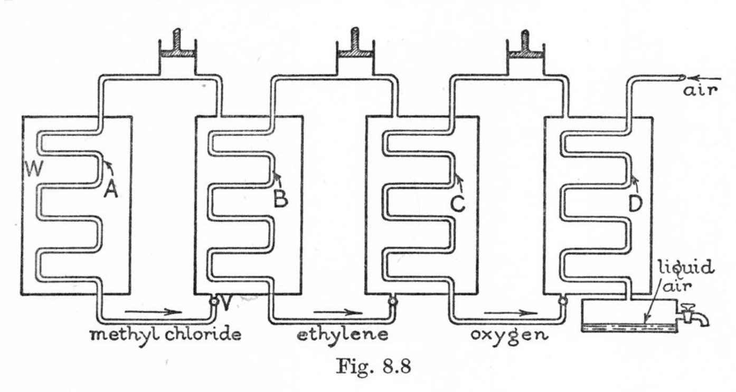

Fig. 8.8

19. Linde's method for liquefaction of air.

If the molecules of a gas have an attraction for each other, the gas will do work against the attractive forces when it expands, since the molecules become more separated. The energy for this *internal work* is provided by the heat in the gas itself if no heat enters or leaves it, and the gas is therefore cooled (see also p. 172). JOULE and LORD KELVIN devised an experiment to find out whether such a cooling took place, by allowing gases to expand through a fine orifice from a high to a low pressure, and they discovered that most gases then decreased in temperature. The cooling which takes place when a gas does internal work is known as the **Joule-Kelvin effect,** and LINDE liquefied air in 1896 by using this phenomenon.

Traces of carbon dioxide and water-vapour are first removed from the air by passing it through lime and calcium-chloride tubes. The air is then compressed to about 200 atmospheres, and the heat generated by this process is abstracted by passing the air through a water-bath. It is now passed through a central tube M (fig. 8.9), actually in the form of a coil, and then issues through a fine orifice V to a new pressure of 40 atmospheres. On account of the Joule-Kelvin effect the air is cooled, although not sufficiently to liquefy it, and the gas is made to flow through

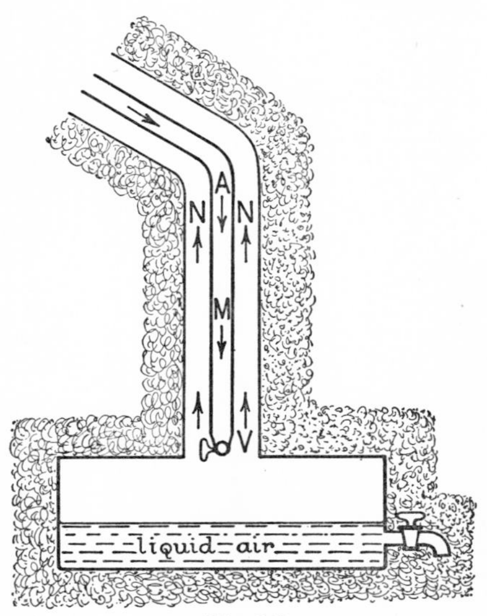

Fig. 8.9

a tube N surrounding M, before it is carried away to the atmosphere. The down-coming air thus becomes progressively cooled, and at some stage the critical temperature of air (—190° C.) is reached and passed. At this stage about a quarter of the air passing through M is liquefied on expansion through V.

20. Claude's (external-work) method for liquefaction of air.

When a gas does external work, e.g. in driving the piston of an engine, the gas becomes cooled if no heat is supplied to it, i.e. if it does work under adiabatic conditions. This is the basis of another method, used by CLAUDE, for the liquefaction of air and other gases, and the *principle* of the method is illustrated in fig. 8.10.

The gas to be liquefied, e.g. air, is compressed to about 40 atmospheres. The heat produced by the compression is then removed, and the air enters A and divides at B into two parts.

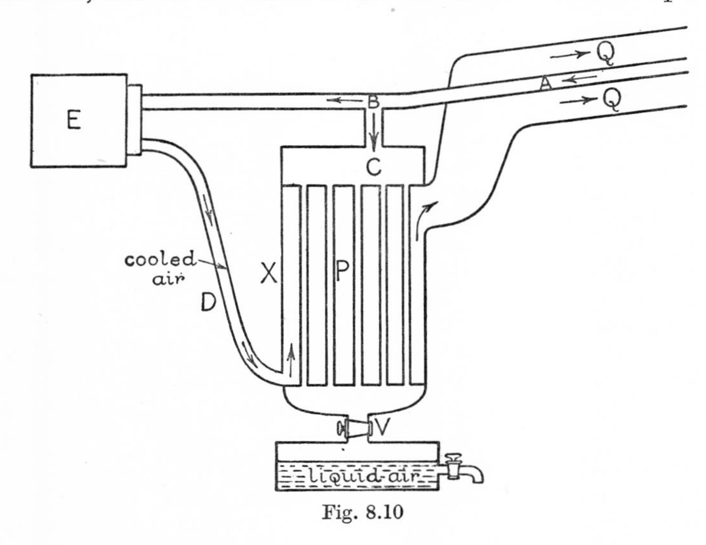

Fig. 8.10

About four-fifths of the air passes to an engine E, where it expands to one atmosphere and does external work in driving the engine. The air consequently becomes cooled, is returned by E through D to a chamber containing pipes P, and then passes back through Q to the compressor. The pipes P pass one-fifth of the air from A, and this is progressively cooled by the cold air passing round it in X. In this way the temperature becomes much lower than the critical temperature of air. The air entering the apparatus then liquifies, and is drawn off by the tap V.

The *efficiency* of the Claude process of liquefying air, i.e. the ratio of the volume of liquid air produced per hour to the volume of compressed air received per hour, is about the same as that obtained by Linde's method.

Examples on Chapter VIII

1. "The principal specific heat of hydrogen at constant pressure is 3·42 cal./gm./°C." What does this statement mean? What is the definition of the principal specific heat of hydrogen at constant volume?

2. Why is the principal specific heat of a gas at constant pressure greater than that at constant volume? The principal specific heat of a gas at constant volume is 0·2 cal./gm./°C. When 1 gram of the gas is heated at constant pressure until its temperature rises 1° C., 0·42 joules of external work are done. Calculate the principal specific heat of the gas at constant pressure. (J = 4·2 joules per calorie.)

3. Write down the relation between C_p, C_V, and J for 1 gram of a gas. What physical consideration has been omitted in deriving this relation? If $C_p = 0{\cdot}237$, $C_V = 0{\cdot}168$ cal./gm./°C., and the volume of 1 gram of air at N.T.P. (0° C. and 76 cm. mercury pressure) is 775 c.c., calculate a value for J.

4. Draw sketches of the apparatus by which the specific heat of a gas have been determined: (i) at constant volume, (ii) at constant pressure. Write a brief account of the method for (i).

5. What is meant by *isothermal expansion* and by *adiabatic expansion*? What is the relation between pressure and volume in each case. A gas of volume 800 c.c. and 72 cm. mercury pressure expands isothermally to a volume of 900 c.c. Find the new pressure.

6. A gas expands isothermally from a volume of 100 c.c. to 250 c.c. under a constant pressure of 2 atmospheres. What external work has been done by the gas if 1 atmosphere = 10^6 dynes per sq. cm.? Has the gas gained or lost heat during the expansion?

7. The volume of a gas at 15° C. and 80 cm. mercury pressure is 100 c.c. The gas is compressed to a volume of 60 c.c. under adiabatic conditions. Find the new pressure and temperature of the gas (C_p= 0·42, C_V = 0·30 cal./gm./°C.).

8. A gas is compressed isothermally. Draw and discuss curves showing how its volume varies with its pressure, (*a*) if the temperature is above the critical temperature, (*b*) if the temperature is below the

critical temperature. Describe and explain a method of liquefying air. (*N.J.M.B.*)

9. Explain how you would find the specific heat of a gas at constant pressure. Calculate the differences between the specific heats at constant pressure and at constant volume for a perfect gas. (*L.H.S.C.*)

10. What do you understand by the gas constant per gm. of an ideal gas? Show how it is related to the specific heats of the gas at constant pressure and at constant volume. Calculate the value of the gas constant per gm. for hydrogen. [Density of hydrogen at 0° C. and 76 cm. mercury pressure is 0·000 09 gm. per c.c.] (*L. Inter.*)

11. Describe a direct method of determining the specific heat of air at constant pressure, and explain how the result is calculated from the observation. If the density of air at N.T.P. is 0·001 293 gm. per c.c., and its specific heat at constant volume is 0·169 calories per gm. per degree C., calculate its specific heat at constant pressure. [Density of mercury = 13·6 gm. per c.c. at 0° C., $J = 4{\cdot}2 \times 10^7$ ergs per cal.] (*C.W.B.*)

12. State Boyle's law and describe how you would verify it for air over a range of pressures from about half an atmosphere to two atmospheres. Describe how the behaviour of carbon dioxide at various temperatures deviates from Boyle's law. Sketch graphs to illustrate your answer. (*L.H.S.C.*)

13. Describe a method of finding the specific heat of a gas at constant volume. Find an expression for the difference of the specific heats of a perfect gas at constant pressure and constant volume. Apply the expression to find an approximate value of this difference for helium. [Density of helium at 0° C. and 760 mm. pressure = 0·18 gm. per litre; density of mercury = 13·6 gm. per c.c.; mechanical equivalent of heat = $4{\cdot}2 \times 10^7$ ergs per calorie.] (*O. & C.*)

14. What is meant by an adiabatic change? Describe one method by which the ratio between the two principal specific heats of a gas may be determined. If the difference between these specific heats in the case of hydrogen is 0·97, obtain a value for the mechanical equivalent of heat. [The density of hydrogen at 0° C. and a pressure of 10^6 dynes per sq. cm. is 0·09 gm. per litre.] (*C.H.S.C.*)

15. Distinguish between isothermal and adiabatic changes. If in an adiabatic change the pressure of a gas is doubled, find the fractional change in volume that occurs, assuming that the ratio of the principal

specific heats of the gas is 1·4. If the original temperature of the gas is 0° C., what will be its final temperature? (*C.W.B.*)

16. Define *critical temperature* and explain its importance in connexion with the liquefaction of gases. Describe the experiments by means of which the existence of the critical state for carbon dioxide was established. (*L. Inter.*)

17. Describe the construction and use of *either* (*a*) Bunsen's ice calorimeter *or* (*b*) Joly's steam calorimeter. Explain how the result is calculated. If 1 gm. of water at 100° C. forms 1670 c.c. of steam at standard atmospheric pressure, find the ratio of internal work to external work done when water is converted into steam. [Latent heat of steam = 540 cal. $gm.^{-1}$] (*L.H.S.C.*)

18. What is meant by the critical state of a substance and what three quantities are required to describe the state for a given substance? Give an account of an experimental investigation of this subject. (*L. Inter.*)

19. Define the two principal specific heats of a gas. Why is the distinction between the two specific heats so much more important in the case of gases than in the case of solids or liquids? If the specific heats of air are 0·242 and 0·172, calculate the value of the mechanical equivalent of heat. Take the density of air at N.T.P. to be 1·29 gm. per litre and the density of mercury to be 13·6 gm. per c.c. (*C.W.B.*)

20. What is meant by the terms *adiabatic* and *isothermal*? Show that the pressure p and volume V of a given mass of a perfect gas are related by the expression pV^{γ} = constant for adiabatic changes, and explain the physical significance of γ.

A mass of air at 20° C. is compressed adiabatically to double its initial pressure? What is the final temperature? [$\gamma = 1{\cdot}41$.] (*C.H.S.C.*)

21. Distinguish between *isothermal* and *adiabatic* changes. An ideal gas is compressed isothermally until its volume is reduced to one-tenth of its initial value, and is then allowed to expand adiabatically to its original volume. Finally the pressure is altered at constant volume until the original state is restored. Represent these changes on a pressure-volume diagram and state whether, on the whole, work has been done on or by the gas. If the initial presssure is 15 lb. wt. per sq. in., what is the change of pressure in the last stage of the process? Assume that $\gamma = 1{\cdot}40$. (*L. Inter.*)

CHAPTER IX

Conduction of Heat. Convection

1. Conduction of heat.

If a teaspoon is placed in a cup of hot tea, the other end of the spoon soon becomes warmer, and we say that some heat has passed, or been " conducted ", along the metal from one end to the other. If one end of a poker is placed in a fire the other end soon becomes warm, as heat is conducted along the metal.

The phenomenon of the *conduction of heat* can be understood if we consider the condition of the molecules of the various parts of a poker, for example, as soon as one end of it is placed in a fire. Each of the molecules is vibrating about some mean or " anchored " position (see p. 146); when the end of the poker is placed in a fire, the molecules at this place vibrate faster on account of the heat received. This is an example of the conversion of heat energy to mechanical energy. The to-and-fro motion of the molecules disturbs the vibrating molecules in the next section of the poker and gives them additional energy, so that they also begin to vibrate faster. In this way a transfer of energy (heat) occurs from one section of the metal to the next, until the other end of the poker is reached. It should be carefully noted that the *average* position of the molecules remains unchanged while the transfer of energy takes place, and the *conduction* of heat may hence be defined as *the transfer of heat from one part of a substance to another in which the average position of the intervening material remains constant.*

2. The steady state in the lagged bar.

Consider a thick metal rod AB, with one end maintained at a constant temperature by steam, for example, and the other maintained at a lower constant temperature, say room temperature. The bar is " lagged ", i.e. surrounded by layers of cotton-wool which prevent any heat escaping from the surface of the bar, and the bulbs of thermometers are placed in holes drilled in the bar at equal intervals to measure the temperatures of the different sections of the bar.

Before the steam circulates round the end A of the bar, the thermometers indicate that the temperatures of all the sections are the same. When the steam passes round A, heat flows from

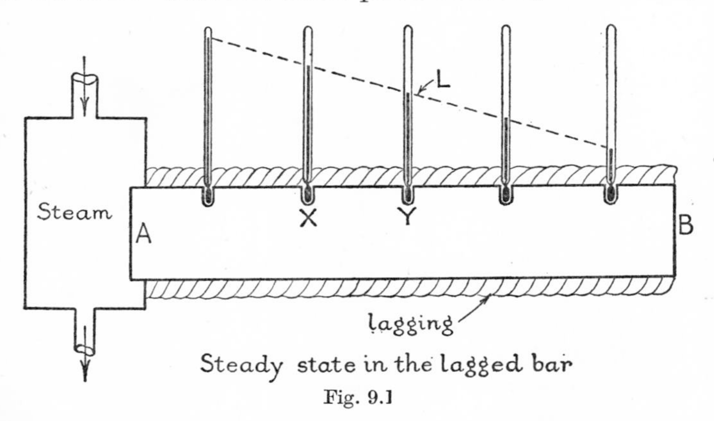

Fig. 9.1

this end through the bar and observation shows that the readings on the thermometers begin to alter. After some time, however, the temperature of each cross-section of the bar is observed to be constant, and a **steady state** is now said to exist along the bar AB. Experiment shows that, in the case of a lagged bar, the temperatures of the sections decrease *uniformly* with the distance from the hottest end, as shown by the straight line L, which passes through the readings on each thermometer (fig. 9.1).

3. Fundamental formulæ in conduction.

In all experiments relating to conduction of heat, measurements are taken only when the steady state in the substance is reached, i.e. when the temperatures of its sections are constant, as in the case just considered. Since no heat is lost from the surface of the lagged bar in fig. 9.1, and the temperature of each section of the bar is constant, we can say that, in the steady state, the quantity of heat flowing per second through the section at X must be equal to that flowing through the section at Y and, in fact, to the quantity of heat flowing per second through any section of the bar.

Experiment shows that the quantity of heat Q flowing through a small part PR of a lagged bar of uniform cross-section in the steady state is proportional to each of three quantities (fig. 9.2). They are:

(*a*) *the time* τ, i.e. the longer the time, the greater is the quantity of heat flowing through a given section;

(*b*) *the area* A *of the cross-section*, i.e. the larger the area, the greater is the quantity of heat flowing through the section in a given time;

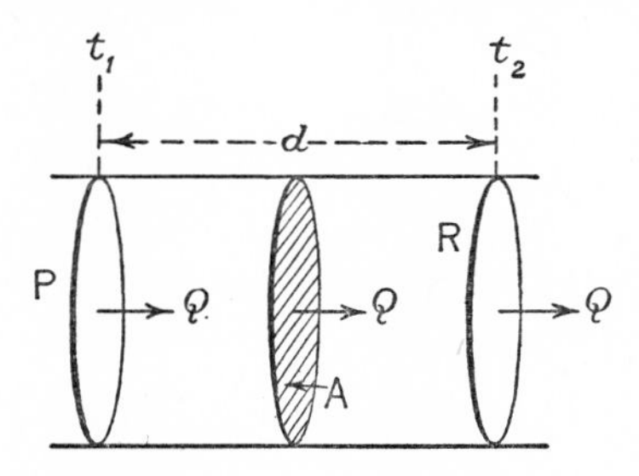

Fig. 9.2

(*c*) *the temperature gradient* g established between the ends of PR. The temperature gradient g is defined as the ratio $\frac{\text{temperature difference between P and R}}{\text{length of PR}}$, and hence $g = \frac{t_1 - t_2}{d}$, where t_1 is the temperature of P, t_2 is the temperature of R, and d is the length of PR. Thus if $t_1 = 75°$ C., $t_2 = 68°$ C., and $d = 10$ cm., the temperature gradient between P and Q is

$$\frac{75 - 68}{10} = 0{\cdot}7° \text{ C. } \textit{per cm.}$$

Thus the quantity of heat Q flowing through any section in the steady state is proportional to $\tau A g$, or $Q \propto \tau A \frac{t_1 - t_2}{d}$.

$$\therefore\ Q = k\tau A \frac{t_1 - t_2}{d}, \quad . \quad . \quad . \quad . \quad (47)$$

where k is a constant of the material of the bar known as its **thermal conductivity.** Since $Q/\tau = kA(t_1 - t_2)/d$, from (47), it can also be stated that the quantity of heat per second (Q/sec.) flowing through a section is given by

$$\boldsymbol{Q/\text{sec.} = kA \times (\text{temperature gradient}).} \quad . \quad (48)$$

The formulæ in (47) and (48) are fundamental equations in conduction, and the student is advised to commit them to memory.

4. Definition and units of thermal conductivity.

Suppose we have a specimen of a material which has a length of 1 cm. and an area of cross-section of 1 sq. cm., e.g. a centimetre cube of the material (fig. 9.3). If we imagine a temperature difference of 1° C. established across the opposite faces of the specimen, the temperature gradient is 1° C. per cm., and in the steady state the quantity of heat per second flowing through the specimen is given, from (48), by $Q/\text{sec.} = k \times 1 \times 1 = k$, since $A = 1$ sq. cm. Thus $k = Q/\text{sec.}$ in this case. The thermal conductivity k of a substance may hence be defined as *the quantity of heat per second flowing normally through the opposite faces of a unit cube of the material* **in a steady state,** *when the temperature difference between the opposite faces is one degree.*

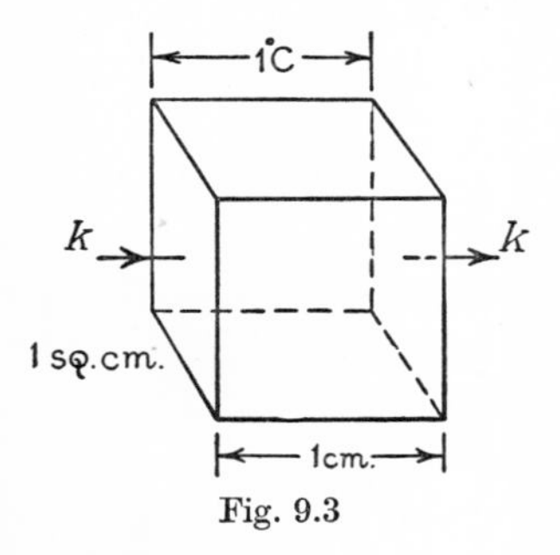

Fig. 9.3

Since $k = \dfrac{Q/\text{sec.}}{A \times (\text{temperature gradient})}$, from (48), the units of k in the centimetre-gram-second (c.g.s.) system are " calories per second per sq. cm. per unit temperature gradient "; in the foot-pound-second (f.p.s.) system, the units of k are " British Thermal units per second per sq. ft. per unit temperature gradient ", the unit temperature gradient being 1° F. per ft.

Alternatively, in the c.g.s. system the units of k are given, from (48), by

$$\frac{\text{calories/sec.}}{\text{sq. cm.} \times {}^\circ\text{C./cm.}}, \quad \text{or} \quad \frac{\text{calories}}{\text{sec.} \times \text{cm.} \times {}^\circ\text{C.}};$$

hence the units of k can be expressed as " cal. sec.$^{-1}$ cm.$^{-1}$ °C.$^{-1}$ "

Copper is an excellent conductor of heat, and experiment shows that its thermal conductivity k is 0·92 cal./sec./sq. cm./unit temperature gradient, i.e. 0·92 c.g.s. units. The thermal conductivity of aluminium and lead are respectively 0·5 and 0·08 c.g.s. units; the thermal conductivity of glass is about 0·002 c.g.s. units; and the thermal conductivity of air, a very poor conductor, is about 0·000 058 c.g.s. units. Glass is thus a bad conductor of heat; so are cement and brick.

5. Analogy between conduction of heat and conduction of electricity.

It may assist the student at this stage if it is pointed out that the conduction of electricity through metals is a phenomenon analogous to the conduction of heat through metals. In the former case, a steady flow of electricity is obtained along a metal soon after a constant potential difference, a " potential gradient ", is established between its ends. In an analogous way, a steady flow of heat is obtained along a metal after a time, when a constant temperature gradient is established between its ends. Further, experiments show that the quantity of electricity flowing per second past any section of the wire, i.e. the electric current, is proportional to the potential difference between the ends of the wire if the condition of the metal is unaltered; this is Ohm's law. Similarly, the quantity of heat per second (Q/sec.) flowing through any section of a *given length* of a metal in the steady state is proportional to the temperature difference between its ends. Thus heat flows along a metal whenever a temperature difference is established between its ends. Experiments show that a good conductor of heat is also a good conductor of electricity, and thus pure metals are good conductors of heat and electricity.

6. The steady state in an unlagged bar.

So far we have considered the case of a lagged bar. Suppose AZ (fig. 9.4*a*) is an unlagged (bare) bar, with one end A maintained at steam temperature, for example, so that a temperature

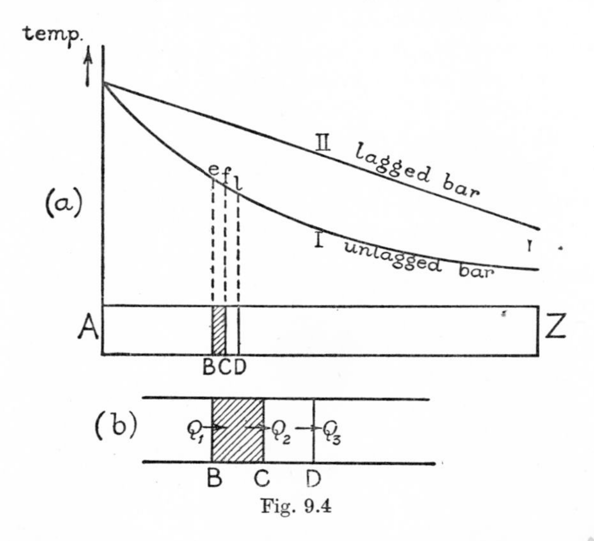

Fig. 9.4

gradient is set up along the bar in the direction AZ. Unlike the case of the lagged bar, however, some heat is lost by radiation from the sides of AZ, and when a steady state is reached, the temperatures of the different sections of the bar decrease from A along a curve shown by I in fig. 9.4.

To explain the temperature variation in the steady state, suppose Q_1 is then the quantity of heat entering the section B of the bar per second (fig. 9.4*b*). Since some heat is lost by radiation from the sides of BC, the quantity of heat per second Q_2 passing through the section C is less than Q_1. Similarly, the quantity of heat per sec. Q_3 passing through the section D is less than Q_2. On the average, then, the quantity of heat flowing per second through a section of the unlagged bar in the steady state becomes progressively smaller as we proceed from A to Z. Now the temperature gradient g across a small portion of the bar in the steady state is $\frac{Q/\text{sec.}}{kA}$ from (48), where k and A are constants for a given bar. Hence, since Q/sec. decreases from A to Z, g decreases from A to Z. The temperature gradient thus diminishes along AZ, as shown by the curve I; the gradient of the temperature-distance curve between fl, for example, is less than the gradient between ef. Curve II illustrates the *uniform* temperature gradient obtained when the bar is lagged. In this case the quantity of heat per second (Q/sec.) flowing through every section of the bar in the steady state is constant (p. 193), and hence at every section

$$\text{the temperature gradient} = g = \frac{Q/\text{sec.}}{kA} = \text{a constant.}$$

7. Methods of measuring the thermal conductivity of solids.

The methods for measuring the thermal conductivity of solids can be divided into two classes:

(i) methods for solids which are good conductors of heat, e.g. copper and brass;

(ii) methods for solids which are bad conductors of heat, e.g. glass, ebonite, rubber.

8. Searle's method for a good conductor.

G. F. C. Searle, of Cambridge University, designed an apparatus which can be used for measuring the thermal conductivity of any good conductor. A thick cylindrical bar S of the specimen is well lagged by layers of wool or felt and a chest is built round one end A of the bar (fig. 9.5). Holes are drilled into the bar at places E, H about 10 cm. apart, and are filled with mercury so that the bulbs of thermometers placed in the holes are in good thermal contact with the sections of the bar at E and H. A copper coil C, soldered round the bar, has a steady flow of water passing in at D and out at B, and the inlet and outlet temperatures are measured by thermometers.

Steam is passed into the chest, and the temperatures of the thermometers begin to rise. After a time, the readings on the thermometers become constant, indicating that a *steady state* has been reached, and the readings are then taken. The

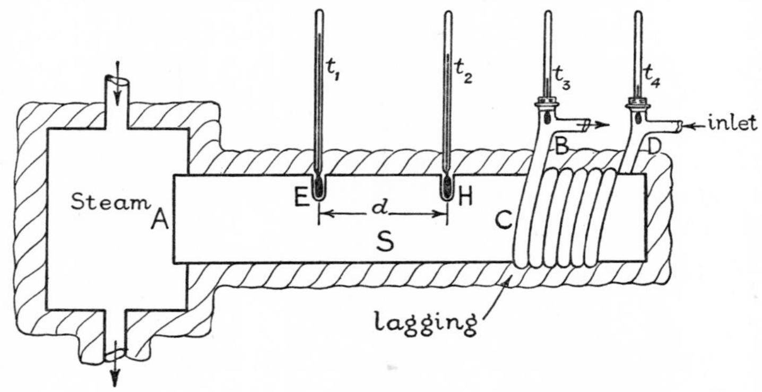

Fig. 9.5

steady flow of water through the coil C is measured by means of a beaker and a stop-clock, and if m gm. flow in τ sec., the quantity of heat per second (Q/sec.) flowing through the bar $= m(t_3 - t_4)/\tau$, where t_3, t_4 are the temperatures at B, D respectively. But $Q/\text{sec.} = kA \times$ temperature gradient $= kA(t_1 - t_2)/d$, where d is the distance btween E and H, A is the area of cross-section of the bar, and t_1, t_2 are the temperatures at E, H respectively.

$$\therefore\ kA\,\frac{t_1 - t_2}{d} = \frac{m(t_3 - t_4)}{\tau}.$$

Hence k can be calculated as the other quantities in the equation are known. The area of cross-section A $= \pi r^2$, where r is the radius of the cylindrical bar, and r can be measured by means of calipers.

9. Methods for bad conductors.

We have now to consider various methods which have been devised to find the thermal conductivity k of bad conductors, such as cardboard, ebonite, glass, and rubber, for example. In order to obtain an appreciable quantity of heat flowing per second through the specimen in a steady state, (*a*) a high temperature gradient must be set up across it, and (*b*) a large area of cross-section must be used. This means, in practice, that a thin specimen of large cross-sectional area must be used in the experiment. Further, the heat lost per second in the steady state from the sides of the specimen must be very small, in which case the fundamental equation $Q/\text{sec.} = kA \times$ (temperature gradient) can be applied to the flow of heat through the specimen.

10. Lees' method for a bad conductor in the form of a disc.

C. H. Lees, of London University, devised a method of measuring the thermal conductivity of a bad conductor in the form of a disc; the method is thus applicable to such materials as cardboard or ebonite. The disc X, which is thin, is sandwiched between two circular nickel-plated brass plates M, N, which are much thicker than X, and the upper plate M forms the bottom of a hollow cylinder P through which steam can be passed (fig. 9.6). The temperatures of M and N can be obtained from thermometers T_1, T_2 respectively, which are placed inside holes drilled in M, N. In the experiment, steam is passed into P, and the readings on T_1, T_2 are taken when they are constant, indicating that a steady state is obtained. Neglecting the amount of heat lost per second from the sides of X, which is very small because the surface area of the sides is very small, we have $Q/\text{sec.} = kA(t_1 - t_2)/d$, where $Q/\text{sec.}$ is the quantity of heat per second flowing through X in the direction MN, A is the area of cross-section of X, k is its thermal conductivity, t_1, t_2 are the respective temperatures on T_1, T_2, and d is the small *thickness* of the disc.

A separate experiment is performed to find the quantity of heat flowing per second (Q/sec.) through the disc in the steady state, which is equal to the heat lost per second by radiation from the exposed surface of N. To find the heat lost by radiation, P and M are removed, leaving X above N; N is gently warmed by a burner until its temperature exceeds the value t_2, and then N is allowed to cool. Readings of the temperature are taken at equal intervals of time until it has a value some degrees lower

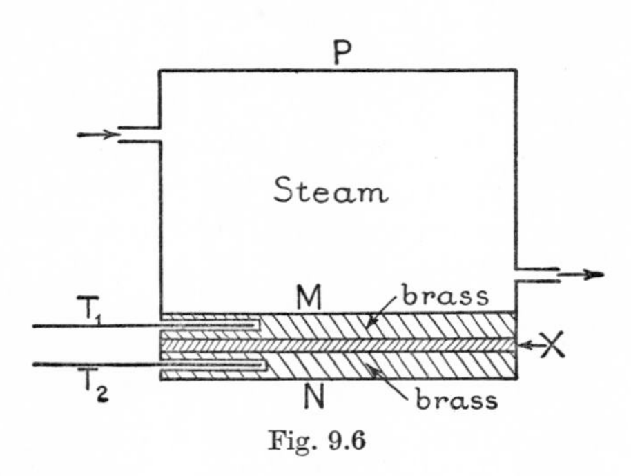

Fig. 9.6

than t_2, and the cooling curve is plotted. The rate of cooling in °C. per sec. at the temperature t_2 is then found by drawing the appropriate tangent to the curve; we shall suppose the value is a° C. per sec. As the conditions under which N has cooled are the same as in the first part of the experiment, the heat lost per sec. by N at t_2° C. by cooling = the heat flowing per second (Q/sec.) through X in fig. 9.6. But the heat lost per sec. by N at t_2° C. = msa cal. per sec., where m is the mass of N and s is its known specific heat.

$$\therefore \ Q/\text{sec.} = msa.$$

But

$$Q/\text{sec.} = kA\,\frac{t_1 - t_2}{d}$$

$$\therefore \ msa = kA\,\frac{t_1 - t_2}{d}.$$

Knowing m, s, a, A, t_1, t_2, and measuring d with a micrometer screw-gauge, the thermal conductivity k can be calculated from this equation.

11. Method for bad conductor in the form of a tube.

The thermal conductivity of a solid, such as glass, in the form of a tube, can be measured by the apparatus shown in fig. 9.7*a*. The tube XY is surrounded by a jacket A, and water flows through the tube from X to Y at a steady rate. When the

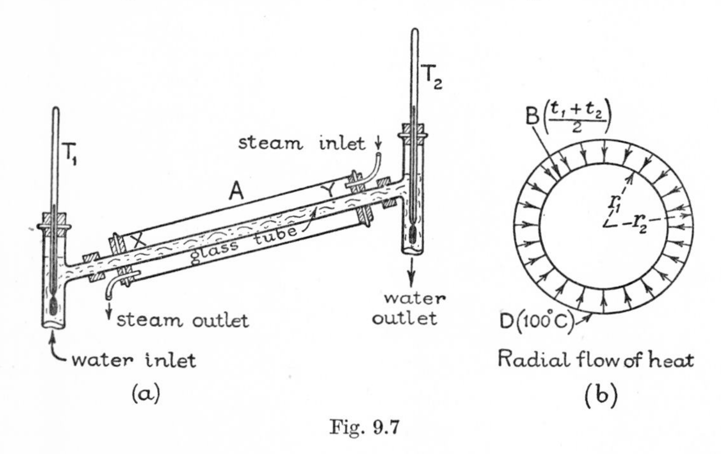

Fig. 9.7

steam circulates round XY heat passes through the tube to the flowing water inside it, which therefore becomes warmed, and after a time the outlet temperature of the water, indicated by the reading on the thermometer T_2, becomes constant. A steady state is now obtained, and the temperature t_2 on T_2 is noted.

Suppose the length of XY is l, and r_1, r_2 are the internal and external radii of the tube respectively. The average radius r of the tube is then $\frac{1}{2}(r_1 + r_2)$, and the surface area A of the tube $= 2\pi rl = \pi(r_1 + r_2)l$. The temperature of the outside surface D of the tube is the temperature of the steam, 100° C. say, and the temperature of the interior surface B is the average temperature $\frac{1}{2}(t_1 + t_2)$ of the flowing water, where t_1 is the inlet temperature of the water (fig. 9.7*b*). Consequently the temperature gradient across the thin tube $= \dfrac{\text{temperature difference}}{\text{thickness}} =$ $[100 - \frac{1}{2}(t_1 + t_2)]/(r_2 - r_1)$, and hence the quantity of heat per second flowing from D to B in the steady state is given by

$$Q/\text{sec.} = kA\,\frac{100 - \frac{1}{2}(t_1 + t_2)}{r_2 - r_1} = k\pi(r_1 + r_2)l\,\frac{100 - \frac{1}{2}(t_1 + t_2)}{r_2 - r_1},$$

where k is the thermal conductivity of the material of the tube. The quantity of heat per second is $m(t_2 - t_1)$, where m is the mass of water per second flowing through XY, as the water is warmed from a temperature t_1 to a temperature t_2.

$$\therefore\ m(t_2 - t_1) = k\pi(r_1 + r_2)l\,\frac{100 - \frac{1}{2}(t_1 + t_2)}{r_2 - r_1}.$$

Thus k can be calculated, as the other quantities in the equation are known.

A piece of thick twisted wire is often placed along the tube XY to mix the water flowing through it. It should be noted that the heat flows through the tube along the *radii* of the cross-section, as represented by the arrows in fig. 9.7*b*, and this flow of heat is therefore called a *radial flow*. In distinction, the heat flows along the bar in fig. 9.5 in parallel directions, and this is termed a *rectilinear flow* of heat.

12. Determination of the thermal conductivity of a rubber tube.

The thermal conductivity of a rubber tube can be found by first passing steam through it for a short time. The tube is then picked up, with the steam still issuing from it, and a fixed length of it, XMY, is immersed inside a calorimeter containing water, which has been cooled several degrees below room temperature by the addition of ice (Fig. 9.8*a*). The temperature of the water is then noted at equal intervals of time as it rises from its initial temperature corresponding to P (fig. 9.8*b*) to a temperature N above the room temperature t_1; from this graph the rise in temperature per second, $a°$ C. per sec. say, at the temperature t_1 is obtained by drawing the corresponding tangent l to the curve.

When the water and calorimeter are at the same temperature as the room (t_1) no heat is lost by them to the surroundings. Thus the quantity of heat flowing per second (Q/sec.) through the rubber tube when immersed in the water is equal to the heat per second gained by the water and

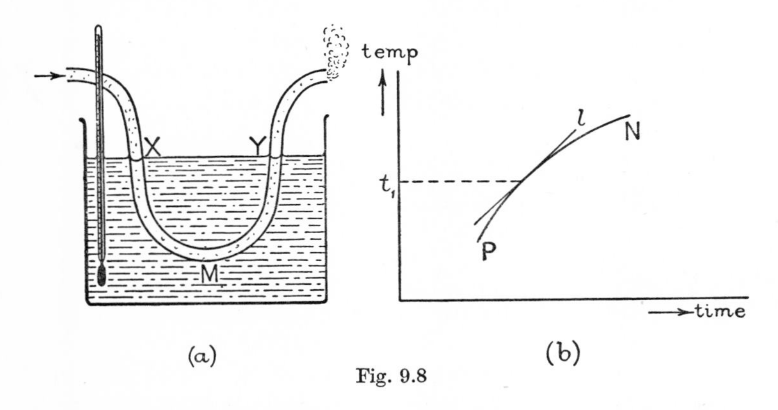

Fig. 9.8

calorimeter at the temperature t_1. Hence Q/sec. $= Wa$ cal./sec., where W is the total water equivalent of the water and calorimeter. But Q/sec. $= kA \times$ temperature gradient.

$$\therefore \; Q/\text{sec.} = k\pi(r_1 + r_2)l\,\frac{t - t_1}{r_2 - r_1},$$

since the area A through which the heat is conducted is $\pi(r_1 + r_2)l$, and the temperature gradient is $(t - t_1)/(r_2 - r_1)$, where l is the length of XMY, r_1, r_2 are the external and internal radii of the tube, and t is the temperature of the steam (compare the case of the hollow tube, p. 201–2). Thus

$$Wa = k\pi(r_1 + r_2)l\,\frac{t - t_1}{r_2 - r_1}.$$

The thermal conductivity k of the rubber can hence be calculated, as the other quantities in the equation are known.

13. Comparison of thermal conductivities by Ingenhausz's method.

About 1790, INGENHAUSZ developed a simple method of *comparing* the thermal conductivity of two metals. The two metals A, B have exactly the same dimensions and are in the form of long bars; their surfaces are electroplated, polished, and completely covered with wax. One end of each bar is inserted into a vessel C, and small pieces of lead shot are equally spaced and attached to the bars along their entire length (fig. 9.9).

Hot water, maintained at a constant temperature, is poured into the vessel C. As the heat is conducted along each bar the wax melts and the lead shot fall off. After a time, when the *steady state* is reached, a length l_1 of A has had wax melted from

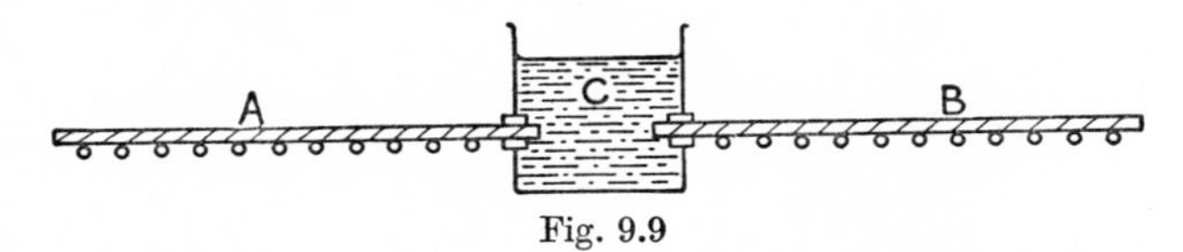

Fig. 9.9

it, and B has then had a different length l_2 of wax melted from it. It can be shown by mathematics beyond the scope of this book that *the thermal conductivities are proportional to the squares of the lengths of wax melted when the steady state has been reached,*

i.e.
$$\frac{k_1}{k_2} = \frac{l_1^2}{l_2^2}, \qquad (49)$$

where k_1, k_2 are the thermal conductivities of A, B respectively. The number of lead shot which have fallen off is proportional to the length of wax melted as the shot are spaced at equal intervals, and hence $k_1/k_2 = n_1^2/n_2^2$, where n_1, n_2 are the numbers of the shot which have fallen from A, B respectively in the steady state.

Iron has a greater thermal conductivity than bismuth, but *initially* (i.e. before the steady state is reached) the wax is observed to melt at a faster rate along a bismuth rod. This surprising observation is explained by the fact that the rate at which the wax melts initially depends on the speed with which the *temperature* "travels" along the bar; the thermal capacity per unit volume of the bar, as well as the thermal conductivity, thus enters into the consideration of the temperature in the initial stage of Ingenhausz's experiment. For iron the density $\rho = 7{\cdot}86$ gm. per c.c., $s = 0{\cdot}11$, and hence $\rho s = 0{\cdot}86$; for bismuth, $\rho = 9{\cdot}8$ gm. per c.c., $s = 0{\cdot}03$, and hence $\rho s = 0{\cdot}29$. The thermal capacity of unit volume of bismuth is thus less than that of iron, and the temperature rise initially obtained can hence be greater in the bismuth bar than in the iron bar. A similar case occurs when copper and bismuth (or aluminium) are used in Ingenhausz's experiment, as the wax melts faster initially from the bismuth (or aluminium) bar; the thermal capacity per unit volume of bismuth is less than that of copper.

The above are general considerations, and more accurately, it can be shown that the speed with which the wax melts initially depends on the *diffusivity* of the substance, which is defined as $k/\rho s$, where k is the thermal conductivity, ρ is the density, and s is the specific heat. The interested reader should consult *Theory of Heat*, Preston (Macmillan), which also contains the proof of Ingenhausz's relation $k_1/k_2 = l_1^2/l_2^2$ for the steady state.

Example 1.—Explain what is meant by the thermal conductivity of a substance. Describe a method by which the thermal conductivity of a bad conductor, such as ebonite, may be measured.

A vessel, having an external surface area of 250 sq. cm. and walls 2 mm. thick, is filled with lumps of ice mixed with water, and then placed in a water-bath maintained at 95° C. How many grams of ice will melt per minute when conditions become steady? Latent heat of fusion of ice = 80 cal. per gm.; thermal conductivity of the material of the vessel = 0·002 c.g.s. units.] (*C.W.B.*)

First part.—The thermal conductivity k is defined on p. 194. The thermal conductivity of ebonite can be found by Lees' disc method, p. 199.

Second part.—In the steady state, the quantity of heat passing per second through the walls of the vessel is given by $Q/\text{sec.} = kA \times$ temperature gradient.

But $k = 0{\cdot}002$ c.g.s., $A = 250$ sq. cm., temp. gradient $= (95 - 0)/0{\cdot}2°$ C. per cm.

$$\therefore\ Q/\text{sec.} = 0{\cdot}002 \times 250 \times 95/0{\cdot}2 \text{ cal. per sec.}$$

$$\therefore\ Q/\text{minute} = 0{\cdot}002 \times 250 \times 95 \times 60/0{\cdot}2 = 14{,}250 \text{ cal. per min.}$$

But the latent heat of fusion of ice = 80 cal. per gm.

$$\therefore \text{ mass of ice melted per minute} = \frac{14250}{80} = 178\tfrac{1}{8} \text{ gm.}$$

Example 2.—What do you understand by the coefficient of thermal conductivity? One end of a cylindrical metal rod, 2 mm. in diameter, is screwed into a copper block weighing 132 gm. The other end projects into a steam jacket and can be maintained at a temperature of 100° C. The length of the exposed rod between the steam jacket and the face of the block is 10 cm. When the temperature of the apparatus is 10° C., steam is turned into the jacket and the initial rate of rise of temperature of the copper block is observed to be 1° C. per min. Assuming that no heat escapes from the surface of the rod, find (*a*) the number of calories of heat passing through the rod from the steam jacket in one second, (*b*) the coefficient of thermal conductivity of the material of which the rod is made. [The specific heat of copper is 0·09 cal. per gm. per °C.] (*N.J.M.B.*)

First part.—See text.

Second part.—(*a*) The heat conducted through the rod initially raises the temperature of the copper block at the rate of 1° C. per min., or 1/60° C. per sec.

$$\therefore \text{ heat per sec. supplied to copper block} = Q/\text{sec.}$$

$$= \text{mass} \times \text{sp. ht.} \times \text{temp. rise/sec.}$$

$$= 132 \times 0{\cdot}09 \times 1/60 = 0{\cdot}198 \text{ cal./sec.}$$

This is the heat passing through the rod from the steam jacket in one second.

(*b*) The temperature gradient across the exposed rod when the steam is turned on $= (100 - 10)/10 = 9°$ C. per cm. The area A of cross-section of the rod $= \pi r^2 = \pi \times 0{\cdot}1^2$ sq. cm., as $r = 1$ mm. $= 0{\cdot}1$ cm. The heat passing per second through the rod is 0·198 cal. from our previous result, and since the heat per second $= kA \times$ temperature gradient, it follows that

$$0{\cdot}198 = k \times \pi \times 0{\cdot}1^2 \times 9.$$

$$\therefore k = \frac{0{\cdot}198}{3{\cdot}14 \times 0{\cdot}01 \times 9} = 0{\cdot}70 \text{ cal./sq. cm./sec. unit temp. gradient.}$$

Example 3.—Define *thermal conductivity* and describe *briefly* the essentials of a method of measuring this quantity for a good conductor.

The temperature inside a boiler is 105° C. The wall of the boiler is 2 cm. thick and is lagged with 4 cm. thickness of a material whose thermal conductivity is 1/9 of that of the material of the boiler. When in the steady state the temperature of the outside surface of the lagging in contact with the air is 10° C. What is the temperature of the common surface of the boiler and the lagging? (*L.H.S.C.*)

First part.—See text.

Second part.—Let $t =$ temperature in °C. of the common surface of the boiler and the lagging. The temperature gradient across the wall of the boiler is then $(105 - t)/2°$ C. per cm., and the temperature gradient across the lagging is $(t - 10)/4°$ C. per cm. Thus if A is the area of the wall and also the area of the lagging material, and k and $k/9$ are the respective thermal conductivities, the quantities of heat passing per second through the wall and the lagging in the steady state are respectively

$$kA\,\frac{105 - t}{2} \quad \text{and} \quad \frac{k}{9}\,A\,\frac{t - 10}{4} \text{ cal. per sec.}$$

But in the steady state, the quantity of heat passing per second through the wall = the quantity of heat passing per second through the lagging.

$$\therefore\ kA\,\frac{105 - t}{2} = \frac{k}{9}\,A\,\frac{t - 10}{4}.$$

$$\therefore\ \frac{105 - t}{2} = \frac{t - 10}{36}.$$

$$\therefore\ 19t = 1900,$$

$$\therefore\ t = 100^\circ\ \text{C}.$$

14. Convection.

If a given mass of liquid is heated its volume increases, and hence the density (mass per unit volume) of the liquid decreases. If we imagine a beaker of water heated by a flame beneath it, the part of the water at the bottom will become hot before any other part, and its density will therefore diminish compared with the water above it. The hot water thus rises to the top, carrying the heat with it, and the cold water falls to the bottom, where it becomes heated in turn and rises. In this way the whole of the water becomes hotter and hotter.

The transfer of heat from one place to another by the movement of the substance itself between these places is called **convection.** In the case of conduction, the average position of the substance remains unaltered while the heat is transferred from one place to another (p. 191). Hot-water systems function by the process of convection, the hot water rising and carrying the heat with itself, leaving the cold water to sink to the boiler and become hot in turn. Convection cannot take place in solids because the particles cannot move freely, and it occurs in gases with more ease than in liquids. A " radiator " in a room warms it mainly by the process of convection, the place of the hot air near the radiator being taken by other and colder air.

15. Thermal conductivity of liquids.

Apart from mercury, liquids are bad conductors of heat. In determining the thermal conductivity k of a liquid, the main precaution is to ensure that no convection can take place, as this would spoil the experiment, and for this purpose the temperature of the *top* of the liquid is made greater than the bottom.

Lees' disc method for bad solids (p. 199) can be adapted for measuring the thermal conductivity of a liquid. Four flat copper discs of about the same diameter, A, B, C, D, are set up horizontally with a heating coil between A and B, a glass slab G between B and C, and the liquid L in an ebonite ring E between C and D (fig. 9.10). When conditions are steady, the temperatures of B, C, D are measured by thermocouples, and since the thermal conductivity of the glass G had been previously determined, the quantity of heat flowing per second down through C is known. By subtracting the heat flowing per second through E (determined by a subsidiary experiment with air in place of the liquid), the heat flowing per second through L is determined; and since the temperature difference between C and D, and the area of L are known, the thermal conductivity of the liquid can be calculated.

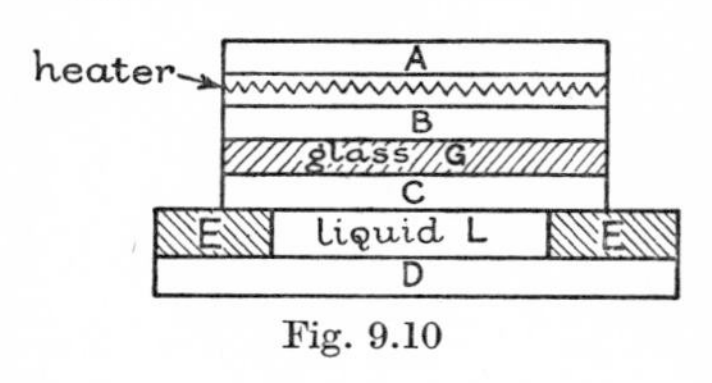

Fig. 9.10

16. Thermal conductivities of gases.

Gases are very poor conductors of heat, e.g. the thermal conductivity of air is about 0·000 06 c.g.s. units. On this account the film of gases on the under side of a boiler reduces considerably the temperature immediately underneath the boiler, and the scale formed must be cleaned from the boiler periodically.

The task of determining the thermal conductivity of a gas is more formidable than for a liquid, as radiation as well as convection effects are liable to occur in the case of the gas. Fig. 9.11 illustrates the *principle* of a method for determining the thermal conductivity k of a gas. Three plane polished plates, D, B, C, are made of copper and silverplated, and C is cooled by a stream of water so that its temperature is constant. B is heated electrically by a coil inside it, and is surrounded by a ring G similarly heated; D is also heated electrically and has an insulator S above it. By adjusting the currents in D, G, B, the temperatures of these metals can be made the same, and after a steady state is reached the temperatures t_1, t_2 of B, C are recorded by means of thermocouples.

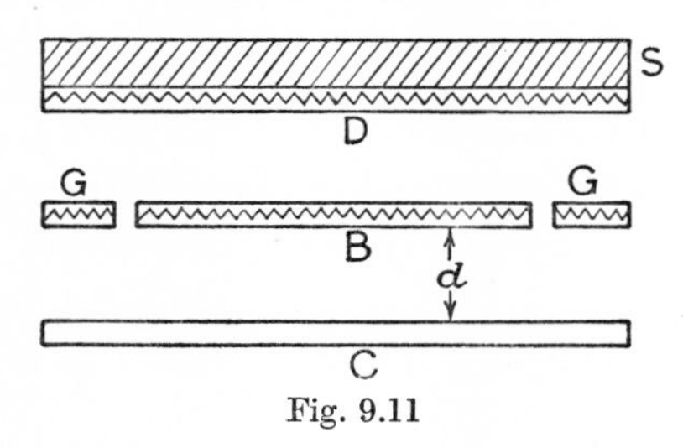

Fig. 9.11

Since B and D are at the same temperature there is no convection between them. Further, as B is at a higher temperature than C, there is no convection between B and C. There is no radiation between B and D since they are at the same temperature, and the radiation between B and C is small since the plates are silverplated. No conduction takes place between D, B and G, B since they are at the same temperature, and the heat flows downward from B to C, the guard ring G ensuring that the flow of heat is perpendicular to B and C. The rate of heat supplied to B, and the temperatures of B and C are known, and since Q per sec. $= kA(t_1 - t_2)/d$, where d is the distance between B and C, and A is the area of B, the thermal conductivity k of the gas can be calculated.

Examples on Chapter IX

1. The opposite sides of a solid cube of side 5 cm. are maintained at temperatures of (i) 100° C. and 15° C., (ii) 20° C. and −5° C. Calculate the temperature gradient in each case.

2. Write down the expression for the quantity of heat per second flowing through a substance in the steady state. Two opposite faces of a solid copper cube of side 20 cm. are maintained at temperatures of 85° C. and 5° C. respectively. Calculate the heat flowing through the cube in the steady state in 5 min. ($k = 0{\cdot}9$ c.g.s. units for copper.)

3. Name two different units of *thermal conductivity*. The thickness of a glass window is 2 mm., and it has an area of 8000 sq. cm. If one side of the glass has a temperature of 16° C. and the other has a temperature of −4° C., calculate the quantity of heat flowing through the glass in 10 seconds. (k for glass $= 0{\cdot}000\,3$ c.g.s. units.)

4. The ends of a long cylindrical bar are maintained at a constant difference of temperature. Draw a sketch of the temperature variation of the different sections of the bar in the steady state if it is (i) unlagged, (ii) lagged. Explain briefly the reason for the temperature variation in both cases.

5. How is the quantity of heat flowing per second through the bar in the steady state measured in Searle's method of determining thermal conductivity? What is the advantage of lagging the bar?

6. What difficulties arise in experimental methods of measuring the thermal conductivity of (i) liquids, (ii) gases? State briefly how the difficulties may be overcome.

7. Define *thermal conductivity* and describe a method for comparing the thermal conductivities of copper and iron. The ends of a uniform metal bar are maintained at 100° C. and 0° C. respectively, and the surface of the bar is lagged so that no heat escapes from it. Explain how the temperature of the bar varies along its length when a steady state is attained. How will this variation of temperature be altered if the hotter half of the bar is composed of a metal whose thermal conductivity is twice that of the metal composing the cooler half, the join of the two metals being perpendicular to the axis of the bar? (*N.J.M.B.*)

8. Describe a method of determining the thermal conductivity of a solid of high conductivity. The metal of a boiler is 1·5 cm. thick. Find the difference of temperature between its faces if 32 kg. of

water is evaporated from the boiler per sq. metre per hour. Why is this difference so much less than that between the flue gases and the water in the boiler? [Latent heat of steam = 540 calories per gm.; thermal conductivity of metal of boiler = 0·15 c.g.s. unit.] (*C.H.S.C.*)

9. Describe an experiment for finding the thermal conductivity (*a*) of a metal rod, and (*b*) of a piece of cardboard. Give reasons for the differences in the two cases. (*L.H.S.C.*)

10. Give an account of a method of finding the thermal conductivity of a substance such as glass. A glass tube of length 30 cm., external diameter 10·2 mm., and internal diameter 9·8 mm., is immersed in a tank containing a large amount of ice and water. If water at 30° C. enters the tube and leaves at 20° C., how much ice is melted in one minute? [k = 0·000 3 c.g.s. units for glass.] (*L. Inter.*)

11. What is meant by the statement that the thermal conductivity of brickwork is 0·001 2 c.g.s. centigrade units? Calculate the heat passing per hour through the brick walls, 25 cm. thick, of a room 5 metres square and 3 metres high, if the inside and outside surfaces have temperatures of 15° C. and 0° C. respectively. [Include doors and windows in the area of the walls.] (*N.J.M.B.*)

12. State the laws of heat conduction, and describe a method for the measurement of the specific conductivity of a good conductor. A boiler supplies steam to a 100 h.p. turbine, whose efficiency is 15 per cent. The temperature of the water is 150° C. and that of the outer boiler-wall 300° C. What is the minimum surface of the boiler exposed to the furnace if the thickness of the wall is 4 mm.? [Conductivity of the material of the boiler = 0·9 calories per sec. per sq. cm. per unit temperature gradient; 1 h.p. = 746 watts; mechanical equivalent of heat $4{\cdot}2 \times 10^7$ ergs per calorie.] (*O. & C.*)

13. Define thermal conductivity. Water contained in a closed thin-walled cylindrical copper tank, of radius 30 cm. and height 1 metre, is maintained at 60° C. by means of an electric heater immersed in the water, the outside temperature being 20° C. The tank is lagged over its whole surface by a layer of felt 1 cm. thick. If the drop in temperature in the thin copper walls is neglected, and the thermal conductivity of felt is 9×10^{-5} c.g.s. units, find the wattage of the heating element. What will be the cost of running the heater for a week if the cost of electrical energy is 1*d.* per Board of Trade Unit (kilowatt-hour)? [J = 4·18 joules per calorie.] (*C.W.B.*)

14. Define the quantity *thermal conductivity*. Give an account of

a method of measuring its value for a metal. An electric heater placed in a small hole at the centre of a metal sphere of diameter 5 cm. is supplied with energy at the rate of 100 watts. Find the gradient of temperature (*a*) at a distance of 1 cm. from its centre, (*b*) at its outer surface. Assume that the steady state has been attained, and that the thermal conductivity of the metal is 0·2 [the units being the calorie, the centimetre, the second, and the degree centigrade]. (*L.H.S.C.*)

15. Define the thermal conductivity of a substance. If the numerical value of the coefficient for a substance is 0·003 when the units of mass, length, time, and temperature are one gram, one centimetre, one second, and one degree centigrade respectively, what will be its numerical value when these units are changed to one pound, one foot, one second, and one degree fahrenheit respectively? One end of a uniform bar is kept in steam and the other in melting ice. Show that when a steady state is reached, the distribution of temperature along the bar is linear if the bar is lagged so that there is no loss of heat by radiation. [1 lb. = 450 gm.; 1 ft. = 30·5 cm.] (*O. & C.*)

16. Define *thermal conductivity.* How would you determine the thermal conductivity of glass using *either* a glass plate *or* a glass tube? Find the heat conducted per square metre per hour (*a*) through a brick wall 12 cm. thick, (*b*) through the same wall covered on one side with a layer of cork 3 cm. thick if, in each case, the difference of temperature between the exposed surfaces is 20 deg. C. Assume that the thermal conductivities of cork and brick are $1{\cdot}0 \times 10^{-4}$ and 12×10^{-4} c.g.s. centigrade units respectively. (*N.J.M.B.*)

17. Define *thermal conductivity,* and state the unit in which it is measured in the c.g.s. system. Describe briefly how you would measure the thermal conductivity of copper. How much heat is conducted per hour through a window 0·6 cm. thick and one square metre in area, when the difference in temperature of the two sides of the glass is 20° C.? [Thermal conductivity of glass = $2{\cdot}5 \times 10^{-3}$ c.g.s. units.] (*C.H.S.C.*)

CHAPTER X

Radiation and Pyrometry

We have already seen that "conduction" and "convection" are processes in which the heat is carried from one place to another by the movement of the substance concerned. The heat per day from the sun which reaches the earth, however, (an enormous quantity of heat) passes through a considerable region in which there is little or no material substance, and hence heat can pass through a vacuum. In this case we speak of the heat *radiated* by the sun. **Radiation** *is the name given to the transfer of heat when the medium takes no part in the transfer.* When we sit in front of a fire the heat reaches us mainly by the process of radiation, since air is a bad conductor of heat and little convection takes place towards us. In this section we shall use the term "radiant heat" to denote the heat radiated by an object, and shall defer until later the nature of radiant heat (p. 216).

1. Detection of radiant heat.

The most sensitive method of detecting or measuring radiant heat is one which utilizes a number of thermocouples in series. A "thermocouple" is the name given to two unlike metals joined together at their ends. When one of the junctions is at a higher temperature than the other, a small electric current flows in the circuit (see p. 11). A *thermopile* is the name given to a series arrangement of thermocouples; fig. 10.1*a* illustrates a thermopile made of two unlike metals A, B, such as bismuth and antimony, with a moving-coil mirror galvanometer connected to its terminals. All the junctions *h* are blackened and brought to an open side of a container, while the other junctions

c are silvered and highly polished and brought to the opposite side. When radiant heat falls on the junctions h, they are warmed, and an electric current flows in G, which increases as the amount of radiant heat increases. A cone is placed across the blackened junctions h of the thermopile T so as to define the *direction* of the radiant heat received (fig. 10.1*b*).

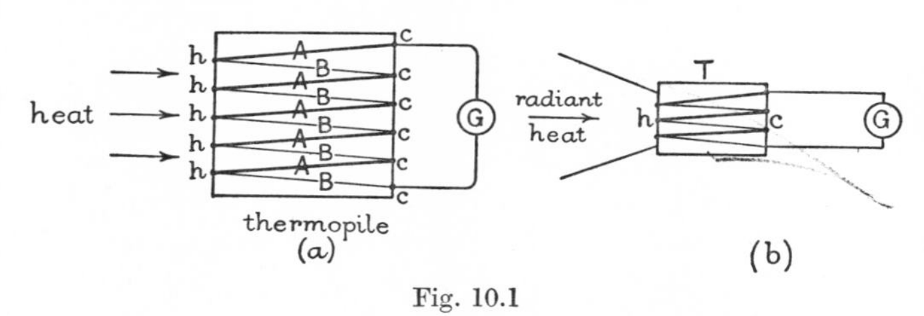

Fig. 10.1

2. Leslie's experiment on the total emissive power of surfaces.

In 1804 Sir John Leslie published the results of a research which he called *An Experimental Inquiry into the Nature and Propagation of Heat*. He coated three of the vertical sides of a cube C with a dull black or lampblack surface, a green paint, a white paint, and polished the fourth side brightly. Hot water

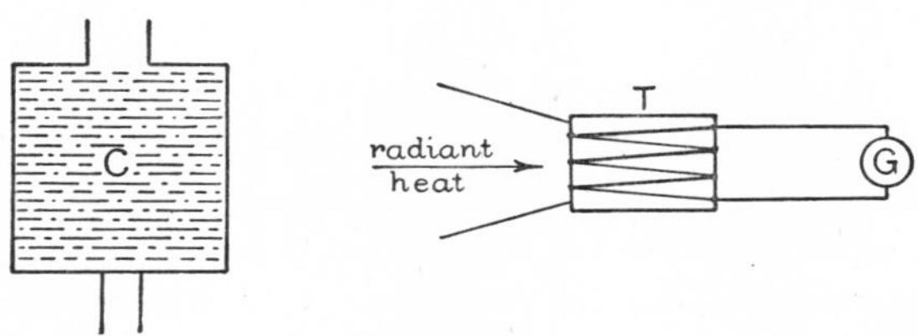

Fig. 10.2

was placed inside C and, by turning the cube round, each side was presented in turn, at the same distance, to a detector of radiant heat. Nowadays we should use a thermopile T (fig. 10.2). The experiment showed that the radiant heat from the black surface was greater than that obtained from any other surface, and the radiant heat from the highly polished surface was least.

By coating the bulb of a sensitive thermometer with lamp-black and other materials, Leslie also showed that a dull black surface was an excellent absorber of heat and that a highly polished, silvered surface was a very poor absorber of heat. It was thus apparent that *a good absorber of heat is a good radiator of heat, and that a poor absorber of heat is a poor radiator of heat.* This experimental result can also be proved theoretically (p. 225), but it should be noted here that we should expect a surface which allows heat to pass through it easily to do so in *either* direction, inward to the body or outward; and hence a good absorber of heat should also be a good radiator. Similarly, a surface which allows little heat to pass through it inward to the body (a poor absorber) also allows little heat to pass through it in an outward direction, i.e. it is a poor radiator.

3. Prévost's Theory of Exchanges.

Suppose that a small hot sphere A, covered with lampblack, is placed inside a larger hollow cold sphere B, similarly coated, so that A is entirely surrounded by B. Experiment shows that, as A becomes colder, B becomes warmer, until eventually A and B are at the same temperature.

The temperature of A begins to fall because heat is radiated from a hot to a cold body (p. 95). It must not be thought, however, that the rôle of B is a passive one while this happens. According to Prévost's " Theory of Exchanges ", *there is a constant stream of radiant heat from a cold to a hot body*, i.e. from B to A, as well as from A to B; but initially the amount of radiant heat emitted per sq. cm. per sec. by B is less than that emitted per per sq. cm. per sec. by A. Hence there is a net gain of radiant heat by B, which thus rises in temperature. Conversely, the amount of radiant heat emitted per sq. cm. per sec. by A is initially greater than that emitted per sq. cm. per sec. by B, and hence the temperature of A decreases. Eventually, the streams of radiant heat from A and from B become equal, and at this stage their temperatures become equal. We now have an example of " dynamic " equilibrium, in the sense that A and B continue to emit radiant heat but that their temperatures are constant.

If A is replaced by a blackened sphere C which is colder than the surrounding sphere B, then B initially emits more radiant heat to C than C emits to B. The temperature of the latter therefore diminishes while that of C rises. A dynamic equilibrium is eventually obtained between the streams of radiant energy, when the temperatures of A and B become equal.

Illustrations of the Theory of Exchanges, given above for the case of two bodies at different temperatures, can be extended to any number of bodies.

4. Properties of radiant heat.

At the beginning of the nineteenth century scientists began to investigate the properties and nature of radiant heat; it was shown that radiant heat could be reflected from a surface, and refracted into a medium, according to the same laws as light.

The *reflection of radiant heat* can be demonstrated by placing a hot metal sphere at the focus of a concave mirror A, and positioning another concave mirror B some distance away from A and in front of it. A thermopile placed at the focus of B shows that radiant heat is received from A, and this could have occurred only by radiant heat reflected from A and then from B according to the same laws governing the reflection of light. In this experiment the mirror B and the thermopile must be protected, of course, from receiving radiant heat directly from the hot sphere.

The *refraction of radiant heat* was first demonstrated by Sir William Herschel in 1800, when moving the blackened bulb of a thermometer through the visible spectrum of the sun. He found that an appreciable rise in temperature occurred when the bulb was placed in the dark region beyond the red, indicating that radiant heat from the sun had been refracted by the prism used. Fig. 10.3 illustrates the principle of an experiment to show the refraction of radiant heat. A white-hot source S and two concave mirrors A, B are arranged so that a parallel beam of light is reflected from B towards a quartz prism P (a glass prism cannot be used as glass absorbs radiant heat). In the absence of the concave mirror C an impure spectrum is formed on a screen D, but if a mirror C is used, a pure spectrum can be focused on to a thermopile T which enables the amount of radiant heat in a narrow part of the spectrum to be examined. A small deflection is obtained in the thermopile as it is moved from the violet to

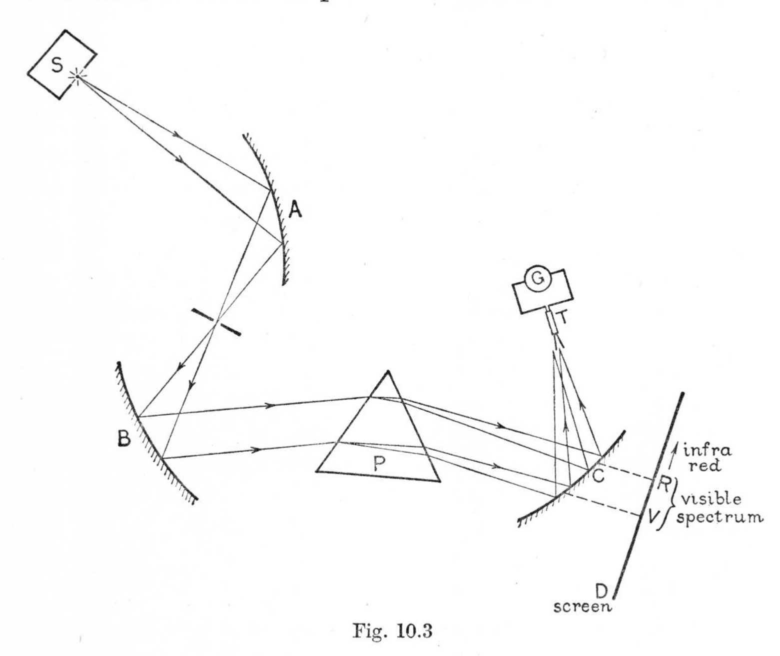

Fig. 10.3

the red end, but beyond the red, in a region of darkness, the deflection increases rapidly before returning to zero farther on. Thus radiant heat can be refracted. Other experiments show that the phenomenon of *interference* is exhibited by radiant heat; and as light and radiant heat are both cut off simultaneously at the time of a solar eclipse, it is evident that the velocity of light and of radiant heat is the same. All experiments, in fact, show that the nature of radiant heat and light is the same.

5. Infra-red (heat) rays.

Clerk Maxwell proved in 1863 that light is due to electric and magnetic vibrations which travel together in space. The *electromagnetic waves* which characterize visible light have a wavelength λ in the range 0·000 035 to 0·000 078 centimetres. Heat rays are called **infra-red** rays because they occur beyond the red end of the visible spectrum (p. 217), and infra-red rays are electromagnetic waves which have a wavelength λ in the range 0·000 075 to 0·04 centimetres. Infra-red rays thus have a longer wavelength than rays in the visible spectrum. Radio waves have longer wavelengths than infra-red rays, while ultra-violet rays, X-rays, and gamma rays have wavelengths smaller than those in the visible spectrum, decreasing in that order. Electromagnetic waves have a velocity c equal to about 3×10^{10} centimetres per second (186,000 miles per second), and the frequency f of the vibrations is related to the wavelength λ by the relation $c = f\lambda$, which applies to any wave-motion.

Although we experience different sensations from radiant heat and light, it can be seen that the only difference between them is their difference in wavelength (or frequency). Both are forms of energy which travel in space as electromagnetic waves. Glass is *adiathermanous* (opaque) to infra-red rays, whereas quartz and rock salt are *diathermanous* (transparent) to them.

6. Black-body radiation, or full radiation.

We have already seen that a blackened surface is an excellent absorber of radiant heat. *A perfectly black body is defined as one which absorbs every wavelength incident on it,* and the nearest approach to the realization of a black body is a sphere with a small hole in it and a lampblacked interior surface. If radiation of any wavelength enters the hole, most of it is absorbed by the surface; the very small amount of radiation diffusely reflected suffers further reflection at the blackened walls inside the sphere, and none remains to emerge from the hole. Thus the hole (not the sphere) constitutes a " black body ".

A body which is a good absorber of radiation of a certain wavelength is also a good emitter of the radiation of that wavelength (see p. 225). Consequently, a black body, which absorbs every wavelength, must also emit every wavelength. **Black-body radiation** is defined as the radiation obtained from a perfectly black body, and if the whole of the sphere described on p. 218 could be raised to a uniform very high temperature, the radiation issuing from the hole would contain every possible wavelength. The inside of the sphere would then appear to be white-hot if the hole were viewed, and ANDRADE has stated, " The glowing heart of a furnace is an ideal (black-body) radiator, for it is practically a small hole surrounded by glowing bodies all at one temperature ". When the furnace is cold the heart of the furnace is perfectly black.

In practice black-body radiators are obtained only with specially constructed apparatus (see below). A hot copper sphere, or the glowing filament of an electric lamp, are not black-body radiators, as certain wavelengths are missing from their spectra. Further, some of the wavelengths present do not contain as much energy as that present in the same wavelengths from a black body, and in this connexion a better name for black-body radiation is *full* (or *total*) *radiation*. The net radiation from any non-black radiator X will be equal to that emitted by a perfectly black body at some lower temperature, T say, and we can therefore refer to the " black-body temperature " T of X, although it is not a black-body radiator.

7. Distribution of energy in black-body radiation.

In 1899 LUMMER and PRINGSHEIM carried out an important investigation into the energy obtained from a black-body radiator. They used a long narrow porcelain tube coated with black cobalt oxide, and surrounded by two other porcelain tubes. The two inner tubes were electrically heated by platinum ribbon wound along their entire length, and a porcelain diaphragm, which acted as the radiator, was placed in the middle of the innermost blackened tube. The radiation which emerged from the porcelain diaphragm along the axis of the tube was black-body radiation, and by means of concave mirrors, a fluorite prism, and a special thermopile, as shown in fig. 10.3, it was possible to investigate the energy distributed among the various wavelengths in the whole range of the black-body radiation.

Fig. 10.4 illustrates how the energy in different wavelengths E_λ varies with the wavelength λ for different temperatures of the black-body radiator. At a given temperature, 1650° K., for

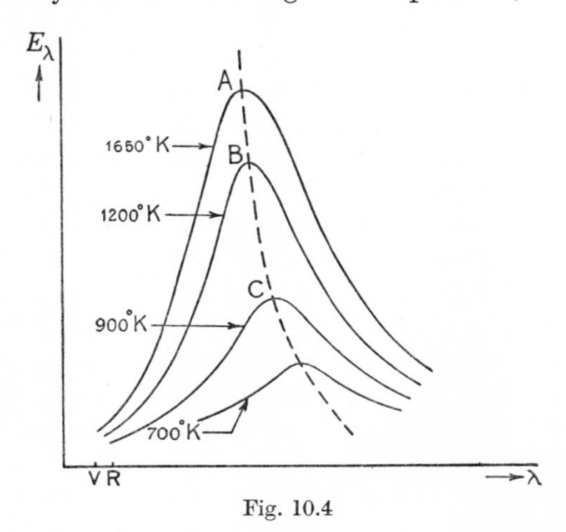

Fig. 10.4

example, there is very little radiant energy in the visible spectrum V — R, but the energy increases to a maximum as longer (infra-red) wavelengths are reached and then decreases to zero. The same variation of E_λ with λ is shown at any temperature of the black body, but the wavelength associated with the maximum energy increases with decreasing temperature.

8. Planck's and Wien's laws.

The expression for the energy E_λ in a particular wavelength λ engaged the attention of many eminent mathematical physicists towards the end of the nineteenth century. Lord Rayleigh and SIR JAMES JEANS obtained a formula for E_λ on the basis that the radiation was emitted *continuously* from the black body, which was not borne out by the experimental results (fig. 10.4). In 1900 MAX PLANCK proposed the then revolutionary principle that the radiation was emitted in definite amounts known as *quanta*, i.e. that the stream of radiation was *discontinuous*. Planck's quantum theory is outside the scope of this book, and we can do no more than quote his result for E_λ, which experiment confirms for all values of λ and T. *Planck's formula or law* states that

$$E_\lambda = \frac{a}{\lambda^5(e^{b/\lambda T} - 1)}, \quad . \quad . \quad . \quad . \quad . \quad (50)$$

where a, b are constants and λ, T are respectively the wavelength and absolute temperature of the black body. Thus the energy in a given narrow band of wavelengths depends only on the average wavelength λ of that band and the absolute temperature T of the black body, and this fact is utilized in optical pyrometry (see p. 227).

The wavelength λ_{max} associated with the maximum energy in the black-body radiation corresponds to the peaks of the curves in fig. 10.4. In 1896 WIEN proved that

$$\lambda_{max} \propto \frac{1}{T}, \quad . \quad . \quad . \quad . \quad . \quad . \quad (51)$$

where T is the absolute temperature of the black body, and hence the peaks of the curves in fig. 10.4 lie on a rectangular hyperbola. Experience confirms Wien's law qualitatively. Thus when iron is heated continuously, colour changes take place which start at dull red and proceed through orange to yellow; showing that, as the temperature increases, λ_{max} becomes smaller and enters the range of the visible spectrum.

9. Stefan's law.

Planck's and Wien's laws concern the energy in a very narrow band of wavelengths of the radiation emitted from a black body. In 1879 STEFAN made a lucky guess at the law relating the *total* radiation from a hot body and its temperature, following a study of some experimental results, and suggested that *the total radiation E emitted from a given body is proportional to the fourth power of its absolute temperature T.* Thus $E \propto T^4$, and hence

$$E = \sigma T^4, \qquad (52)$$

where σ is a constant known as *Stefan's constant.* The fourth-power law was deduced from theoretical arguments by BOLTZMANN in 1884, who showed that it was only true for a black body, and it is therefore frequently called the *Stefan-Boltzmann law.* The total energy E is related to E_λ by $E = \int_{\lambda=0}^{\lambda=\infty} E_\lambda d\lambda$, and is hence represented by the total area enclosed by the corresponding energy-distribution ($E_\lambda - \lambda$) curve, and the axis of λ.

Since $E = \sigma T^4$, and the radiation from a body is expressed in ergs per sq. cm. per sec. (see p. 213), it follows that σ is expressed in "ergs per sq. cm. per sec. per degree^4". The numerical value of σ is about $5{\cdot}67 \times 10^{-5}$. If a black-body radiator X, initially at an absolute temperature T_1° K., is placed inside a black-body enclosure Y at a lower temperature T_0° K., X emits an amount of radiation σT_1^4 and receives an amount σT_0^4 from Y. Thus the net amount of heat lost per sq. cm. per second by X is $\sigma T_1^4 - \sigma T_0^4$, or $\sigma(T_1^4 - T_0^4)$; the heat gained per sq. cm. per second by Y is also given by $\sigma(T_1^4 - T_0^4)$.

10. Approximations from Stefan's law.

When the absolute temperature T_1 of a black-body radiator is *high* compared with the absolute temperature T_0 of the black-body enclosure, T_0^4 may be neglected compared with T_1^4. In this case the heat lost per sq. cm. per second by the black-body radiator is σT_1^4 to a good approximation. Thus, if black-body radiators at temperatures of 1000° C. and 1200° C. are placed in turn in a black-body enclosure at a temperature of 15° C., the respective heats lost per sq. cm. per second by the hot bodies are in the ratio $(1000 + 273)^4 : (1200 + 273)^4$, or $1273^4 : 1473^4$.

When the absolute temperature T_1 of a black-body radiator is only *slightly higher* than that of the black-body enclosure, it can be shown that the heat lost per second by the radiator is proportional to the *difference in temperature* between itself and the enclosure. Thus suppose T_0 is the enclosure temperature, and we write T_1 as $(T_0 + x)$, where x is the difference in temperature between T_1 and T_0. Then the heat lost per second $= \sigma(T_1^4 - T_0^4), = \sigma[(T_0 + x)^4 - T_0^4]$, from Stefan's law. Now $(T_0 + x)^4 - T_0^4 = 4T_0^3x + 6T_0^2x^2 + 4T_0x^3 + x^4$. As T_0 is 300° K. for a temperature of 27° C., for example, and x is assumed small, e.g. less than 30° C., it can be seen that $6T_0^2x^2$ $4T_0x^3$, and x^4 can all be neglected compared with $4T_0^3x$. Thus the heat lost per sec. $= 4\sigma T_0^3x$. Consequently, the heat lost per second is proportional to the difference in temperature (x) in an enclosure of given temperature when the black-body-radiator temperature is slightly higher than the enclosure temperature.

Example.—Give an account of Stefan's law of radiation, explaining the character of the radiating body to which it applies and how such a body can be experimentally realized.

If each square cm. of the sun's surface radiates energy at the rate of $1{\cdot}5 \times 10^3$ cal. sec.$^{-1}$ cm.$^{-2}$ and Stefan's constant is $5{\cdot}7 \times 10^{-5}$ erg sec.$^{-1}$ cm.$^{-2}$ deg. abs.$^{-4}$, calculate the temperature of the sun's surface in degrees centigrade, assuming Stefan's law applies to the radiation. (*L. Inter.*)

First part.—See text.

Second part.—From Stefan's law, $E = \sigma T^4$. The energy per sq. cm. per sec. from the sun $= E = 1{\cdot}5 \times 10^3$ calories $= 1{\cdot}5 \times 10^3 \times 4{\cdot}2 \times 10^7$ ergs, as $4{\cdot}2 \times 10^7$ ergs are equivalent to 1 calorie of heat. Thus if T is the absolute temperature of the sun,

$$1{\cdot}5 \times 10^3 \times 4{\cdot}2 \times 10^7 = 5{\cdot}7 \times 10^{-5}\, T^4.$$

$$\therefore T = (1{\cdot}5 \times 10^3 \times 4{\cdot}2 \times 10^7/5{\cdot}7 \times 10^{-5})^{\frac{1}{4}}$$

$$= \left(\frac{6{\cdot}3}{5{\cdot}7} \times 10^{15}\right)^{\frac{1}{4}} = 5765° \text{ K.}$$

$\therefore$ temperature in deg. C. $= 5765 - 273 = 5492$.

11. Emissive power and absorptive power.

Total emissive power.—The " total emissive power " e of the surface of a body is defined as " the total energy emitted per square centimetre per second " from it. e is thus expressed in " ergs per sq. cm. per sec.", and its magnitude depends on the nature and temperature of the surface. The definition of total emissive power given above applies to the surface of any radiating body; in the special case of a black body the total emissive power is denoted by E, and obeys Stefan's law.

Emissive power for a wavelength λ.—We have already seen that the radiation from a body contains various wavelengths. The " emissive power of a surface for a given wavelength λ ", represented by e_λ, is defined by the statement: " $e_\lambda \delta\lambda$ is the energy emitted per square centimetre per second in the range of wavelengths λ to $\lambda + \delta\lambda$." Thus, from the definition of total emissive power e, it follows that $e = \int e_\lambda d\lambda$, the integral being taken over the range of wavelengths emitted by the surface of the body. In the special case of black-body radiation, the emissive power for a wavelength λ will be denoted by E_λ, and E_λ depends on the temperature of the body and the wavelength concerned (Planck's law, p. 221).

The *total absorptive power* a of a body is defined as " the fraction of the incident energy absorbed ". The *absorptive power for a given wavelength* λ is defined as " the fraction of the incident energy absorbed between the wavelengths λ and $\lambda + \delta\lambda$ ", and will be denoted by a_λ. Thus $a = \int a_\lambda d\lambda$.

12. Kirchhoff's law.

In 1833 Ritchie showed by experiment that the ratio of the total emissive power of a surface to its total absorptive power is a constant. In 1860 Kirchhoff showed that this constant was the same for all surfaces, and the following argument can be used to prove this law of radiation.

Consider an object A placed inside a black-body enclosure, e.g. a blackened sphere with a small hole in it (p. 218), and suppose that A and the enclosure are at the same temperature. Then the energy flow per square cm. per second inside the enclosure is E, where E depends only on the temperature, and the energy absorbed by the object A is aE ergs per sq. cm. per sec., where a is the total absorptive power of A. But in dynamic equilibrium A emits as much energy per square cm. per second as it absorbs.

$$\therefore \ e = aE,$$

where e is the total emissive power of A. Thus

$$\frac{e}{a} = E. \qquad \qquad (53)$$

But E is a constant at a given temperature. Hence *the ratio of the total emissive power of a body to its total absorptive power is a constant equal to the total emissive power of a black body at the same temperature.*

The same argument as above can also be used to prove that

$$\frac{e_\lambda}{a_\lambda} = E_\lambda, \quad \ldots \ldots \ldots \quad (54)$$

where e_λ, a_λ are the respective emissive and absorptive powers of the surface for a given wavelength λ, and E_λ is the emissive power for that wavelength of a black body at the same temperature. Thus $\frac{e_\lambda}{a_\lambda}$ is a constant, and hence *Kirchhoff's law*, as expression (54) is called, proves that *a good emitter of a certain wavelength is a good absorber of that wavelength.* Experiment shows that the spectrum of a white-hot source of light is crossed by two close dark lines if the light is intercepted by a sodium flame before it is incident on the prism, and that these lines correspond to the wavelengths of the two lines in the light emitted by the sodium flame. This is an example of the statement that a good emitter of a certain wavelength is a good absorber of that wavelength.

13. Pyrometry, or the measurement of very high temperatures.

In Chapter I we saw that platinum resistance and gas thermometers are standard instruments which can be used for measuring high temperatures. These instruments cannot be used to measure temperatures above 1500° C., however, as the bulb containing the wire or gas would melt if it came into contact with the very hot object.

The laws of radiation are utilized for measuring very high temperatures. A *pyrometer* is such an instrument, and is used extensively in industry to measure the temperatures of furnaces of all descriptions. For example, pyrometers are used at glass works, at kilns for making bricks, and at steel and iron works, where the processes concerned must be regulated at certain known high temperatures.

14. Féry's total-radiation pyrometer.

In 1902 FÉRY designed a pyrometer known as a "total-radiation" pyrometer, because it utilizes the total radiation E

emitted from a hot object (p. 222). The essential features of the instrument are illustrated in fig. 10.5*a*. C is a highly polished, silvered, concave mirror, which can be moved to or fro along the axis of a tube X by means of a screw D. The tube is pointed at the furnace whose temperature is required, and after reflection at C the radiation is focused on to the blackened junction of a thermopile T whose other (silvered) junction is shielded from the radiation. The temperature of the furnace is obtained directly from the reading on the millivoltmeter G connected to T, as G is calibrated in degrees centigrade or degrees fahrenheit.

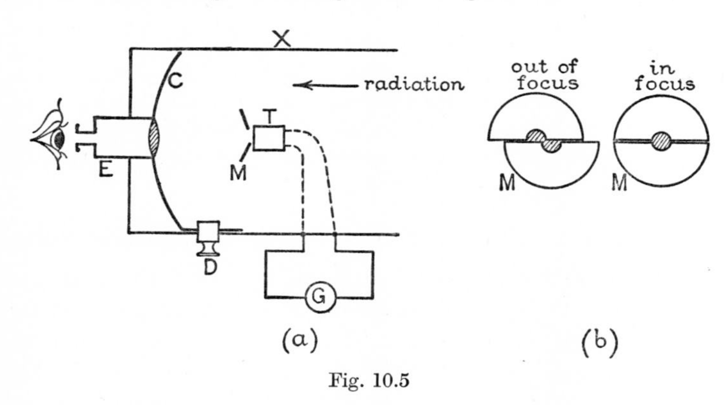

Fig. 10.5

Two conditions must be fulfilled before the reading on G is observed. In the first place, the image of the hot body in the concave mirror C must *overlap* the blackened thermopile junction, i.e. the hot body must not be too far away from the pyrometer. In this case, halving the distance of the hot body from C increases the area of its image four times; but the amount of radiation falling on C is four times as much as previously, and hence the energy per sq. cm. per sec. on the thermojunction is the same as before. The reading on G is thus constant.

In the second place, the radiation from the hot body must be brought to a focus on the blackened junction of T. For this purpose Féry arranged two small semicircular mirrors M near the thermojunction which are slightly inclined to each other from the vertical (fig. 10.5*a*). The centres of the mirrors are cut away so that they form a limiting diaphragm for the radiation received by T. When the mirrors are viewed through the eyepiece E through C, and the rays from the hot body reflected by C are not convergent on to the line of intersection of the two mirrors, the latter are seen displaced, as illustrated in fig. 10.5*b*. The screw D is then turned so that C is moved, and when the mirrors M are not seen displaced relative to each other, the radiation is focused on to the thermojunction T.

15. The Optical Pyrometer.

Féry's pyrometer utilizes the *total* radiation from the hot object. About 1900, however, a pyrometer was designed which utilizes a very narrow band of wavelengths in the radiation from a glowing hot object, and this type of pyrometer is known as an OPTICAL PYROMETER.

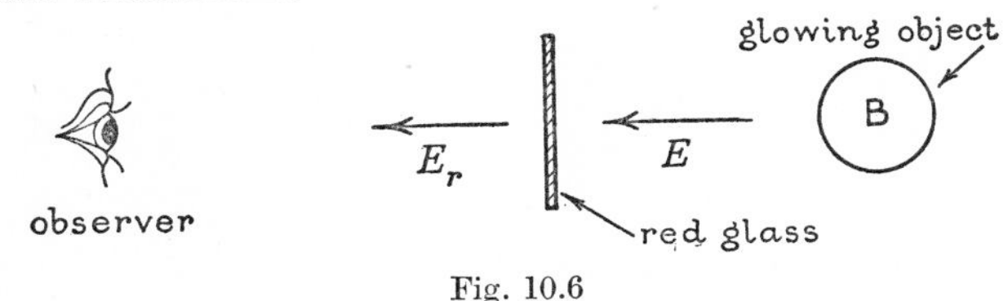

Fig. 10.6

Theory.—The principle of the optical pyrometer can be understood by reference to fig. 10.6, in which B is a glowing black-body radiator and is viewed through a sheet of red glass by an observer. The glass cuts off all wavelengths except a narrow band corresponding to the wavelengths of red light; and hence the *brightness* or intensity E_r of the red light observed is that due to the energy in this band of wavelengths in the total radiation E from the hot object B. From Planck's law, the brightness of the red light depends only on its wavelength and on the absolute temperature of B (see p. 221).

Suppose now that another glowing black-body radiator C (not shown) is viewed through the same red glass. If the brightness of the red light due to C is the same as that due to B, the temperatures of B and C must be the same, from Planck's law, because the wavelength of the light received by the observer is the same in both cases. Thus, if the temperature of C is known, the temperature of B is also known.

Practical arrangement.—We are now in a position to understand the design of an optical pyrometer which is illustrated in fig. 10.7. An image I of a glowing furnace A, for example, is formed by the lens L, and is viewed through a piece of red glass R and an eye-piece by an observer O, who thus sees the red light in the

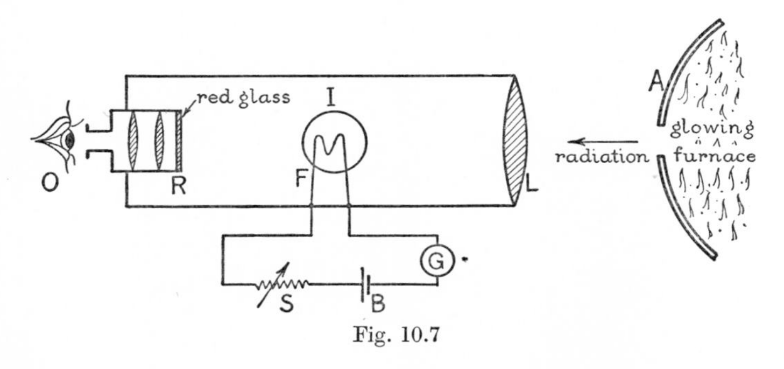

Fig. 10.7

radiation from A. The filament F of an electric lamp is in the same plane as I, and is connected to a 2-volt battery B, a rheostat S, and an ammeter G whose scale is graduated in degrees centigrade or fahrenheit. This has been done by a separate or calibration experiment, in which the temperatures of the filament F corresponding to various currents in it have been determined by using Planck's law (p. 221).

The current through F controls its temperature. Hence, as the rheostat S is varied, F will appear brighter than the background of the image I of the hot furnace in some cases, and in others it will appear darker than the background of I. For some position of S, the filament F merges into the background and is indistinguishable from it; in this case, since the brightness of the red light from F and from I is the same, the temperatures of F and I are the same. The reading on G is then the temperature of the hot furnace. This type of optical pyrometer is often called a *disappearing-filament pyrometer*, because the filament merges or " disappears " into the background formed by I when the reading on G is taken.

Unlike the total-radiation pyrometer, the optical pyrometer cannot be used to measure the temperatures of hot objects which are not glowing, as wavelengths in the visible spectrum are required for its operation. This is a disadvantage of the optical pyrometer. The optical pyrometer is considered more accurate than the total-radiation pyrometer, however, as the theory concerned in the optical pyrometer is relatively less affected by the fact that the hot body may not be a "black-body" radiator.

16. Extension of the thermometer scale above 1500° C.

The temperature of a hot object can be found by using a thermocouple which has been previously calibrated by a gas thermometer, and hence the total-radiation pyrometer, which utilizes a thermocouple (p. 226), can be used directly to measure temperatures up to the limit of the range of a gas thermometer, which is 1500° C. This is also the limiting temperature of the filament of a lamp, as the filament would grow thinner by evaporation if the temperature were higher than 1500° C.

Nevertheless, it is possible to extend the range of pyrometers above 1500° C., and this has involved the use of a disc from which a small sector has been cut away. As an illustration, suppose that this sector has an angle of 20°, and the disc is rotated in front of a very hot furnace at a constant speed of more than 40 revolutions per second. The radiation obtained beyond the disc has now been reduced in the ratio 20° : 360°, i.e. 1 : 18, and we shall suppose that the temperature indicated on a total-radiation pyrometer on which the radiation falls is 1120° C., or 1393° K.

The total radiation from the hot furnace is σT^4, where σ is Stefan's constant (p. 222), and hence the radiation beyond the disc is $\frac{1}{18}\sigma T^4$. But the radiation falling on the pyrometer appears to be that emitted from a body of 1393° K.

$$\therefore \frac{1}{18}\sigma T^4 = \sigma 1393^4,$$

assuming black-body radiation.

$$\therefore T = (18)^{\frac{1}{4}} \times 1393 = 2870^\circ \text{ K}.$$

Thus the temperature of the hot body is 2597° C.

In general the choice of the size of the angle of the sector depends on the magnitude of the temperature of the hot body, and the method can be applied to obtain a measure of the sun's temperature. A sectored disc can also be used to extend the range of the optical pyrometer beyond 1500° C., as the brightness of the image beyond the rotating sector is diminished in a ratio depending on the angle of the sector. The calculation for the temperature of the hot body is not as straightforward as that for the case of the total-radiation pyrometer. The brightness of the image of the hot body has also been reduced in a known ratio by using special absorbing glass.

Examples on Chapter X

1. "A good emitter of radiation is also a good absorber of radiation." Give two examples which justify this statement, and describe an experiment to verify one of your answers.

2. Define a *black-body radiator*. Can such a radiator be realized experimentally? Draw sketches showing roughly how the energy in a black-body radiator varies with the different wavelengths for (i) 700° C., (ii) 1000° C., (iii) 1500° C.

3. State Stefan's law of radiation. A hot metal sphere at 1000° C. cools to 900° C. If the temperature of the room containing the sphere is constant at 20° C., compare the rate of cooling of the sphere at these two temperatures, assuming it acts as a black-body radiator. Compare also the rates of cooling when the sphere reaches a temperature of 60° C. and 40° C. respectively.

4. Draw labelled sketches showing how the reflection and refraction of radiation can be demonstrated. What connexion is there

between radiation and luminous energy, and what evidence shows that the speed of radiation is the same as the speed of light?

5. Define *Stefan's constant*, and state its units. The temperature of a furnace is 1727° C. Calculate the heat radiated per sq. cm. per sec. by the furnace, assuming black-body radiation. (Stefan's constant $\sigma = 5 \cdot 7 \times 10^{-5}$ c.g.s. units.)

6. The temperature of a furnace, which is not glowing, is 500° C. Name the pyrometer you would use to determine its temperature, and draw a labelled sketch of its principal features. What other instrument could also be used?

7. Draw a careful sketch of an optical pyrometer. How is it used to measure the temperature of a glowing furnace?

8. Distinguish between conduction, convection, and radiation of heat, giving your conception of the way in which each takes place. The bulb of a thermometer is coated with a very thin layer of lamp-black. How will its readings compare with those of an uncoated thermometer placed near it in the open (*a*) in bright sunshine, (*b*) on a clear and dry night, (*c*) on a damp and cloudy night? In each case give reasons for your answer. (*N.J.M.B.*)

9. Write a brief essay on the radiation of energy from a hot body. Include in your account a description of experiments showing that the radiation can be reflected and refracted. (*L.H.S.C.*)

10. Give a brief survey of the different methods for measuring the temperature of a furnace, describing in detail the method which you consider most suitable. (*L. Inter.*)

11. Give an account of the different ways in which a body may lose heat. Explain how the losses of heat from a vacuum flask are reduced. (*O. & C.*)

12. Describe one experiment to show that a polished metal surface is a poor absorber of heat, and one experiment to show that such a surface reflects a high proportion of a beam of light falling on it. Briefly compare heat and light radiations from the standpoint of (*a*) velocity, (*b*) effect at a distance, (*c*) simple refraction, (*d*) transmission through material substances. (*N.J.M.B.*)

13. A block of metal is heated and (*a*) exposed to ordinary atmospheric conditions, or (*b*) placed in a high vacuum. State concisely the factors that govern the rate at which its temperature falls under conditions (*a*) and (*b*). Energy is supplied at the rate of 165 watts to a closed cylindrical canister 5 cm. in radius and 15 cm. high, filled with water and exposed to the air of the room, which is at 15° C. It is found that the temperature of the water remains steady at 80° C.

Find the rate of heat loss per unit area of the vessel per degree C. excess temperature. Estimate also the fall of temperature in a minute, when the energy supply is shut off. Neglect the weight of the canister itself. (*L.H.S.C.*)

14. In what ways does radiant heat resemble light? Describe briefly facts or experiments which demonstrate these points of resemblance. (*L. Inter.*)

15. Draw graphs to indicate very approximately the distribution of energy in the spectrum of (*a*) a black body, (i) at 400° C., (ii) at 1400° C.; (*b*) of the sun. How is the distribution of energy affected by inserting a sheet of glass in the path of the radiant energy? Use your statement to explain the use of glass for fire-screens and greenhouses. (*L. Inter.*)

16. Describe an experiment to show (*a*) that the spectrum of an incandescent solid includes both visible and invisible radiations, (*b*) how the fraction of incident radiation transmitted by glass depends on the temperature of the source of the radiation.

The sun's rays are focused by a concave mirror of diameter 12 cm. fixed with its axis towards the sun on to a copper calorimeter, where they are absorbed. If the thermal capacity of the calorimeter and its contents is 59 cal. per deg. C. and the temperature rises 8 deg. C. in 2 minutes, calculate the heat received in 1 minute by a square metre of the earth's surface when the rays are incident normally. (*N.J.M.B.*)

17. Describe the processes by which a body can gain heat from its surroundings. Discuss the processes involved in (*a*) the heating of a room by a coal fire, (*b*) the heating of water in a metal vessel by means of a gas flame. Water at 10° C. is contained in an open vessel of which the sides and base are well lagged. If the temperature of the air is 0° C., describe and explain the changes in the temperature of the water at the bottom of the vessel. (*C.H.S.C.*)

APPENDIX

Units in Heat

It is meaningless to express the result of an experiment as a number, without adding the **units** in which the result has been calculated; as a simple example, it is meaningless to state that the melting-point of a certain solid is 35, without specifying whether the latter is °C. or °F. The following summary is intended to emphasize the units of various physical quantities encountered throughout the book.

Absolute temperature of melting ice.	273° **K.**
Temperature of melting ice.	0° **C.** or 32° **F.**
Linear coefficient of expansion of brass (α).	0·000 018 **per °C.,** or 0·000 010 **per °F.**
Superficial coefficient of expansion of brass (β).	0·000 036 **per °C.,** or 0·000 02 **per °F.**
Cubical coefficient of expansion of mercury (γ).	0·000 18 **per °C.,** or 0·000 10 **per °F.**
Volume coefficient of a gas (α_p).	0·003 66 **per °C.**
Pressure coefficient of a gas (α_V).	0·003 66 **per °C.**
Quantity of heat (Q).	**calories** or **B.Th.U.**
Specific heat of copper (s).	0·095 **cal. per gm. per °C.** (*or B.Th.U. per lb. per °F.*).
Thermal capacity.	**cal. per °C.** (*or B.Th.U. per °F.*).
Water equivalent (W).	**grams** (of water).
Latent heat of fusion of ice (L).	80 **cal. per gm.**
Latent heat of vaporization of steam (L).	540 **cal. per gm.**
Mechanical equivalent of heat (J).	4·18 × 10^7 **ergs per cal.,** or 4·18 **joules per cal.,** or 778 **ft.-lb. per B.Th.U.**
Thermal conductivity of copper (k).	0·92 **cal. per sec. per sq. cm. per unit temp. gradient,** or 0·92 **c.g.s. units** (or in *B.Th.U. per sec. per sq. ft. per unit temp. gradient*).
Radiant energy.	**ergs,** or **calories.**

Answers to Examples

CHAPTER I

1. (i) 25° C., (ii) 87·5° C., (iii) 31·3° C. 3. 16° C. 5. (i) 63·9° C., (ii) 164·3° C. 13. 77·5 cm. 16. 444·1, 421·6° C.

CHAPTER II

1. 0·000 01 per °F., 0·000 022 5 per °R. 2. (i) 30·009 36 yd., (ii) 0·143 in. 3. 2401·27, 2399·16 sq. ft. 4. 2·000 23 sec. 6. $3·43 \times 10^4$ kgm. wt. 10. 4·1 sec. 11. $30·2 \times 10^6$ dynes. 12. $47·1 \times 10^7$ dynes.

CHAPTER III

1. 0·122 c.c. 3. (i) 203, (ii) 202·7 c.c. 4. 13·59, 13·35 gm./c.c. 5. 0·000 53, 0·000 557 per °C. 8. 76·28 cm. 9. 37·55 gm. 10. 963·9 gm. 13. 2·57 c.c. 15. 20·54 cm. 16. (*a*) 1·055 : 1, (*b*) 0·001 09 per °C. 17. 0·000 375 sq. cm. 18. 62·38 gm.

CHAPTER IV

1. 0·003 66 per °C., 478 c.c. 2. 1/491 per °F., −273° C., −459° F. 3. 373° K., (i) 78·6, (ii) 73·2 cm. 4. 130·8° C. 5. 23·4 ft. 6. 241·3 c.c. 7. (i) $2·88 \times 10^6$, (ii) $2·88 \times 10^7$; 0·985 gm. 8. $12·17 \times 10^7$ ergs, 12·17 joules. 9. 0·079 6 gm. 10. 15 ft. 12. 77·4 cm. 13. 306 cm. water. 15. $\frac{T}{V}\left(\frac{p_1v_1}{T_1} + \frac{p_2v_2}{T_2}\right)$. 16. 32·9 c.c. 17. 26. 18. 56·3 ft. 19. $1·84 \times 10^5$, $2·15 \times 10^5$ cm./sec. 20. (i) $3·55 \times 10^{11}$, (ii) $3·11 \times 10^{11}$.

CHAPTER V

1. 16·7° F. 2. 12 gm., 80° C. 3. (i) 156,250; (ii) 1815 cal. 4. (i) 79 cal./gm., (ii) 5·67 gm. 6. 156·5 gm. 7. 0·33 cal./gm./°C.

8. 0·37 c.c., s = 0·3 cal./gm./°C. 9. 12·1 gm. 11. 1·7 cm. 12. 991° F. 14. 10 gm. 15. 59·6 cal./gm. 16. 0·53 cal./gm./°C. 17. 2·6 ohms. 19. 0·086 cal./gm./°C. 21. 20° C. 23. $\pi d^2 x \rho L/4(1 - \rho)mt$.

CHAPTER VI

7. 58·8 per cent. 8. 2·6 cm. 13. 722 mm. 15. 44·6 per cent. 16. 11·3 cm. 19. 153·8 c.c. 21. 23·34 cm. 22. 1681·2 mm.

CHAPTER VII

1. 12·9 B.Th.U., 1·29° F. 2. 1·59° C. 3. 10^4 cal., 12·6 min. 4. 0·19° F. 7. 7·39 × 10^{10} ergs, 4·1 joules/cal. 8. 0·95 : 1. 9. 0·23° C. 10. 0·64 lb. wt. 11. 4·17 joules/cal. 12. (*a*) 23·8 cal., (*b*) 25° C. 14. 778·7 ft.-lb. 15. 1/9.

CHAPTER VIII

2. 0·3 cal./gm./°C. 3. 4·17 × 10^7 ergs/cal. 5. 64 cm. 6. 15 × 10^7 ergs. 7. 163·5 c.c., 80·3° C. 10. 4·12 × 10^7 ergs/gm./°K. 11. 0·237 cal./gm./°C. 13. 0·49 cal./gm./°C. 14. 4·2 × 10^7 ergs/cal. 15. 62/100, 59·9° C. 17. 12·36 : 1. 19. 4·11 × 10^7 ergs/cal. 20. 85·4° C. 21. On the gas; 9·03 lb. wt./sq. in.

CHAPTER IX

1. (i) 17° C./cm., (ii) 5° C./cm. 2. 432,000 cal. 3. 2400 cal. 7. Junction temp. = $66\frac{2}{3}$° C., i.e. ratio of gradients = 1 : 2. 8. 4·8° C. 10. 53 gm. 11. 1·56 × 10^6 cal. 12. 351 sq. cm. 13. (i) 284 watts, (ii) 4s. 14. (*a*) 167, (*b*) 26·7 cal./cm. 15. 0·000 2. 16. (*a*) 72,000, (*b*) 18,000. 17. 3 × 10^6 cal.

CHAPTER X

3. (i) 1·525, (ii) 2 : 1. 5. 9·12 × 10^8 cal. 13. (i) 0·009 6 cal./sec. (ii) 2° C. 16. 20,860 cal.

INDEX